Glencoe Science Ecology
Contents in Brief

Teacher Wraparound Edition

Student Edition

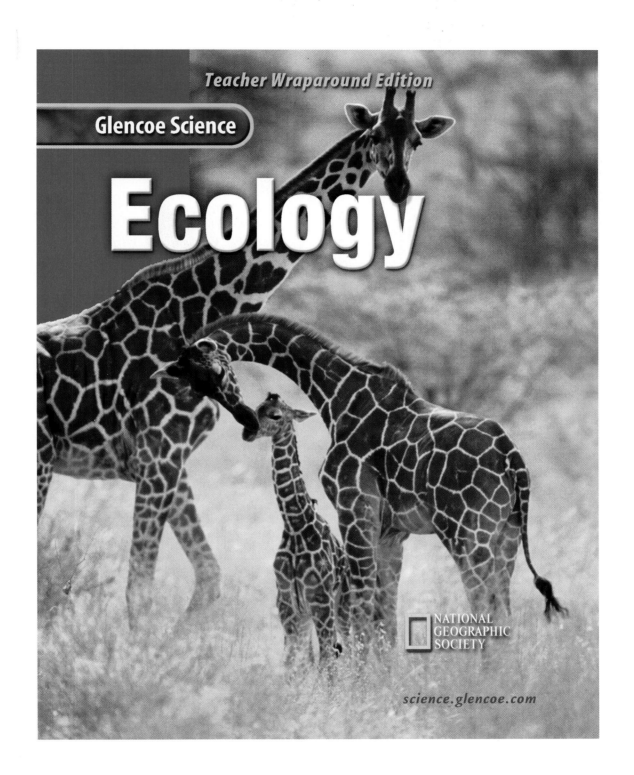

Teacher Wraparound Edition

Glencoe Science

Ecology

NATIONAL GEOGRAPHIC SOCIETY

science.glencoe.com

Glencoe McGraw-Hill

New York, New York   Columbus, Ohio   Woodland Hills, California   Peoria, Illinois

GLENCOE SCIENCE
Ecology

Student Edition
Teacher Wraparound Edition
Interactive Teacher Edition CD-ROM
Interactive Lesson Planner CD-ROM
Lesson Plans
Content Outline for Teaching
    Directed Reading for Content Mastery
    Foldables: Reading and Study Skills
Assessment
    Chapter Review
    Chapter Tests
    ExamView Pro Test Bank Software
    Assessment Transparencies
    Performance Assessment in the Science Classroom
    The Princeton Review Test Practice Booklet
Spanish Directed Reading for Content Mastery
Spanish Resources
Reinforcement
Enrichment

Activity Worksheets
Section Focus Transparencies
Teaching Transparencies
Laboratory Activities
Science Inquiry Labs
Critical Thinking/Problem Solving
Reading and Writing Skill Activities
Mathematics Skill Activities
Cultural Diversity
Laboratory Management and Safety
Mindjogger Videoquizzes and Teacher Guide
Interactive Explorations and Quizzes CD-ROM
    with Presentation Builder
Vocabulary Puzzlemaker Software
Cooperative Learning
Environmental Issues in the Science Classroom
Home and Community Involvement
Using the Internet in the Science Classroom
Dinah Zike's Teaching Science with Foldables

Glencoe/McGraw-Hill

A Division of The **McGraw·Hill** Companies

Send all inquiries to:

Glencoe/McGraw-Hill
8787 Orion Place
Columbus, OH 43420

ISBN 0-07-825589-9

Printed in the United States of America

1 2 3 4 5 6 7 8 9 10 027/043 10 09 08 07 06 05 04 03 02 01

Authors, Reviewers, and Consultants

for the *Custom Curriculum Series*

Authors

Alton Biggs
Biology Teacher
Allen High School
Allen, Texas

Lucy Daniel, PhD
Teacher/Consultant
Rutherfordton-Spindale
High School
Rutherfordton, North Carolina

Cathy Ezrailson
Science Department Head
Academy for Science and Health
Professions
Conroe, Texas

Ralph M. Feather Jr., PhD
Science Department Chair
Derry Area School District
Derry, Pennsylvania

Nicholas Hainen
Chemistry/Physics Teacher
Worthington City Schools
Worthington, Ohio

Patricia Horton
Mathematics/Science Teacher
Summit Intermediate School
Etiwanda, California

Norman G. Lederman, PhD
Professor of Science and Math
Education
Oregon State University
Corvallis, Oregon

Deborah Lillie
Math and Science Writer
Sudbury, Massachusetts

Thomas McCarthy, PhD
Science Department Chair
St. Edwards School
Vero Beach, Florida

Edward Ortleb
Science Consultant
St. Louis Public Schools
St. Louis, Missouri

Susan Leach Snyder
Earth Science Teacher,
Consultant
Jones Middle School
Upper Arlington, Ohio

Peter Rillero, PhD
Professor of Science Education
Arizona State University West
Phoenix, Arizona

Eric Werwa, PhD
Department of Physics and
Astronomy
Otterbein College
Westerville, Ohio

Dinah Zike
Educational Consultant
Dinah-Might Activities, Inc.
San Antonio, Texas

Margaret K. Zorn
Science Writer
Yorktown, Virginia

Reviewers

Sandra K. Enger, PhD
Coordinator
UAL Institute for Science Education
Huntsville, Alabama

Lee Meadows, PhD
Associate Professor of Science Education
University of Alabama
Birmingham, Alabama

Gilbert Naizer, PhD
Assistant Professor of Elementary Education
Texas A&M University
Commerce, Texas

Kimberly S. Roempler, PhD
Associate Director
Eisenhower National Clearinghouse
for Math and Science
The Ohio State University
Columbus, Ohio

Cultural Diversity Consultants

Nedaro Bellamy
Associate Director,
Rice Model Science Laboratory
Lanier Middle School, Houston ISD
Houston, Texas

Joyce Hilliard-Clark, PhD
Director, Imhotep Academy
North Carolina State University
Raleigh, North Carolina

Inclusion Strategies Consultant

Barry Barto
Special Education Teacher
John F. Kennedy Elementary School
Manistee, Michigan

Glencoe Science Custom Curriculum Series

Teach science your way!

With the 15 Life, Earth, and Physical Science titles in our modular series, you can select the science topics you want to cover and customize your science curriculum in any way you choose.

The Glencoe Custom Curriculum Series provides:

- Flexibility—you can easily meet your curriculum requirements.
- Convenience—the books are easy for students to carry and ideal for whenever locker space isn't available.
- A sense of accomplishment—as students complete each book, they can see the progress they're making.

A **Life's Structure and Function**
1 Exploring and Classifying Life
2 Cells
3 Cell Processes
4 Cell Reproduction
5 Heredity
6 Adaptations Over Time

B **From Bacteria to Plants**
1 Bacteria
2 Protists and Fungi
3 Plants
4 Plant Reproduction
5 Plant Processes

C **Animal Diversity**
1 Introduction to Animals
2 Mollusks, Worms, Arthropods, and Echinoderms
3 Fish, Amphibians, and Reptiles
4 Birds and Mammals
5 Animal Behavior

D **Human Body Systems**
1 Structure and Support
2 Nutrients and Digestion
3 Circulation
4 Respiration and Excretion
5 Control and Coordination
6 Regulation and Reproduction
7 Immunity and Disease

E **Ecology**
1 Interactions of Life
2 The Nonliving Environment
3 Ecosystems
4 Conserving Resources
5 Conserving Life

Correlation to Benchmarks

The five **Life Science** books in the *Custom Curriculum Series* address many of the Benchmarks for Science Literacy.

A	Life's Structure and Function
B	From Bacteria to Plants
C	Animal Diversity
D	Human Body Systems
E	Ecology

Benchmark	Book and Chapter
4 **The Physical Setting**	
4B. The Earth	A6, C1, E2, E3
4C. Processes That Shape the Earth	A6, E2, E4
4D. Structure of Matter	A3, E2
4E. Energy Transformation	A3, B5, E1, E3
5 **The Living Environment**	
5A. Diversity of Life	A1, A2, A5, B1, B2, B3, B4, B5, C1, C2, C3, C4, E5
5B. Heredity	A4, A5, B4
5C. Cells	A2, A3, A4, B1, B2, C1, D7
5D. Interdependence of Life	B1, B2, B4, C1, C2, C4, C5
5E. Flow of Matter and Energy	A3, B1, B2, B5, E1, E2, E3, E4, E5
5F. Evolution of Life	A1, A4, A5, A6, B1, B2, B3, C1, C2, C3, C4, D7
6 **The Human Organism**	
6A. Human Identity	D1, D2, D3, D4, D5, D6, D7
6B. Human Development	D6
6C. Basic Functions	C5, D1, D2, D3, D4, D5, D6, D7
6D. Learning	C5, D5
6E. Physical Health	B1, B2, C1, D1, D2, D3, D4, D5, D6, D7
8 **The Designed World**	
8F. Health Technology	A2, A5, B1, B2, C1, D1, D2, D3, D4, D5, D6, D7
9 **The Mathematical World**	
9A. Numbers	All Math Skills and Problem-Solving Activities
9B. Symbolic Relationships	All Math Skills and Problem-Solving Activities
9C. Reasoning	All Math Skills and Problem-Solving Activities
10 **Historical Perspectives**	
10G. Explaining the Diversity of Life	A1, A4, A5, C1, C2, C3, C4
10I. Discovering Germs	A2, B1
12 **Habits of Mind**	
12A. Values and Attitudes	A1, All "Oops, Accidents in Science!," "Science and History," and "Science and Language Arts" features
12B. Computation and Estimation	Math Skills and Problem-Solving Activities
12D. Communication Skills	All Activities and Skill Builders

Correlation to National Science Education Standards

The following chart illustrates how the five **Life Science** books in the *Custom Curriculum Series* address the National Science Education Standards.

Content Standard	Book, Chapter, and Section
(UCP) Unifying Concepts and Processes	
1. Systems, order, and organization	A1-4, A2-1, A2-2, A3-3, B2-1, B2-2, B3-1, B5-1, B5-2, D1-1, D1-2, D1-3, D2-2, D3-1, D4-1, D4-2, D5-1, D5-2, D6-1, D6-2, D7-1, E1-1, E1-2, E1-3, E2-1, E2-2, E2-3, E3-1, E3-2, E3-3, E5-1, E5-2
2. Evidence, models, and explanation	A1-1, A1-2, A1-3, A3-1, A5-1, A5-2, A5-3, B1-2, D7-2, E4-1, E4-2, E4-3
3. Change, constancy, and measurement	A4-1, A4-2, A4-3, B4-1, C2-1, C2-2, C2-3, C2-4, C3-1, C3-2, C3-3, C3-4, C4-1, C4-2, C5-1, C5-2, D2-1, D6-2, E3-1
4. Evolution and equilibrium	A3-2, A4-2, A4-3, A6-1, A6-2, A6-3, D7-3, E5-1, E5-2
5. Form and function	A2-1, A2-3, B1-1, B2-1, B2-2, B3-2, B3-3, B4-2, B4-3, C1-1, C1-2, C1-3, D3-2, D3-3, D6-1, D6-3
(A) Science as Inquiry	
1. Abilities necessary to do scientific inquiry	A1-1, A1-4, A2-1, A2-2, A2-3, A3-1, A3-2, A3-3, A4-1, A4-3, A5-1, A5-2, A5-3, A6-1, A6-3, B1-1, B1-2, B2-1, B2-2, B3-2, B3-3, B4-1, B4-2, B4-3, B5-1, B5-2, C1-1, C1-2, C1-3, C2-3, C2-4, C3-1, C3-2, C3-3, C3-4, C4-1, C4-2, C5-1, C5-2, D1-1, D1-2, D1-3, D2-1, D2-2, D3-1, D3-2, D3-3, D4-1, D4-2, , D5-1, D5-2, D6-2, D6-3, D7-1, D7-2, D7-3, E1-1, E1-2, E1-3, E2-1, E2-2, E2-3, E3-2, E3-3, E4-1, E4-2, E4-3, E5-1, E5-2
2. Understandings about scientific inquiry	A1-1, A1-3, A1-4, A6-1, C5-2
(B) Physical Science	
1. Properties and changes of properties in matter	A1-1, A3-1, E2-2, E2-3
2. Motions and forces	D1-1, D1-2, E2-3
3. Transfer of energy	A3-3, E2-3
(C) Life Science	
1. Structure and function in living systems	A1-2, A1-3, A1-4, A2-1, A2-2, A2-3, A3-1, A3-2, A3-3, A4-1, A4-3, A6-1, A6-2, A6-3, B1-1, B2-1, B2-2, B3-1, B3-2, B3-3, B4-1, B4-2, B4-3, B5-1, B5-2, C1-1, C1-2, C1-3, C2-1, C2-2, C2-3, C2-4, C3-1, C3-2, C3-3, C3-4, C4-1, C4-2, D1-1, D1-2, D1-3, D2-1, D2-2, D3-1, D3-2, D3-3, D4-1, D4-2, D5-1, D5-2, D6-1, D6-2, D6-3, D7-1, D7-2, D7-3, E1-1, E1-2, E1-3, E2-1, E2-2, E2-3, E5-1, E5-2
2. Reproduction and heredity	A2-3, A4-2, A4-3, A5-1, A5-2, A5-3, A6-1, A6-2, A6-3, B1-1, B2-2, B4-1, B4-2, B4-3, C2-3, C3-2, C3-3, C3-4, C4-1, C4-2, C5-2, D6-2, D6-3
3. Regulation and behavior	A3-2, B1-1, B5-1, B5-2, C1-1, C1-2, C1-3, C2-4, C3-1, C3-2, C3-3, C3-4, C4-1, C4-2, C5-1, C5-2, D1-3, D2-2, D5-1, D5-2, D6-1, D6-2, D6-3, D7-1, D7-2, D7-3
4. Populations and ecosystems	A1-2, A3-3, B1-2, C1-2, C3-2, C3-3, C3-4, C4-2, E1-1, E1-2, E1-3, E2-1, E2-2, E2-3, E3-1, E3-2, E3-3, E5-1, E5-2
5. Diversity and adaptations of organisms	A6-1, A6-2, A6-3, B1-1, B2-1, B2-2, B3-1, B3-2, B3-3, B4-2, B4-3, C1-1, C1-2, C1-3, C2-1, C2-2, C2-3, C2-4, C3-1, C3-2, C3-3, C3-4, C4-1, C4-2, C5-1, C5-2, D7-1, D7-2, D7-3, E3-2, E3-3, E5-1, E5-2
(D) Earth and Space Science	
1. Structure of the Earth system	E2-1, E2-2, E2-3
2. Earth's history	A1-3, A6-1, A6-2
3. Earth in the solar system	E2-3
(E) Science and Technology	
1. Abilities of technological design	A5-3, D7-3
2. Understandings about science and technology	A2-3, A4-3, A5-3, B3-3, B4-3, D2-2, D7-3, E4-2, E4-3
(F) Science in Personal and Social Perspectives	
1. Personal Health	A2-3, A5-2, B1-2, C1-3, D1-2, D1-3, D2-1, D2-2, D3-2, D3-3, D4-1, D4-2, D6-2, D6-3, D7-1, D7-2, D7-3, E4-2
2. Populations, resources, and environments	C1-2, C2-1, C2-2, C2-4, C4-2, E2-1, E2-2, E2-3, E3-1, E3-2, E3-3, E4-1, E4-2, E4-3, E5-1, E5-2
3. Natural hazards	E3-1
4. Risks and benefits	B3-2, D7-3, E4-1, E4-2, E4-3
5. Science and technology in society	A1-4, A4-3, A5-3, B1-2, B2-2, B3-3, B4-3, C3-4, E1-3, E4-1, E4-2, E4-3, E5-1, E5-2
(G) History and Nature of Science	
1. Science as a human endeavor	A1-1, A3-3, A4-3, A5-3, A6-1, A6-3, B2-2, B5-2, C2-4, C4-2, C5-2, D5-2, D7-3, E1-3, E3-3, E4-3
2. Nature of science	A1-4, A6-2, A6-3, B1-2, B3-3, D1-3
3. History of science	A1-3, A1-4, A2-3, A5-1, A6-1, A6-2, A6-3, C1-3, C4-2, C5-1, D1-3, D3-3, D4-2, D7-2, E1-3

Technology Resources

Online Science

The Glencoe Science Web site **science.glencoe.com** is an invaluable resource for all teachers and students. You will find current information, Web links, chapter content, and Internet activities that allow students to connect to other students worldwide.

ExamView Pro Computer TestMaker Software

Use this software to design and create your own test instruments in minutes. This versatile program allows you to create paper tests, tests for your school LAN system, or tests posted to a class Web site.

Interactive CD-ROM Program

This program provides students the opportunity to develop hypotheses, manipulate variables, build presentations, review content, and think critically.

Interactive Lesson Planner

Here's the perfect solution for help in planning your lessons and organizing your resources. Every page of your Teacher Classroom Resources is available in this product at the click of a mouse.

MindJogger Videoquizzes

The interactive quiz-show format of this program, with three levels of difficulty, provides excitement for your students in reviewing key concepts for every chapter. It's a fun way to help you assess students' understanding of science content.

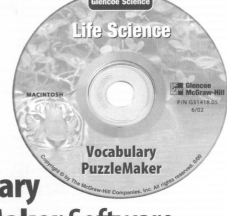

Vocabulary PuzzleMaker Software

This software program allows you to create crossword puzzles, jumble puzzles, or word searches in minutes to review chapter vocabulary. The puzzles can be printed or played on the computer screen.

Guided Reading Audio Program
English/Spanish

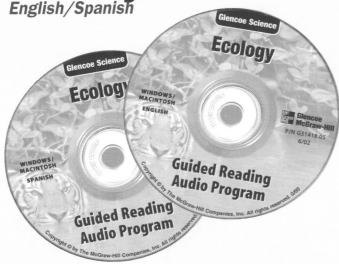

Students can listen to complete chapter texts read in English and Spanish. They're perfect for students who are auditory learners or for English Language Learners.

Interactive Teacher Edition

You can view your entire *Teacher Wraparound Edition* and Teacher Classroom Resources on your computer screen. Export all worksheet masters to your own word processor for editing, if you choose.

Teacher Classroom Resources

Chapter Resources Booklets

We've organized all of the materials you need for each chapter into convenient chapter-based booklets! The Fast File system provides an easy way to stay organized.

Each **Chapter Resources** booklet contains:

Reproducible Student Pages

Assessment
- Chapter Review
- Chapter Test

Hands-On Activities
- Activity Worksheets for each activity in the *Student Edition*
- Two additional laboratory activities
- Foldables: Reading and Study Skills

Meeting Individual Needs
- Extension and Intervention
- Directed Reading for Content Mastery

- Directed Reading for Content Mastery *in Spanish*
- Reinforcement
- Enrichment
- Note-taking Worksheets

Transparency Activities
- Section Focus Activity
- Teaching Transparency Activity
- Assessment Transparency Activity

Teacher Support and Planning
- Content Outline for Teaching
- Spanish Resources
- Teacher Guide and Answers

Additional Resources

Glencoe Professional Series

Foldables: Improving Reading and Study Skills

Students love Foldables because they're fun. Teachers love them because they're effective.

What is a Foldable?

Foldables are three-dimensional, interactive graphic organizers. As students fold paper, cut tabs, write, and manipulate what they have made, they are kinesthetically involved in learning. These unique, hands-on tools for studying and reviewing were created exclusively for Glencoe Science by teaching specialist Dinah Zike.

Foldables are Useful!

Reading in the Content Area

Foldables help students develop ways of organizing information that are fun and creative. These useful activities help students practice basic writing skills, find and report main ideas, organize information, review key vocabulary terms, and much more!

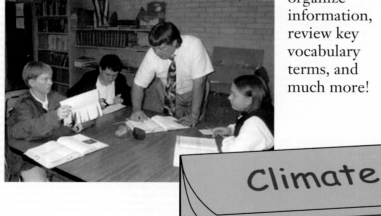

Every chapter begins with a Foldable activity. Students make the physical structure of a Foldable that incorporates one of many prereading strategies. Then, as students read through the chapter and do the activities, students record information as they learn it in the appropriate part of the foldable. In the Chapter Study Guide, the After You Read feature gives students a strategy for using the fold they made to help them review the chapter concepts.

FOLDABLES Reading & Study Skills

Before You Read

Dinah Zike Study Fold Purpose to find out what students know about the similarities and differences between bir... *See After You Read in the Study Guide at the end of this chapter.*

For ... in **Dinah Zi**... Science Web...

After You Read

After students have read the chapter and completed the Foldable described in Before You Read, have them do the following activity.

Number the characteristics you have written under the flap. Give your fold to a partner. On another sheet of paper, draw a Venn diagram and label it. Have your partner read each characteristic and its number out loud, mixing them up. Write the number of the characteristic where it belongs on your paper. Then repeat the process with your partner's fold, while you read the characteristics and have him or her write the numbers. Check your answers to make sure they are correct.

Dinah Zike

Review One advantage of Foldables is that they result in an organized study guide. The Foldables then can be used not only while preparing for the chapter test, but they can also be used for reviewing for unit tests, end of course exams, and even standardized tests.

Assessment Foldables present an ideal opportunity for you to probe the depth of your students' knowledge. You'll get detailed feedback on exactly what they know and what misconceptions they may have.

Climate
polar
temperate
tropical
temperate
polar

Foldables are Easy!

Anyone who has paper, scissors, and maybe a stapler or some glue can implement Foldables in the classroom. Glencoe's Foldables have been tested with teachers and middle school students to make sure the directions are easy for both students and teachers. After doing a couple of them, your class will quickly become seasoned experts. Don't be surprised if you find them inventing their own for use in projects and reports in all of their classes!

A message from **the creator of Foldables,** Dinah Zike

You might not know my name or me, but I bet you have seen at least one of my graphic organizers or folds used in supplemental programs or teacher workshops. Today, my graphic organizers and manipulatives are used internationally. I present workshops and keynote presentations to over 50,000 teachers a year, sharing the manipulatives I began inventing, designing, and adapting over thirty years ago. Around the world, students of all ages are using them as daily work, note-taking activities, student-directed projects, forms of alternative assessment, science lab journals, quantitative and qualitative observation books, graphs, tables, and more. But through all my years of teaching, designing, and publishing, my materials had never been featured in a middle school textbook. When Glencoe/McGraw-Hill approached me to share some of my three-dimensional, manipulative graphic organizers with you in this new and innovative science series, I was thrilled.

Working with Glencoe, we all had the vision that Foldables should be an integral part of the curriculum, not simply tacked on. What we ended up with was a strategy that will help students read and learn science concepts. One of the advantages of using the same manipulative repeatedly is that students are immersed in what they are learning. It is not out of sight and out of mind. How long is your average student actively involved with a duplicated activity sheet? Ten minutes? Fifteen? Students will use the Foldable at the beginning of each chapter, before reading the chapter, during reading, and after reading. That's a lot of immersion!

Dinah Zike

Students often make personal, educational, and career choices on their own that can influence the rest of their lives. Throughout their school years, they acquire skills that help them make these decisions. The development of keen mathematical skills can ensure that students have a wide variety of life options.

Principles and Standards for School Mathematics of the National Council of Teachers of Mathematics describes the foundation of mathematical concepts and applications that can provide students with the necessary mathematical skills to help achieve their life goals.

The ten categories of mathematical concepts and applications, as shown in the table below, allow students to increase their abilities to visualize, describe, and analyze situations in mathematical terms.

In *Glencoe Custom Curriculum Series*, each Math Skill Activity and Problem-Solving Activity provides students with the opportunity to practice and apply some of the mathematical concepts and applications described in the Standards. These activities serve to reinforce mathematical skills in real-life situations, thus, preparing students to meet their needs in an ever-changing world.

A	Life's Structure and Function	C	Animal Diversity	E	Ecology
B	From Bacteria to Plants	D	Human Body Systems		

Correlation of Math Skills Activities and Problem Solving Activities in the Life Science books, *Glencoe Custom Curriculum Series,* to NCTM Standards Grades 6–8

Standard	Book and Page
1. Number and Operations	D-11, A-13, E-15, C-25, D-40, A-46, C-52, A-74, D-78, E-80, C-82, D-104, A-109, B-112, E-114, E-129, A-133, D-133, C-147, D-147, D-185
2. Algebra	D-11, E-15, C-25, E-40, C-52, A-74, E-80, C-82, B-112, E-114, D-133, B-135, D-147
3. Geometry	D-11, A-46
4. Measurement	D-11, E-15, D-40, E-40, A-46, E-80, C-82, D-133
5. Data Analysis and Probability	A-13, D-78, E-114, C-117, E-129, A-133, B-135, C-147, D-185
6. Problem Solving	D-11, A-13, E-15, B-20, C-25, D-40, B-41, C-52, B-70, A-74, D-78, E-80, C-82, D-104, A-109, B-112, E-114, C-117, A-133, B-135, C-147, D-147, A-159, D-185
7. Reasoning and Proof	D-40, B-41
8. Communication	A-13, E-15, B-20, D-40, B-41, A-46, C-52, B-70, D-78, C-82, D-104, A-109, E-114, C-117, E-129, C-147, A-159, D-185
9. Connections	D-11, A-13, E-15, B-20, C-25, D-40, E-40, B-41, A-46, C-52, B-70, A-74, D-78, E-80, C-82, D-104, A-109, B-112, E-114, C-117, E-129, A-133, D-133, B-135, C-147, D-147, A-159, D-185
10. Representation	E-40, B-70, D-78, E-114, E-129, A-133

Materials List

It is assumed that goggles, laboratory aprons, tap water, textbooks, paper, calculators, pencils, and pens are available for all activities.

All laboratory activities have been thoroughly reviewed by a safety expert.

All full-length labs were bench tested by Science Kit to ensure quality and safety.

Materials support is provided by Science Kit® & Boreal® Laboratories. Call Science Kit at 1-800-828-7777 to get your activity materials folder. This folder makes it easy for you to order materials and equipment for the program.

Consumables

Item	EXPLORE ACTIVITY Page	Mini LAB Page	Activity Chapter/Section
Aluminum foil	93		4-2
Cardboard boxes			4-2
Cloth		133	1-2
Cotton balls			5-1
Cotton swabs			5-1
Die			5-2
Dishwashing liquid		38	5-1
Food coloring			5-1
Food-banana		133	1-2
Food-chocolate chip cookie		96	
Food-leaf lettuce			1-1
Food-raw liver			1-1
Food-raw meat			1-1
Food-vegetable oil			5-1
Food-vinegar		135	
Food-whole fruit		17	
Glue			4-2
Graph paper			3-1
Grass clippings			2-1
Labels		47	
Leaves			2-1
Orange peel			1-2
Paper plate		96	
Paper towels		17, 135	2-2, 5-1
Paper, colored			5-2
pH indicator paper		103	
Plastic bags, self-sealing (2)		135	
Plastic container lids			1-2
Plastic sheets, clear			4-2
Plastic wrap			4-1
Pond debris/sediment		78	
Poster board		72	4-2
Rubber band(s)		133	4-1
Seeds, mustard (100)		135	

Materials List

Consumables *continued*

Item	EXPLORE ACTIVITY Page	Mini LAB Page	ACTIVITY Chapter/Section
Seeds, radish		13	2-2
Sponge			5-1
String	125		4-2
Tape	125		4-1, 4-2
Toothpick(s)		96	
Water	93	38, 72, 78, 103, 135	1-1, 1-2, 2-1, 2-2, 5-1

Non-Consumables

Item	EXPLORE ACTIVITY Page	Mini LAB Page	ACTIVITY Chapter/Section
Baking pan	93		
Balance			2-2
Basin	93	13	
Beaker(s)	93		5-1
Binoculars			3-1
Bowl, plastic			1-1
Clock		38	
Clock with second hand			4-1
Coat hangers, wire			4-2
Compass			3-1
Container with lid, clear plastic		78	
Cookware, black			4-2
Culture containers			1-2
Cup		103, 135	2-2
Feathers			5-1
Fruit fly culture kit			1-2
Graduated cylinder			2-1
Hand lens	7, 125	78	1-1, 1-2, 3-1
Household fertilizer, 3 different brands		47	
Jar		38, 133	2-1
Knife, plastic		17	
Lamp with 100 W lightbulb			4-1
Net		78	
Reference-field guides	125		3-1
Reference-globe	35		
Reference-weather references	35		
Reference-world map	35		
Sand	93		
Scale			2-2
Sink		72	

Non-Consumables *continued*

Item	EXPLORE ACTIVITY Page	Mini LAB Page	Activity Chapter/Section
Sod	7		
Soft-drink bottles, clear, 1 L (2)			4-1
Soil	93	13, 38	2-1, 4-1
Spray bottle	93		
Stopwatch			4-2
Thermometer(s)			3-1, 4-1, 4-2
Toothbrush			5-1
Watch		38	
Watering can		13	

Live Organisms

Item	EXPLORE ACTIVITY Page	Mini LAB Page	Activity Chapter/Section
Fruit flies			1-2
Guppies (several)			1-1
Houseplant	63		
Moss	93		
Planarians (several)			1-1
Plants, aquatic		78	
Plants, potted (2)		13	

Lab Safety

The activities in *Glencoe Custom Curriculum Series* have been tested in the laboratory and have been reviewed by safety consultants. Even so, there are no guarantees against accidents. For additional help, refer to the *Laboratory Management and Safety* booklet, which contains safety guidelines and masters to test students' lab and safety skills.

General Guidelines

- Post safety guidelines, fire escape routes, and a list of emergency procedures in the classroom. Make sure students understand these procedures. Remind them at the beginning of *every* lab session.

  - Understand and make note of the Safety Symbols used in each activity.

  - Have students fill out a safety contract. Students should pledge to follow the rules, to wear safety attire, and to conduct themselves in a responsible manner.

- Know where emergency equipment is stored and how to use it.

- Supervise students at all times. Check assembly of all setups.

- Perform all activities before you allow students to do so.

- Instruct students to follow directions carefully.

- Make sure that all students are wearing proper safety attire. They should secure long hair and loose clothing.

Handling Chemicals

- Always wear safety goggles, gloves, and an apron when handling chemicals. Treat all chemicals as potentially dangerous.

- Never ingest chemicals. Use proper techniques to smell solutions.

- Use a fume hood when handling chemicals that are poisonous or corrosive or that give off a vapor.

- *Always add acids to water, never the reverse.*

- Prepare solutions by adding the solid to a small amount of distilled water, then diluting with water to the volume listed. If you use a hydrate that is different from the one specified, adjust the amount of hydrate to obtain the correct concentration.

- Consider purchasing premixed solutions from a scientific supply house.

- Maintain appropriate MSDS (Materials Safety Data Sheets).

- Do not permit wearing contact lenses, even with safety glasses; splashing chemicals could infuse under a lens and cause eye damage.

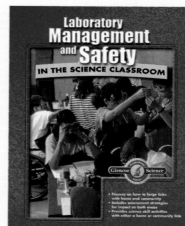

Disclaimer

Glencoe/McGraw-Hill makes no claims to the completeness of this discussion of laboratory safety and chemical handling. The material presented is not all-inclusive, nor does it address all of the hazards associated with handling, storage, and disposal of chemicals, or with laboratory management.

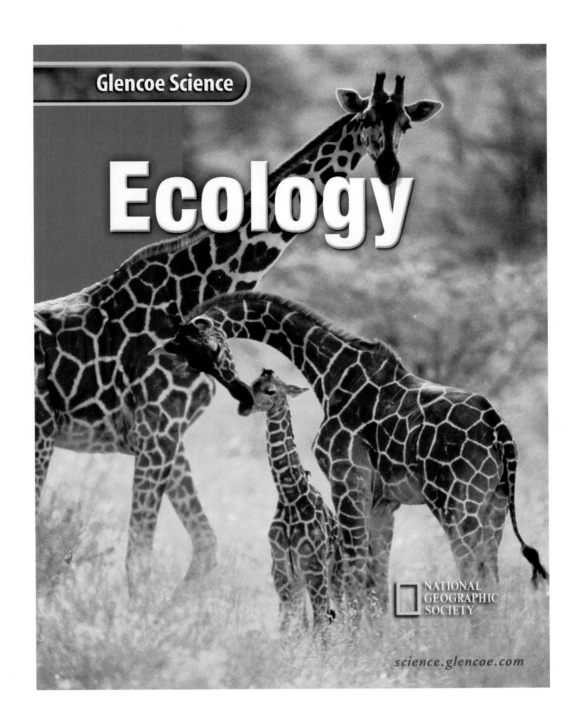

Glencoe Science

Ecology

NATIONAL GEOGRAPHIC SOCIETY

science.glencoe.com

Glencoe McGraw-Hill

New York, New York   Columbus, Ohio   Woodland Hills, California   Peoria, Illinois

Glencoe Science

Ecology

Student Edition
Teacher Wraparound Edition
Interactive Teacher Edition CD-ROM
Interactive Lesson Planner CD-ROM
Lesson Plans
Content Outline for Teaching
Dinah Zike's Teaching Science with Foldables
Directed Reading for Content Mastery
Foldables: Reading and Study Skills
Assessment
   Chapter Review
   Chapter Tests
   ExamView Pro Test Bank Software
   Assessment Transparencies
   Performance Assessment in the Science Classroom
   The Princeton Review Standardized Test Practice Booklet
Directed Reading for Content Mastery in Spanish
Spanish Resources
English/Spanish Guided Reading Audio Program
Reinforcement

Enrichment
Activity Worksheets
Section Focus Transparencies
Teaching Transparencies
Laboratory Activities
Science Inquiry Labs
Critical Thinking/Problem Solving
Reading and Writing Skill Activities
Mathematics Skill Activities
Cultural Diversity
Laboratory Management and Safety in the Science Classroom
Mindjogger Videoquizzes and Teacher Guide
Interactive Explorations and Quizzes CD-ROM with
   Presentation Builder
Vocabulary Puzzlemaker Software
Cooperative Learning in the Science Classroom
Environmental Issues in the Science Classroom
Home and Community Involvement
Using the Internet in the Science Classroom

"Study Tip," "Test-Taking Tip," and the "Test Practice" features in this book were written by The Princeton Review, the nation's leader in test preparation. Through its association with McGraw-Hill, The Princeton Review offers the best way to help students excel on standardized assessments.

The Princeton Review is not affiliated with Princeton University or Educational Testing Service.

Glencoe/McGraw-Hill

A Division of The McGraw·Hill Companies

Cover Images: Three generations of reticulated giraffes are shown in this photo.

Send all inquiries to:
Glencoe/McGraw-Hill
8787 Orion Place
Columbus, OH 43240

ISBN 0-07-825588-0
Printed in the United States of America.
1 2 3 4 5 6 7 8 9 10 027/043 06 05 04 03 02 01

Authors

Peter Rillero, PhD
Professor of Science Education
Arizona State University West
Phoenix, Arizona

Dinah Zike
Educational Consultant
Dinah-Might Activities, Inc.
San Antonio, Texas

Consultants

Content

Michael A. Hoggarth, PhD
Department of Life and Earth
Sciences
Otterbein College
Westerville, Ohio

Dominic Salinas, PhD
Middle School Science Supervisor
Caddo Parish Schools
Shreveport, Louisiana

Safety

Sandra West, PhD
Associate Professor of Biology
Southwest Texas State University
San Marcos, Texas

Reading

Elizabeth Babich
Special Education Teacher
Mashpee Public Schools
Mashpee, Massachusetts

Math

Teri Willard, EdD
Department of Mathematics
Montana State University
Belgrade, Montana

Reviewers

Michelle Bailey
Northwood Middle School
Houston, Texas

Maureen Barrett
Thomas E. Harrington Middle
School
Mt. Laurel, New Jersey

Desiree Bishop
Baker High School
Mobile, Alabama

Janice Bowman
Coke R. Stevenson Middle School
San Antonio, Texas

Linda V. Forsyth
Merrill Middle School
Denver, Colorado

Amy Morgan
Berry Middle School
Hoover, Alabama

Michelle Punch
Northwood Middle School
Houston, Texas

Darcy Vetro-Ravndal
Middleton Middle School of
Technology
Tampa, Florida

Billye Robbins
Lomax Junior High School
LaPorte, Texas

Series Activity Testers

José Luis Alvarez, PhD
Math/Science Mentor Teacher
Yseleta ISD
El Paso, Texas

Nerma Coats Henderson
Teacher
Pickerington Jr. High School
Pickerington, Ohio

Mary Helen Mariscal-Cholka
Science Teacher
William D. Slider Middle School
El Paso, Texas

José Alberto Marquez
TEKS for Leaders Trainer
Yseleta ISD
El Paso, Texas

Science Kit and Boreal Laboratories
Tonawanda, New York

CONTENTS

Interdisciplinary Connections/Activities

Glencoe Science Ecology
Contents in Brief

Teacher Wraparound Edition

Student Edition

Conservation and Native Americans

Introduction

This feature introduces students to the concepts of conservation and resource management. Students will also read that all species on Earth are interconnected and about how each interacts with and affects the environment. The ideas of conservation and resource management are presented through the example of the traditional practices of Native North Americans. The feature also stresses the concept that ideas in science change as humans gain new knowledge, but also that some ideas from history are still valid.

1 Motivate

Why is conservation of resources important? Possible answer: Some resources are of limited supply. Have students make a list of what resources they use everyday. **Which of these resources may need to be conserved?** Answers will vary. **What resources do you conserve?** Possible answers: water, paper (wood), fossil fuels (electricity), plastics

Conservation and Native Americans

Figure 1
Salmon were the major food source of the Pacific Northwest Native Americans.

Figure 2
Native Americans did not waste any part of nature. This Blackfoot shirt was made with hair, porcupine quills, and feathers.

A cool breeze blows through the trees lining the Columbia River in the state of Washington as a shiny salmon darts through the water. Every year these fish make the difficult journey upstream to lay their eggs in the same waters where they began their lives.

Many years ago, before Europeans came to North America, Native Americans of the northwest depended on salmon. At the first sign of autumn, the salmon run would start. Native American oral histories tell of rivers being so full of the fish that you almost could walk across them to the other side. The native people harvested and dried enough fish to sustain them for the entire year. They also had a deep respect for the salmon. The belief that the fish had a spirit was shown by the tradition of thanking the salmon's spirit for its sacrifice before it was eaten.

Respect for Life

Native American tradition is to respect all animals and their spirits that gave their life to feed and clothe the people. On the Great Plains, the Cheyenne and other native peoples had strict rules against killing more bison than they needed. They believed in using every part of the animal. They used as much of the animal as possible for food. The animal's fat was used in cooking. Tools were made from bones. Clothing, shoes, and blankets were made from hides. Even the bisons' stomachs were used as water pouches.

Respect for life extended to plants and crops for Native Americans. The Iroquois of the northeastern United States celebrated festivals in honor of the "three sisters"—corn, squash, and beans—their essential foods. The Maya who once lived in what is now southern Mexico and Central America, felt that if someone cut down a tree unnecessarily, that person's life would be shortened.

Curriculum Connection

History Have students research the history of Native American fishing in the Pacific Northwest. **Which fish were an important source of food? What methods were used to catch the fish? Were there other uses for the fish besides food?** Possible answers: Herring, salmon, cod, halibut, and flounder; fish were caught with spears, harpoons, trawls, weirs, nets, and hooks on lines. In one case, the skeleton of a fish was used in a ceremony. The oil of some fish was used for flavoring foods.

Every year, in the late spring or early summer, native peoples living on the Plains, including the Cree, Kiowa, Shoshone, and others, celebrated the cycle of life with the Sun Dance. This ceremony, which is performed by many tribes today, stresses the regeneration of life and humans' connection to Earth. Native Americans expressed thankfulness for Earth's gifts—the return of flowers and crops in the spring and summer, and the sacrifice made by animal spirits as they give their bodies to sustain the people. Their tradition recognizes that people must cooperate with nature so that revival and rebirth can continue.

Figure 3
Agriculture students experiment with the Native American practice of growing several types of plants in one area.

Respect for Earth

Native Americans felt a deep connection to Earth. While some European settlers viewed the New World as a wilderness ready to be tamed, the native peoples believed in living in harmony with Earth. They didn't understand the European desire to own and develop land. To the Native Americans, everyone shared the land. You could no more own the land than you could own the air. The Lakota chief Black Elk once spoke of each human's responsibility to Earth in this way: "Every step that we take upon You should be done in a sacred manner; every step should be taken as a prayer."

Figure 4
Native American artist Helen Hardin titled this piece *Father Sky Embracing Mother Earth.*

THE NATURE OF SCIENCE E ◆ 3

2 Teach

Content Background

Resources can be classified as renewable, those that are constantly recycled or replaced by nature, or nonrenewable, those that are used up more quickly than they can be replaced by natural processes. Fossil fuels such as coal, oil, and natural gas are examples of nonrenewable resources. Renewable energy resources include solar power, wind, or water.

Other resources such as groundwater or fisheries can be depleted if they are overexploited. When the removal rate of adult fish from an area exceeds their rate of reproduction, this can result in increasingly smaller numbers in the population. If overharvesting of a particular species continues for an extended period of time, the fish can disappear from an area. During the nineteenth century, halibut was overfished so drastically from the northwestern Atlantic that even today the numbers of halibut caught in this area are very low.

Discussion

How are all species on Earth interconnected? Possible answer: Species are connected by food webs and by the global environment. Pollutants in the air and ocean can have far reaching effects. Issues such as the depletion of the ozone layer, the greenhouse effect, and global warming can affect all species on Earth.

Content Background

The Iroquois planted the "three sisters" (corn, squash, and beans) together, taking advantage of the natural characteristics of each plant to help the others grow. The corn plants provided shade for the bean plants. The bean and squash vines grew up and around the tall stalk of the corn. The bean plants provided a usable form of nitrogen to surrounding plants. The squash plants also grew close to the ground around the base of the corn and beans, which helped to reduce soil erosion. Also, the prickly foliage of squash vines deter some animals that eat corn.

Activity

Have students each choose one resource and devise a plan to reduce their use of the resource by ten percent. For example, they could choose a fossil fuel such as natural gas, which may be the fuel used to heat their home, heat water, provide electricity, or provide energy for the stove; water; or paper (wood). Suggest students examine a gas or electric bill, count how many pieces of paper are used, or estimate water usage by examining statistics of average use in order to determine how much of the resource their families use in a week. Conservation strategies may include turning off lights or televisions when not in the room or turning off water while brushing teeth. Have students write out their plans and follow them for a week, recording their results.

THE NATURE OF SCIENCE

Figure 5
Early industrial development led to environmental pollution.

Figure 6
Recycling and using nonpolluting types of energy, such as solar energy, are two of the ways Americans are becoming more environmentally conscious.

Need for Conservation

When Europeans began to settle throughout America, it seemed that their way of life would completely replace Native American conservation practices. Many farming techniques used by the new settlers eroded fertile topsoil. Some of the wildlife, which had been treasured and respected by the native peoples, was driven to either extinction or near extinction.

New technology greatly affected the environment. The steam and diesel engines, commercial oil drilling, burning of coal, and industrial development led to waste and pollution.

In recent years, Americans have become more aware of the need for conservation. In 1970, the Environmental Protection Agency was created with the goal of safeguarding the environment. Paper, plastic, glass, and metal are widely recycled. Many items that were once considered waste are now being reused. Although pollution is still a problem, Americans are returning to practices that are more like traditional Native American ways.

Science

The practice of modifying human behavior to preserve Earth is known as conservation. Conservation involves managing the use of natural resources found in many different environments. In this book, you will learn about how all species on Earth are connected and how they can affect their environments.

History of Science

History is a record of people's achievements and their mistakes. Science history teaches that scientific ideas are not limited to scientists. Many people of different ethnic backgrounds, professions, and ages—male and female—have contributed to today's conservation movement. Studying the history of science reminds people that even though accepted views may change, humans constantly gain a better understanding of nature.

Visual Learning

Figure 7 Unlike petroleum based packing beads, some new packing beads are being manufactured from wheat, corn, or potato starch. Packing beads made from starch are biodegradable. They can also be recycled or composted. **What other items could be used in packing that are recyclable or biodegradable?** Possible answers: paper, newspaper, wood shavings, crumpled plastic grocery bags

Connections

Throughout their history, Native Americans have understood the importance of living in harmony with nature. They practiced conservation as a way of life, not just a passing fad. The people of the northwest understood that fishing for more salmon than they needed would endanger the next year's supply. Today, people are learning this same lesson as some traditional fishing grounds are closed because of overharvesting.

Recall the Mayan belief about how unnecessarily cutting down a tree shortened one's life. It is now known that plants provide oxygen and remove carbon dioxide from the air. Scientists warn that cutting down rain forest trees might lead to a buildup of carbon dioxide in the atmosphere. This could add to the trend in rising, global average temperatures known as global warming.

Native Americans on the Plains realized the importance of using every part of the bison, learning to live with their minimum needs, and limiting their use of natural resources. This model is being followed today, in some ways, through the effort to reduce, reuse, and recycle.

As new knowledge replaces old, it's tempting to think that only new ideas are worthwhile. Native American traditions of conservation show that this is not always true. These traditions once were disregarded but the value of their conservation is now known.

Figure 7
Many items that you use every day are made of recycled material. These packing beads are made from a wheat product.

Figure 8
The amount of land covered by rain forests is decreasing daily.

You Do It

In 1950, rain forests covered about 30 percent of Earth's land areas. Today, only about 7 percent of Earth's land areas are covered with rain forests. Research to find out the history of this change. Explain how following Native American conservation practices might have avoided the problems that face the rain forests today.

THE NATURE OF SCIENCE   E ◆ 5

Extension

Have students analyze their results from the activity. Were they able to reduce their usage of a resource by at least ten percent? Was the percentage of reduction less? Greater? How could they improve their plans? Have students make a conservation poster that shows the goal, the plan, and the results that might encourage other people to try it.

Use Science Words

Word Origin Have students use a dictionary to determine the origin of the word *ecology*. The word is derived from the Greek *ökologie*, the root of which, *oikos*, means "house"; *–logie* means "science."

Quick Demo

Present students with a list of resources and have them classify the resources as renewable or nonrenewable. Discuss with students the reasons why they choose to classify the resources as they did. Possible answers: nonrenewable: coal, oil, natural gas, minerals, metals in Earth's crust; renewable: Sun (solar power), water, air, crops, or wind

3 Assess

Use the question in You Do It to assess understanding. Answers should relate to what is known about the removal of rain forests and should be as specific as possible.

You Do It

Rain forests are being cut down for several reasons including as a source of wood, for space needed as populations expand, and for farmland. Some of the problems that have resulted from deforestation include habitat destruction for many types of plants and animals that live in the forests. It is the plants in the forest itself that holds most of the nutrients. Once the plants have been removed, the soil is nutrient poor and can be easily eroded.

Section/Objectives	Standards		Activities/Features
Chapter Opener	National	State/Local	**Explore Activity:** Examine sod from a lawn, p. 7 **Before You Read,** p. 7
	See p. 6T for a Key to Standards.		
Section 1 Living Earth 🕐 2 sessions 🧱 1 block 1. **Identify** places where life is found on Earth. 2. **Define** ecology. 3. **Observe** how the environment influences life.	National Content Standards: UCP1, A1, C1, C4		**Science Online,** p. 10
Section 2 Populations 🕐 2 sessions 🧱 1 block 1. **Identify** methods for estimating population sizes. 2. **Explain** how competition limits population growth. 3. **List** factors that influence changes in population size.	National Content Standards: UCP1, A1, C1, C4		**MiniLAB:** Observing Seedling Competition, p. 13 **Problem Solving Activity:** Do you have too many crickets?, p. 15 **Science Online,** p. 16 **MiniLAB:** Comparing Biotic Potential, p. 17 **Visualizing Population Growth,** p. 18
Section 3 Interactions Within Communities 🕐 3 sessions 🧱 1.5 blocks 1. **Describe** how organisms obtain energy for life. 2. **Explain** how organisms interact. 3. **Recognize** that every organism occupies a niche.	National Content Standards: UCP1, A1, C1, C4, F5, G1, G3		**Chemistry Integration,** p. 21 **Health Integration,** p. 23 **Activity:** Feeding Habits of Planaria, p. 25 **Activity:** Population Growth in Fruit Flies, pp. 26–27 **Science and History:** You Can Count On It, pp. 28–29

NATIONAL GEOGRAPHIC

Teacher's Corner

PRODUCTS AVAILABLE FROM GLENCOE
To order call 1-800-334-7344:
CD-ROMs
NGS Picture Show: Looking at Ecosystems
NGS Picture Show: Looking at Living Things

Videodisc
STV: Habitats
STV: Water

PRODUCTS AVAILABLE FROM NATIONAL GEOGRAPHIC SOCIETY
To order call 1-800-368-2728:

Videos
Ecosystem: A Struggle For Survival
Pond-Life: Food Web
Web of Life

Activity Materials	Reproducible Resources	Section Assessment	Technology
Explore Activity: a section of sod, hand lens	**Chapter Resources Booklet** Foldables Worksheet, p. 17 Directed Reading Overview, p. 19 Note-taking Worksheets, pp. 33–35	*GLENCOE'S* **ASSESSMENT** *ADVANTAGE*	
Need materials? Contact Science Kit at 1-800-828-7777 or www.sciencekit.com on the Internet.	**Chapter Resources Booklet** Transparency Activity, p. 44 Enrichment, p. 30 Reinforcement, p. 27 Directed Reading, p. 20 **Science Inquiry Labs,** p. 7	Portfolio Activity, p. 10 Performance Skill Builder Activities, p. 11 Content Section Assessment, p. 11 Challenge, p. 11	Section Focus Transparency Interactive CD-ROM/DVD Guided Reading Audio Program
MiniLAB: 2 pots of plants, moist potting soil, radish seeds, watering can, basin, metric ruler **MiniLAB:** whole fruit, plastic knife, paper towels	**Chapter Resources Booklet** Transparency Activity, p. 45 MiniLAB, pp. 3, 4 Enrichment, p. 31 Reinforcement, p. 28 Directed Reading, p. 20 Transparency Activity, pp. 47–48 **Mathematics Skill Activities,** p. 5	Portfolio Curriculum Connection, p. 15 Performance MiniLAB, p. 13 MiniLAB, p. 17 Skill Builder Activities, p. 19 Content Section Assessment, p. 19 Challenge, p. 19	Section Focus Transparency Teaching Transparency Interactive CD-ROM/DVD Guided Reading Audio Program
Activity: small bowl, several planarians, lettuce leaf, raw liver or meat, several guppies, pond or stream water, hand lens **Activity:** fruit flies; fruit fly culture kit; food items (banana, orange peel, or other fruit); water; culture containers; cloth, plastic, or other tops for containers; hand lens	**Chapter Resources Booklet** Transparency Activity, p. 46 Activity Worksheets, pp. 5–6, 7–8 Enrichment, p. 32 Reinforcement, p. 29 Directed Reading, pp. 21, 22 Lab Activities, pp. 9–11, 13–16 **Home and Community Involvement,** p. 47 **Lab Management and Safety,** p. 71	Portfolio Science Journal, p. 23 Performance Skill Builder Activities, p. 24 Content Section Assessment, p. 24 Challenge, p. 24	Section Focus Transparency Interactive CD-ROM/DVD Guided Reading Audio Program

End of Chapter Assessment

GLENCOE'S **ASSESSMENT** *ADVANTAGE*

Blackline Masters	Technology	Professional Series
Chapter Resources Booklet Chapter Review, pp. 37–38 Chapter Tests, pp. 39–42 **Standardized Test Practice by The Princeton Review,** pp. 11–14	MindJogger Videoquiz CD-ROM Explorations and Quizzes Vocabulary Puzzle Makers ExamView Pro Test Bank Interactive Lesson Planner Interactive Teacher's Edition	Performance Assessment in the Science Classroom (PASC)

Transparencies

Section Focus

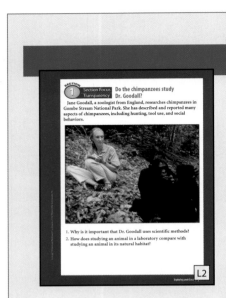

Section Focus Transparency 1 — Do the chimpanzees study Dr. Goodall?

Jane Goodall, a zoologist from England, researches chimpanzees in Gombe Stream National Park. She has described and reported many aspects of chimpanzees, including hunting, tool use, and social behaviors.

1. Why is it important that Dr. Goodall uses scientific methods?
2. How does studying an animal in a laboratory compare with studying an animal in its natural habitat?

L2

Section Focus Transparency 2 — Most Enlightening

Have you ever seen a house plant reaching for the window? Most plants grow toward the light. This bending, called phototropism, is caused by a plant hormone that makes cells on the side away from the light grow longer. Therefore, the plant bends in the direction of the light source.

1. Describe this plant's response to light.
2. What would happen if you gave the pot a half turn?
3. What does this plant need to live?

L2

Section Focus Transparency 3 — How about a field trip?

Is there life on other planets? If there is, it probably doesn't look like aliens in the movies. Some scientists think Europa, a moon of Jupiter, is a candidate for housing extraterrestrial life.

1. Where do living things come from?
2. Can you make a guess as to how life on Earth began?
3. What life-starting components might Europa possess?

L2

This is a representation of key blackline masters available in the Teacher Classroom Resources. See Resource Manager boxes within the chapter for additional information.

Key to Teaching Strategies

The following designations will help you decide which activities are appropriate for your students.

L1 Level 1 activities should be appropriate for students with learning difficulties.

L2 Level 2 activities should be within the ability range of all students.

L3 Level 3 activities are designed for above-average students.

ELL ELL activities should be within the ability range of English Language Learners.

COOP LEARN Cooperative Learning activities are designed for small group work.

LS Multiple Learning Styles logos are used throughout to indicate strategies that address different learning styles.

P These strategies represent student products that can be placed into a best-work portfolio.

Assessment

Assessment Transparency — Exploring and Classifying Life

Directions: Carefully review the table and answer the following questions.

Fruit and Vegetable Seed Germination Rate

Type of seed	Number of seeds	Amount of water added (mL)	Day 3	Day 5	Day 7
Orange	10	50	0	0	1
Lemon	10	50	0	1	1
Cucumber	10	50	6	7	7
Onion	10	50	7	9	10

1. Which hypothesis was probably being tested?
   A Less than 25 percent of vegetable seeds will germinate.
   B Seeds prefer to grow in soil versus sand.
   C Vegetable seeds germinate faster than fruit seeds.
   D A period of one week is required before seeds will germinate.
2. Which of the following would improve an experiment to compare the rate of seed germination?
   F using more types of seeds
   G measuring the length of the plants
   H adding 100mL of water to each seed
   J conducting the experiment for a shorter time
3. Which factor would have the LEAST effect on the results?
   A the amount of light to which the seeds were exposed
   B the amount of soil used for the seeds
   C the color of the pots used
   D the depth the seeds were planted in the soil

L2

Teaching

Teaching Transparency — Modern Classification

Kingdom — Animalia
Phylum — Chordata
Class — Mammalia
Order — Cetacea
Family — Delphinidae
Genus — Tursiops
Species — Tursiops truncatus

L2

Hands-on Activities

Activity Worksheets

Activity — Classifying Seeds

Lab Preview

Directions: Answer these questions before you begin the Activity.

1. Why should seeds that are meant for planting not be tasted or eaten?

2. What is one feature of a seed that might be used for classifying seeds?

Scientists use classification systems to show how organisms are related. How do they determine what features to use to classify organisms? In this activity, you will observe seeds and use their features to classify them.

What You'll Investigate
How can the features of seeds be used to develop a key to identify the seed?

Materials
packets of seeds (10 different kinds)
hand lens
metric ruler

Goals
■ **Observe** the seeds and notice their features.
■ **Classify** seeds using these features.

Safety Precautions
Do not eat any seeds or put them in your mouth. Some may have been treated with chemicals.

Procedure
1. Record the features of each seed in the table below.
2. Use the features to develop a key.
3. Exchange keys with another group. Can you use their key to identify seeds?

Features	Type of Seed
Color	
Length (mm)	
Shape	
Texture	

L2

Laboratory Activities

Laboratory Activity — The Scientific Method

When scientists are asked questions, they may not know the answers. They think of the possible answers, called hypotheses, and experiment to find the correct answers. Using the results of the experiment, they may need to form another hypothesis and test it. This way of solving a problem is called the scientific method.

Strategy
You will predict whether or not red cabbage juice will remain red when chemicals are added to it.
You will test your prediction with an experiment.
You will observe what happens and record your observations.
You will draw conclusions based on your observations.

Materials
apron
goggles
4 test tubes (18 × 150 mm)
test tube rack
labels
3 droppers
graduated cylinder (25 mL)
40 mL red cabbage juice
chemical X (vinegar) Keep containers closed when not in use.
chemical Y (ammonia)
chemical Z (baking soda solution)

Procedure
1. In the space below, predict what will happen to the red cabbage juice when chemicals X, Y, and Z are added to it.

2. Label four test tubes, 1, 2, 3, and 4.
3. Add 10 mL of red cabbage juice to each test tube. **CAUTION:** Do not spill chemicals X, Y, or Z on clothes or skin. Rinse with water if spilled.

6. Add 10 drops of chemical X to test tube 1.
7. Add 10 drops of chemical Y to test tube 2.
8. Add 10 drops of chemical Z to test tube 3.
7. Do not add anything to test tube 4. This is the control. The control is part of the experiment that is not tested.
8. Record your observations in Table 1.

Data and Observations
Table 1

Test tube	Substance added	Color
1		
2		
3		
4		

L2

Meeting Different Ability Levels

Content Outline

Reinforcement

Directed Reading

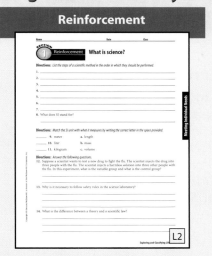

Assessment

Chapter Tests

Enrichment

Spanish Directed Reading

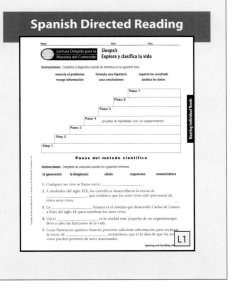

Test Practice Workbook

Chapter Review

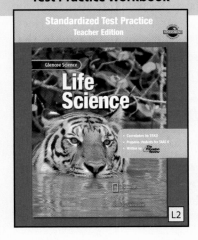

Science Content Background

SECTION 1

Living Earth
Understanding Ecosystems

The biosphere is the total part of Earth where life can exist and includes a great variety of conditions. An ecosystem is a smaller area consisting of the organisms and nonliving features that interact in the system. Sir Arthur George Tansley, a British plant ecologist, coined the word *ecosystem* in 1935.

SCIENCE Online

For additional content background on this topic, go to the Glencoe Science Web site at science.glencoe.com.

SECTION 2

Populations
Population Size

Population size is an important characteristic, but it can be difficult to measure. Animal population size is influenced by the amount of food and space available. Natural populations cannot increase forever. Population density measures how crowded a population is. It is always expressed as the number of individuals per unit area or volume.

Carrying Capacity

When a population's size is no longer increasing, it has reached its carrying capacity. The carrying capacity is the greatest number of individuals in a certain population that a given

Manoj Shah/DRK Photo

environment is capable of supporting under a given set of conditions. If a population is at carrying capacity, the number of organisms born in a given period of time is balanced by the number of organisms that die during that same time. Carrying capacity can vary with changing seasonal conditions. For example, cold winter weather may cause a reduction in the food supply and a resulting decrease in carrying capacity. In summer, when temperatures are favorable and food supplies increase, carrying capacity also increases.

SECTION 3

Interactions Within Communities
Types of Interactions

Organisms within a community interact in many ways. Plants and other photosynthetic organisms produce sugars that they use as food. Animals, fungi, and other non-photosynthetic organisms must consume other organisms for food. In addition to predator/prey or producer/consumer relationships, organisms may participate in symbiotic relationships, such as mutualism, commensalism, and parasitism, or they may compete with other species with similar needs for resources. A single species interacts directly or indirectly with nearly all the other species in its community. For example, a squirrel in a forest interacts not only with the plants it eats or with the predators that eat it but also with the plants it uses for cover or shelter, with insects that share its nest, with other animals that use its abandoned nest for shelter, with the bacteria that live on its skin, and so on.

Student Misconception

Plants do not depend on other organisms.

Refer to the facing page for teaching strategies to address this misconception. Refer to pages 23–24 for content related to this topic.

IDENTIFYING > Misconceptions

Find Out What Students Think

Students may think that . . .

- **Plants do not depend on other organisms.**

- **Organisms do not depend on one another.**

- **Interdependence is primarily predator/prey relationships.**

While most students can draw a picture of a natural community that includes producers, herbivores, and predators, few can explain their selections in terms of ecological relationships. Many students understand that the organisms they have depicted belong in the environment, but they don't understand how the organisms interact with one another and with the nonliving environment. While students may be able to identify predator/prey relationships, or plant/herbivore relationships, they seldom understand other types of relationships, nor do they see how interconnected one organism may be with many other organisms in its environment.

Activity

Have students draw a terrestrial community, using the local environment as a model. Their drawings should include several different types of organisms. Ask students to indicate as many interactions between organisms as they can. Then have them describe, aloud or in essay form, how each organism in the picture interacts with other organisms. Note the types and complexity of interactions that students describe.

Promote Understanding

Activity

After students read Section 3, organize the class into teams of three or four students. Assign each team a color. Have each team make ten or so flags from paper corresponding to their team's color and toothpicks.

- Take the class outside to a grassy or weedy area of the school grounds.

- Have teams hunt for examples of organisms interacting in various ways, including consumption, competition, and symbiosis, and mark each area where an interaction is occurring with a flag. On each flag, team members should identify the type of interaction and write a short description in their Science Journals of what they found. Encourage students to include drawings along with their verbal descriptions.

- After the allotted time, give students time to examine the findings of other teams before gathering up the flags and returning to the classroom.

- Give each team time to summarize their findings. Then have representatives from each team report their findings to the class. Encourage teams to include their drawings of the interactions they observed.

When all teams have reported, discuss the relationships discovered by the class. Focus the discussion on a few organisms identified by most teams. Challenge students to brainstorm a list of ways in which those organisms interact with other organisms.

Assess

After completing the chapter, see *Identifying Misconceptions* in the Study Guide.

Chapter Vocabulary

biosphere
ecosystem
ecology
population
community
habitat
limiting factor
carrying capacity
producer
consumer
symbiosis
mutualism
commensalism
parasitism
niche

What do you think?

Science Journal These are the little mud tunnels that termites build across a non-wood surface to provide protection as they travel back and forth between their nest and their food source.

Interactions of Life

Why would a powerful rhinoceros allow birds to perch on its back? Why aren't these birds safely perched in a tree? How do they find food? You don't have to go to Africa to see birds on the back of a rhino. You can see these animals at zoos or wildlife parks. In this chapter, you will learn how living organisms interact with each other and their surroundings. You also will learn about the roles each organism plays in the flow of energy through the environment.

What do you think?

Science Journal Look at the picture below with a classmate. Discuss what you think this might be or what is happening. Here's a hint: *It's a city within a city.* Write your answer or best guess in your Science Journal.

Theme Connection

Systems and Interactions A discussion of ecosystems, habitats, and communities shows how organisms interact. These interactions within the system affect population sizes and organisms' abilities to survive in their environments.

EXPLORE ACTIVITY

In your lifetime, you probably have taken thousands of footsteps on grassy lawns or playing fields. If you take a close look at the grass, you'll see that each blade is attached to roots in the soil. How do the grass plants obtain everything they need to live and grow? What other kinds of organisms live in the grass? The following activity will give you a chance to take a closer look at the life in a lawn.

Examine sod from a lawn

1. Examine a section of sod from a lawn.

2. How do the roots of the grass plants hold the soil?

3. Do you see signs of other living things besides grass?

Observe

In your Science Journal, answer the above questions and describe any organisms that are present in your section of sod. Explain how these organisms might affect the growth of grass plants. Draw a picture of your section of sod.

FOLDABLES
Reading & Study Skills

Before You Read

Making a Concept Map Study Fold The following Foldable will help you organize information by diagramming ideas about your favorite wild animal.

1. Place a sheet of paper in front of you with the short side at the top. Fold the paper in half from the left side to the right side.

2. Fold from top to bottom to divide the paper into thirds, then open up the three folds.

3. Through the top thickness of paper, cut along each of the fold lines to the side fold, forming three tabs.

4. Label *Organism, Population,* and *Community* across the front of the paper, as shown. Write the name of your favorite wild animal under the *Organism* tab.

5. Before you read the chapter, write what you know about your favorite animal under the top tab. As you read the chapter, write how this animal is part of a population and a community under the middle and bottom tabs.

Organism

Population

Community

E ◆ 7

Purpose Use the Explore Activity to introduce students to characteristics of ecosystems and communities. Explain that they will be learning about interactions among organisms of the same or different species. L1
ELL IS **Kinesthetic**

Preparation Purchase sod from a garden center, or dig up a square of sod, including the soil that surrounds the roots. Temporarily fill the area with soil so you don't leave a divot. Replace the sod when you are finished. Keep the sod in a cool, moist area so that it stays fresh and retains small animal life.

Materials small piece of sod for each group, hand lens (optional)

Teaching Strategy After a few minutes of examination, instruct students to tear the sod in half. This may reveal animals that have moved to the interior of the sod.

Observe

Organisms may include one or more grasses, clover, ants, grasshopper nymphs, earthworms, fungi, or bacteria. The effects of the organisms will vary. A grasshopper might slow the growth of grass, but an earthworm might accelerate it.

✓ Assessment

Process Have students show each other an organism that they observed. Then have them infer the effect of the organism on the grass. Use **Performance Assessment in the Science Classroom,** p. 89.

FOLDABLES
Reading & Study Skills

Before You Read

Dinah Zike Study Fold

Purpose Students develop and use a Foldable concept map to describe a specific animal as part of a population and a community.

📁 For additional help, see Foldables Worksheet, p. 17 in **Chapter Resources Booklet,** or go to the Glencoe Science Web site at **science.glencoe.com.** See After You Read in the Study Guide at the end of this chapter.

SECTION

1

Living Earth

1 Motivate

Bellringer Transparency

Display the Section Focus Transparency for Section 1. Use the accompanying Transparency Activity Master. L2 ELL

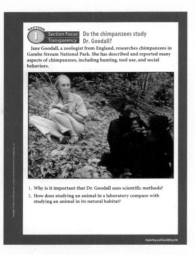

Tie to Prior Knowledge

Ask students to identify several habitats—the places where plants and animals live. Have them describe living and non-living things in those habitats.

Living Earth

As You Read

What You'll Learn
- **Identify** places where life is found on Earth.
- **Define** ecology.
- **Observe** how the environment influences life.

Vocabulary

biosphere	population
ecosystem	community
ecology	habitat

Why It's Important
All living things on Earth depend on each other for survival.

The Biosphere

What makes Earth different from other planets in the solar system? One difference is Earth's abundance of living organisms. The part of Earth that supports life is the **biosphere** (BI uh sfihr). The biosphere includes the top portion of Earth's crust, all the waters that cover Earth's surface, and the atmosphere that surrounds Earth.

✔ **Reading Check** *What three things make up the biosphere?*

As **Figure 1** shows, the biosphere is made up of different environments that are home to different kinds of organisms. For example, desert environments receive little rain. Cactus plants, coyotes, and lizards are included in the life of the desert. Tropical rain forest environments receive plenty of rain and warm weather. Parrots, monkeys, and tens of thousands of other organisms live in the rain forest. Arctic regions near the north pole are covered with ice and snow. Polar bears live on the arctic ice. Seals and walruses hunt for fish in the Arctic Ocean.

Figure 1
Earth's biosphere consists of many environments, including ocean waters, polar regions, and deserts.

Desert

Arctic

Coral reef

Section ✓Assessment Planner

PORTFOLIO
Activity, p. 10
PERFORMANCE ASSESSMENT
Skill Builder Activities, p. 11
See page 32 for more options.

CONTENT ASSESSMENT
Section, p. 11
Challenge, p. 11
Chapter, pp. 32–33

Astronomy INTEGRATION

Life on Earth In our solar system, Earth is the third planet from the Sun. The amount of energy that reaches Earth from the Sun helps make the temperature just right for life. Mercury, the planet closest to the Sun, is too hot during the day and too cold at night to make life possible there. Venus, the second planet from the Sun, has a thick, carbon dioxide atmosphere and high temperatures. It is unlikely that life could survive there. Mars, the fourth planet, is cooler than Earth, with high temperatures of about –33°C. Mars might support microscopic life, but none has been found. The planets beyond Mars probably do not have enough heat and light from the Sun to create the right conditions for life.

Ecosystems

On a visit to Yellowstone National Park in Wyoming, you might see a prairie scene like the one shown in **Figure 2.** Bison graze on prairie grass. Cowbirds follow the bison, catching grasshoppers that jump away from the bisons' hooves. This scene is part of an ecosystem. An **ecosystem** consists of all the organisms living in an area and the nonliving features of their environment. Bison, grass, birds, and insects are living organisms of this prairie ecosystem. Water, temperature, sunlight, soil, and air are nonliving features of this prairie ecosystem. **Ecology** is the study of interactions that occur among organisms and their environment. Ecologists are scientists who study these interactions.

✔ **Reading Check** *What is an ecosystem?*

Figure 2
Ecosystems are made up of living organisms and the nonliving features of their environment. In this prairie ecosystem, cowbirds eat insects and bison graze on grass. *What other kinds of organisms might live in this ecosystem?*

Populations

SCIENCE *Online*

Internet Addresses

_____

_____

_____

Explore the Glencoe Science Web site at science.glencoe.com to find out more about topics in this section.

IDENTIFYING Misconceptions

Uses of the term *population* may lead to confusion. When discussing human population size it is common to simply say population. For example, "What is the population of San Diego?" In ecology, a population refers to all the organisms of a species in an area. A population has many characteristics, only one of which is size.

Activity

Have students observe a natural setting and draw or photograph a habitat that contains visible plant and animal life. Ask students to place their drawings or photographs, along with a list of the populations observed, in their Science Journals. L2 ELL

IS Naturalist P

SCIENCE *Online*

Research Visit the Glencoe Science Web site at **science.glencoe.com** and find out the estimated human population size for the world today. In your Science Journal, create a graph that shows the population change between the year 2000 and this year.

Figure 3
The living world is arranged in several levels of organization.

Populations

Suppose you meet an ecologist who studies how a herd of bison moves from place to place and how the female bison in the herd care for their young. This ecologist is studying the members of a population. A **population** is made up of all the organisms in an ecosystem that belong to the same species. For example, all the bison in a prairie ecosystem are one population. All the cowbirds in this ecosystem make up a different population. The grasshoppers make up yet another population.

Ecologists often study how populations interact. For example, an ecologist might try to answer questions about several prairie species. How does grazing by bison affect the growth of prairie grass? How does grazing influence the insects that live in the grass and the birds that eat those insects? This ecologist is studying a community. A **community** refers to all the populations in an ecosystem. The prairie community is made of populations of bison, grasshoppers, cowbirds, and all other species in the prairie ecosystem. An arctic community might include populations of fish, seals that eat fish, and polar bears that hunt and eat seals. **Figure 3** shows how organisms, populations, communities, and ecosystems are related.

Inclusion Strategies

Learning Disabled Give student pairs a one-inch column of newspaper text. Ask them to find, circle, and count different populations. For example, have them find the population of the letter *P* by circling each *P* and counting to determine population size. Explain that one letter is an organism, each type of letter is a population, and all the types of letters are a community. L1

Resource Manager

Chapter Resources Booklet
　　Reinforcement, p. 27
　　Enrichment, p. 30
Science Inquiry Labs, p. 7

Figure 4
The trees of the forest provide a habitat for woodpeckers and other birds. This salamander's habitat is the moist forest floor.

Habitats

Each organism in an ecosystem needs a place to live. The place in which an organism lives is called its **habitat.** The animals shown in **Figure 4** live in a forest ecosystem. Trees are the woodpeckers' habitat. These birds use their strong beaks to pry insects from tree bark or break open acorns and nuts. Woodpeckers usually nest in holes in dead trees. The salamander's habitat is the forest floor, beneath fallen leaves and twigs. Salamanders avoid sunlight and seek damp, dark places. This animal eats small worms, insects, and slugs. An organism's habitat provides the kinds of food and shelter, the temperature, and the amount of moisture the organism needs to survive.

Section 1 Assessment

1. What is the biosphere?
2. What is ecology?
3. How are the terms *habitat* and *biosphere* related to each other?
4. What is the major difference between a community and a population? Give one example of each.
5. **Think Critically** Does the amount of rain that falls in an area determine which kinds of organisms can live there? Why or why not?

Skill Builder Activities

6. **Forming Hypotheses** Make a hypothesis about how one nonliving feature of the environment would affect the growth of dandelions in that environment. **For more help, refer to the** Science Skill Handbook.
7. **Communicating** Pretend you are a non-human organism in the wild. Describe what you are and list living and nonliving features of the environment that affect you. **For more help, refer to the** Science Skill Handbook.

Habitats

Discussion

Point out that a habitat may describe a very small location, such as a nest in a tree, or a much larger area, such as a freshwater lake. **What is your habitat?** house or apartment **What is the habitat of a humpback whale?** the ocean

3 Assess

Reteach

Have students write a paragraph in their Science Journals explaining the relationships among a population, a community, and an ecosystem. They should include that populations interact to form a community and that communities and nonliving things together make up the ecosystem. L2 IS **Linguistic**

Challenge

Have students research the natural habitat of an organism and then tell the class five interesting things about this habitat. L3 IS **Naturalist**

✓Assessment

Content Provide students with photographs from discarded magazines. Have them identify living and nonliving things in each photograph and explain how the nonliving things might affect living things. Use **Performance Assessment in the Science Classroom,** p. 89.

Answers to Section Assessment

1. the part of Earth that supports life
2. the study of the interactions between organisms and between organisms and their nonliving environment
3. Habitat—place where organisms live; the biosphere includes all Earth's habitats.

4. A population is a single species living in an area. Example: all the maple trees of the Catskill Mountains. A community is all the populations that live in an area. Example: all the species of the Catskill Mountains.
5. Yes; organisms that need a lot of water cannot exist in areas with little rainfall.

6. Hypotheses should indicate that a nonliving factor, such as light, moisture, chemical fertilizers, or pH can have a positive or negative affect on the growth of dandelions.
7. Answers will vary but should include interactions with both the living and nonliving components of the environment.

SECTION

2

Populations

1 Motivate

Bellringer Transparency

Display the Section Focus Transparency for Section 2. Use the accompanying Transparency Activity Master. L2 ELL

Tie to Prior Knowledge

Have students recall the needs of living things. Knowing what living things need to grow and reproduce will be helpful in understanding limiting factors.

Populations

As You Read

What You'll Learn

- **Identify** methods for estimating population sizes.
- **Explain** how competition limits population growth.
- **List** factors that influence changes in population size.

Vocabulary

limiting factor
carrying capacity

Why It's Important

Competition caused by population growth affects many organisms, including humans.

Figure 5
Gila woodpeckers make nesting holes in the saguaro cactus. Many animals compete for the shelter these holes provide.

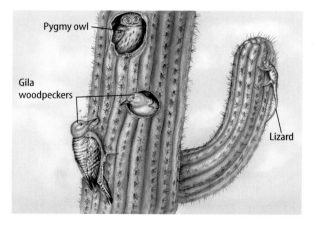

Pygmy owl

Gila woodpeckers

Lizard

Competition

Some pet shops sell lizards, snakes, and other reptiles. Crickets are raised as a food supply for pet reptiles. In the wild, crickets come out at night and feed on plant material. During the day, they hide in dark areas, beneath leaves or under buildings. Pet shop workers who raise crickets make sure that the insects have plenty of food, water, and hiding places. As the cricket population grows, the workers increase the crickets' food supply and the number of hiding places. To avoid crowding, some of the crickets could be moved into larger containers.

Food and Space Organisms living in the wild do not always have enough food or living space. The Gila woodpecker, shown in **Figure 5,** lives in the Sonoran Desert of Arizona and Mexico. This bird makes its nest in a hole that it drills in a saguaro (suh GWAR oh) cactus. If an area has too many Gila woodpeckers or too few saguaros, the woodpeckers must compete with each other for nesting spots. Competition occurs when two or more organisms seek the same resource at the same time.

Growth Limits Competition limits population size. If the amount of available nesting space is limited, some woodpeckers will not be able to raise young. Gila woodpeckers eat cactus fruit, berries, and insects. If food becomes scarce, some woodpeckers might not survive to reproduce. Competition for food, living space, or other resources can prevent population growth.

In nature, the most intense competition is usually among individuals of the same species, because they need the same kinds of food and shelter. Competition also takes place among individuals of different species. For example, after a Gila woodpecker has abandoned its nesting hole, owls, flycatchers, snakes, and lizards compete for the shelter of the empty hole.

12 ◆ E CHAPTER 1 Interactions of Life

Section ✓*Assessment* Planner

PORTFOLIO
Curriculum Connection, p. 15

PERFORMANCE ASSESSMENT
Try at Home MiniLAB, p. 13
MiniLAB, p. 17
Skill Builder Activities, p. 19
See page 32 for more options.

CONTENT ASSESSMENT
Section, p. 19
Challenge, p. 19
Chapter, pp. 32–33

Population Size

Ecologists often need to measure the size of a population. This information can indicate whether or not a population is healthy and growing. Population counts can help identify populations that could be in danger of disappearing.

Some populations are easy to measure. If you were raising crickets, you could measure the size of your cricket population simply by counting all the crickets in the container. What if you wanted to compare the cricket populations in two different containers? You would calculate the number of crickets per square meter (m^2) of your container. The size of a population that occupies a specific area is called population density. **Figure 6** shows human population density in different places in the world.

✓ Reading Check *What is population density?*

Measuring Populations Counting crickets can be tricky. They look alike, move a lot, and hide. The same cricket could be counted more than once, and others could be completely missed. Ecologists have similar problems when measuring wildlife populations. One of the methods they use is called trap-mark-release. Suppose you want to count wild rabbits. Rabbits live underground and come out at dawn and dusk to eat. Ecologists set traps that capture rabbits without injuring them. Each captured rabbit is marked and released. Later, another sample of rabbits is captured. Some of these rabbits will have marks, but many will not. By comparing the number of marked and unmarked rabbits in the second sample, ecologists can estimate the population size.

Humans/2.6km²	
	Over 500
	100–500
	50–99
	10–49
	Under 10

Figure 6
This map shows human population density. *Which countries have the highest population density?*

SECTION 2 Populations **E ◆ 13**

TRY AT HOME
Mini LAB

Observing Seedling Competition

Procedure
1. Fill **two plant pots** with **moist potting soil.**
2. Plant **radish seeds** in one pot, following the spacing instructions on the seed packet. Label this pot "Recommended Spacing."
3. Plant radish seeds in the second pot, spaced half the recommended distance apart. Label this pot "Densely Populated." Wash your hands.
4. Keep the soil moist. When the seeds sprout, move them to a well-lit area.
5. Measure the height of the seedlings every two days for two weeks. Record the data in your **Science Journal.**

Analysis
1. Which plants grew faster?
2. Which plants looked healthiest after two weeks?
3. How did competition influence the plants?

✓ Assessment

Oral Have students explain why the more densely planted seedlings might have grown faster. Have them predict which plants would be healthier if the experiment was continued for another four weeks. Use **Performance Assessment in the Science Classroom,** p. 99.

---

2 Teach

Population Size

TRY AT HOME
Mini LAB

Purpose Students determine if population density affects the growth of certain plants. L2
🅸🅽 **Logical-Mathematical**

Materials 2 plant pots, potting soil, radish seeds, watering can, large basin, metric ruler

Teaching Strategies
- Avoid putting plants in hot areas.
- Have students premeasure water before adding.

Troubleshooting Follow seed packets instructions as to the number of seeds to plant per hole. Thin plants so that the density of seedlings in one pot is twice the density in the other pot.

Analysis
1. In many cases the densely planted seedlings grew faster.
2. The plants with more space will usually look healthier. They may not be as tall, but they look greener, fuller, and more robust.
3. Competition probably caused the less densely planted seedlings to grow better because they were able to get more light.

✓ Reading Check

Answer the size of a population that occupies a specific area

Caption Answer
Figure 6 India, Japan, the Philippines, and South Korea

Population Size,
continued

Discussion

Why would people want to know the population size of organisms such as deer? Ecologists may want the data for research. Game and Fish Departments may want the information to decide how many hunting permits to issue.

Caption Answer

Figure 7 Answers will vary. Students may suggest that they can count the number of wildebeests in the enlarged square, and then multiply by 25, the number of squares in the entire photograph.

Extension

Assume one crabgrass plant produces 100 seeds every season, and each of those sprouts into a plant next season that will also produce 100 seeds. **If you start with one grass plant, how many will you have after three years?**

1: $(1 \times 100) + 1 = 101$;
2: $(101 \times 100) + 101 = 10,201$
3: $(10,201 \times 100) + 10,201 = 1,030,301$

Figure 7
Ecologists can estimate population size by making a sample count. Wildebeests graze on the grassy plains of Africa. *How could you use the enlarged square to estimate the number of wildebeests in the entire photograph?*

Sample Counts What if you wanted to count rabbits over a large area? Ecologists use sample counts to estimate the sizes of large populations. To estimate the number of rabbits in a 100-acre area, for example, you could count the rabbits in one acre and multiply by 100 to estimate the population size. **Figure 7** shows another approach to sample counting.

Limiting Factors One grass plant can produce hundreds of seeds. Imagine those seeds drifting onto a vacant field. Many of the seeds sprout and grow into grass plants that produce hundreds more seeds. Soon the field is covered with grass. Can this grass population keep growing forever? Suppose the seeds of wildflowers or trees drift onto the field. If those seeds sprout, trees and flowers would compete with grasses for sunlight, soil, and water. Even if the grasses did not have to compete with other plants, they might eventually use up all the space in the field. When no more living space is available, the population cannot grow.

In any ecosystem, the availability of food, water, living space, mates, nesting sites, and other resources is often limited. A **limiting factor** is anything that restricts the number of individuals in a population. Limiting factors include living and nonliving features of the ecosystem.

A limiting factor can affect more than one population in a community. Suppose a lack of rain limits plant growth in a meadow. Fewer plants produce fewer seeds. For seed-eating mice, this reduction in the food supply could become a limiting factor. A smaller mouse population could, in turn, become a limiting factor for the hawks and owls that feed on mice.

LAB DEMONSTRATION

Purpose to estimate population size

Materials overhead projector (OHP), 4 sheets of paper, transparency, marker, ruler, cardboard to screen the OHP surface, hole punch

Preparation Punch 100 discs. Draw a grid on the transparency consisting of 25 1.25″ x 1.25″ squares.

Procedure Display the grid. Erect the screen. Evenly sprinkle 25 discs. Position papers to reveal one square. Turn on the OHP; count the discs. Repeat twice. Estimate and then count population size. Repeat for 50 and 100 discs.

Expected Outcome Estimates will approximate actual population size.

✓ Assessment

How could a better estimate be made? Collect data from a greater number of cells. **When would an ecologist use this technique?** when it is difficult or expensive to count all the organisms in an area

Carrying Capacity A population of robins lives in a grove of trees in a park. Over several years, the number of robins increases and nesting space becomes scarce. Nesting space is a limiting factor that prevents the robin population from getting any larger. This ecosystem has reached its carrying capacity for robins. **Carrying capacity** is the largest number of individuals of one species that an ecosystem can support over time. If a population begins to exceed the environment's carrying capacity, some individuals will not have enough resources. They could die or be forced to move elsewhere, like the deer shown in **Figure 8.**

Figure 8
These deer might have moved into a residential area because a nearby forest's carrying capacity for deer has been reached.

✓ **Reading Check** *How are limiting factors related to carrying capacity?*

Problem-Solving Activity

Do you have too many crickets?

You've decided to raise crickets to sell to pet stores. A friend says you should not allow the cricket population density to go over 210 crickets/m^2. Use what you've learned in this section to measure the population density in your cricket tanks.

Identifying the Problem
The table on the right lists the areas and populations of your three cricket tanks. How can you determine if too many crickets are in one tank? If a tank contains too many crickets, what could you do? Explain why too many crickets in a tank might be a problem.

Cricket Population

Tank	Area (m^2)	Number of Crickets
1	0.80	200
2	0.80	150
3	1.5	315

Solving the Problem
1. Do any of the tanks contain too many crickets? Could you make the population density of the three tanks equal by moving crickets from one tank to another? If so, which tank would you move crickets into?

2. The population density of wild crickets living in a field is 2.4 crickets/m^2. If the field has an area of 250 m^2, what is the approximate size of the cricket population? Why would the population density of crickets in a field be lower than the population density of crickets in a tank?

Curriculum Connection

Art Have students research populations that live in areas in which limiting factors severely restrict the kinds of organisms that can live there. Have them make a collage that shows several different populations and environments, such as penguins in Antarctica and cacti in a hot, dry desert.

Activity
Have the classroom represent an ecosystem. Set the carrying capacity of the room at 80 percent of the number of students present. Have the remaining 20 percent of the students stand to the side. Have these "extra" individuals enter the ecosystem through birth or immigration and have others leave through death or emigration so that the size of the population remains steady. ⎣S⎦ **Kinesthetic**

✓ **Reading Check**

Answer Carrying capacity exists because of limiting factors. A shortage of one or more things limits population size.

Problem-Solving Activity

National Math Standards
Correlation to Mathematics Objectives
1, 2, 4, 6, 8, 9

Answers
1. The population densities of the three tanks are 1: 250 crickets/m^2 2: 187.5 crickets/m^2 3: 210 crickets/m^2. Tank 1 has too many crickets. You might try putting some of the extra crickets into tank 2, because it has a lower population density. Tank 3 has the maximum population density allowed.
2. To find this answer, multiply the population density by the area: 250 m^2 × 2.4 crickets/m^2 = 600 crickets. The population density in the field would be much lower than the tank because the crickets have more space to spread out. They are also free from competition.

Biotic Potential What would happen if no limiting factors restricted the growth of a population? Think about a population that has an unlimited supply of food, water, and living space. The climate is favorable. Population growth is not limited by diseases, predators, or competition with other species. Under ideal conditions like these, the population would continue to grow.

The highest rate of reproduction under ideal conditions is a population's biotic potential. The larger the number of offspring that are produced by parent organisms, the higher the biotic potential of the species will be. Compare an avocado tree to a tangerine tree. Assume that each tree produces the same number of fruits. Each avocado fruit contains one large seed. Each tangerine fruit contains a dozen seeds or more. Because the tangerine tree produces more seeds per fruit, it has a higher biotic potential than the avocado tree.

Changes in Populations

Birthrates and death rates also influence the size of a population and its rate of growth. A population gets larger when the number of individuals born is greater than the number of individuals that die. When the number of deaths is greater than the number of births, populations get smaller. Take the squirrels living in New York City's Central Park as an example. In one year, if 900 squirrels are born and 800 die, the population increases by 100. If 400 squirrels are born and 500 die, the population decreases by 100.

The same is true for human populations. **Table 1** shows birthrates, death rates, and population changes for several countries around the world. In countries with faster population growth, birthrates are much higher than death rates. In countries with slower population growth, birthrates are only slightly higher than death rates. In Germany, where the population is getting smaller, the birthrate is lower than the death rate.

Table 1 Population Growth			
	Birthrate*	Death Rate*	Population Increase (percent)
Rapid-Growth Countries			
Jordan	38.8	5.5	3.3
Uganda	50.8	21.8	2.9
Zimbabwe	34.3	9.4	5.2
Slow-Growth Countries			
Germany	9.4	10.8	−1.5
Sweden	10.8	10.6	0.1
United States	14.8	8.8	0.6

*Number per 1,000 people

Figure 9
The mangrove seeds sprout while they are still attached to the parent tree. Some sprouted seeds drop into the mud below the parent tree and continue to grow. Others drop into the water and can be carried away by tides and ocean currents. When they wash ashore, they might start a new population of mangroves or add to an existing mangrove population.

Moving Around Most animals can move easily from place to place, and these movements can affect population size. For example, a male mountain sheep might wander many miles in search of a mate. After he finds a mate, their offspring might establish a completely new population of mountain sheep far from the male's original population.

Many bird species move from one place to another during their annual migrations. During the summer, populations of Baltimore orioles are found throughout eastern North America. During the winter, these populations disappear because the birds migrate to Central America. They spend the winter there, where the climate is mild and food supplies are plentiful. When summer approaches, the orioles migrate back to North America.

Even plants and microscopic organisms can move from place to place, carried by wind, water, or animals. The tiny spores of mushrooms, mosses, and ferns float through the air. The seeds of dandelions, maple trees, and other plants have feathery or winglike growths that allow them to be carried by wind. Spine-covered seeds hitch rides by clinging to animal fur or people's clothing. Many kinds of seeds can be transported by river and ocean currents. Mangrove trees growing along Florida's Gulf Coast, shown in **Figure 9,** provide an example of how water moves seeds.

Mini LAB

Comparing Biotic Potential

Procedure
1. Remove all the seeds from a **whole fruit.** Do not put fruit or seeds in your mouth.
2. Count the total number of seeds in the fruit. Wash your hands, then record this data in your Science Journal.
3. Compare your seed totals with those of classmates who examined other types of fruit.

Analysis
1. Which type of fruit had the most seeds? Which had the fewest seeds?
2. What is an advantage of producing many seeds? Can you think of a possible disadvantage?
3. To estimate the total number of seeds produced by a tomato plant, what would you need to know?

Mini LAB

Purpose Students observe and compare the number of seeds in different types of fruit. L2
ELL IS **Logical-Mathematical**

Materials plastic knives, paper towels, assorted fruits

Teaching Strategies
- Arrange for students to bring in fruits from home.
- Explain that many of our vegetables are actually fruits, including tomatoes, eggplants, and squashes.

Safety Precautions Instruct students on the proper way to handle and use the plastic knives.

Analysis
1. Tomatoes and strawberries have many seeds; avocados and peaches have one seed.
2. Advantage: There is a greater chance that a seed will find an optimal place to grow. Disadvantage: The seeds are small and carry few nutrients.
3. How many tomatoes the plant produces and about how many seeds are produced by each tomato

✔ Assessment

Oral Based on the number of seeds contained in each fruit, which has a greater biotic potential—a nectarine or a watermelon? **Explain.** A watermelon—it contains many seeds, while a nectarine contains only one. Use **PASC,** p. 89.

☑ Active Reading

Four-Corner Discussion This strategy encourages the class to debate a complex issue. Make four signs: Strongly Agree, Agree, Disagree, Strongly Disagree. Place one sign in each corner of the room. Write on the chalkboard a statement that will elicit reactions from students. Have students respond on paper to the statement. After several minutes, direct them to move to the corner with the sign that most closely reflects their opinions. In the corners, students share responses. Each group then selects a spokesperson to report the opinions of the group. After all groups have reported, open the floor for debate. Allow students who have changed their opinions to change corners. Have students conduct a Four-Corner Discussion about the causes of changes in populations.

Visualizing Population Growth

Have students examine the pictures and read the captions. Then ask the following question.

What happens when a population exceeds carrying capacity? Possible answer: There may not be enough resources to support all members of the population. It is likely that members will begin to die from lack of resources such as food and water.

Extension

Have students graph the following data on predator-prey cycles between lynx and snowshoe hares.

Years	# of lynx	# of hares
1845	9,000	18,000
1850	10,000	30,000
1855	36,000	41,000
1860	8,000	12,000
1865	71,000	93,000
1870	5,000	9,000
1875	40,000	61,000
1880	9,000	11,000

What is the pattern between the population numbers of the lynx and the hares? As the number of hares increases, the number of lynx increases. As the larger lynx population feeds on hares, the number of hares decreases, followed by a decrease in the number of lynx.

Figure 10

When a species enters an ecosystem that has abundant food, water, and other resources, its population can flourish. Beginning with a few organisms, the population increases until the number of organisms and available resources are in balance. At that point, population growth slows or stops. A graph of these changes over time produces an S-curve, as shown here for coyotes.

CARRYING CAPACITY

EXPONENTIAL GROWTH

BEGINNING GROWTH

Population

Time

BEGINNING GROWTH During the first few years, population growth is slow, because there are few adults to produce young. As the population grows, so does the number of breeding adults.

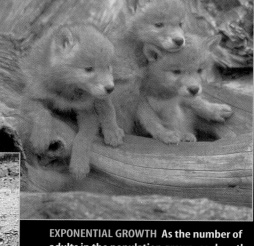

EXPONENTIAL GROWTH As the number of adults in the population grows, so does the number of births. The coyote population undergoes exponential growth, quickly increasing in size.

CARRYING CAPACITY As resources become less plentiful, the birth rate declines and the death rate may rise. Population growth slows. The coyote population has reached the environmental carrying capacity—the maximum number of coyotes that the environment can sustain.

18 ◆ E

Resource Manager

Chapter Resources Booklet
    Transparency Activity, pp. 47–48
    Reinforcement, p. 28

Life Science Critical Thinking/Problem Solving, p. 13

Curriculum Connection

Math The bacteria *E. coli* can double in population size every twenty minutes under suitable conditions. Starting with a single bacterium, have students calculate the length of time it would take for the population to reach 1 million. The population would reach 1 million in only 6 hours and 40 minutes. L2 LS **Logical-Mathematical**

Exponential Growth

Imagine what might happen if a pair of coyotes moves into a valley where no other coyotes live. Food and water are abundant, and there are plenty of areas where female coyotes can build dens for their young. This population grows quickly in a pattern called exponential growth. Exponential growth means that the larger a population becomes, the faster it grows.

After several years, the population becomes so large that the coyotes begin to compete for food and den sites. Population growth slows, and the number of coyotes remains fairly constant. This ecosystem has reached its carrying capacity for coyotes. A graph that describes each stage in this pattern of population growth is shown in **Figure 10.** As you can see in **Figure 11,** Earth's human population shows exponential growth. In the year 2000, Earth's human population reached 6 billion. By the year 2050, it is estimated that Earth's human population could reach 10 billion.

Increase in Human Population

Figure 11
The size of the human population is increasing by about 1.6 percent per year. *What factors affect human population growth?*

3 Assess

Reteach
Ask students to work in groups to (a) guess the size of your school's seventh-grade population, (b) devise a way to more accurately estimate that population size, and (c) give reasons for seventh-grade immigration and emigration. L1 COOP LEARN

Challenge
The number of a certain bacteria doubles every hour. If you start at time zero with one bacterium, how many bacteria will you have after 10 hours? Make a graph showing the number you have every hour. Graphs should show the following data:

Time (hours)	Number of Bacteria	Time (hours)	Number of Bacteria
0	1	6	64
1	2	7	128
2	4	8	256
3	8	9	512
4	16	10	1024
5	32		

✓ Assessment

Performance Have students research the population trends of an endangered species. Ask students to graph the data, showing numbers of individuals on the vertical axis and year on the horizontal axis. Have students describe the growth curve. Use **PASC,** p. 111.

Section 2 Assessment

1. How can an ecologist predict the size of a population without counting every organism in the population?

2. Why does competition between individuals of the same species tend to be greater than competition between individuals of different species?

3. How do birthrates and death rates influence the size of a population?

4. How does carrying capacity influence the number of organisms in an ecosystem?

5. **Think Critically** Why does the supply of food and water in an ecosystem usually affect population size more than other limiting factors?

Skill Builder Activities

6. **Making and Using Tables** Construct a table using the following data on changes in the size of a deer population in Arizona. In 1910 there were 6 deer; in 1915, 36 deer; in 1920, 143 deer; in 1925, 86 deer; and in 1935, 26 deer. Propose a hypothesis to explain what might have caused these changes. **For more help, refer to the** Science Skill Handbook.

7. **Solving One-Step Equations** A vacant lot that measures 12 m × 12 m contains 46 dandelion plants, 212 grass plants, and 14 bindweed plants. What is the population density, per square meter, of each species? **For more help, refer to the** Math Skill Handbook.

Answers to Section Assessment

1. Count the organisms in a portion of an area, and then multiply that number by the number of portions needed to make a whole.

2. Organisms of the same species have similar needs.

3. If birth rate exceeds death rate, population size increases. If death rate exceeds birth rate, population size decreases. If they are equal, population size is maintained.

4. The number of organisms cannot permanently exceed the carrying capacity of the environment.

5. Food and water are critical for survival. Things such as oxygen also are critical, but they usually are not in short supply.

6. Possible answer: The population grew when predators were eliminated. When the deer exceeded the carrying capacity of their environment, their numbers were again reduced.

7. dandelion: 46/144 = 0.3; grass: 212/144 = 1.5; bindweed: 14/144 = 0.1

SECTION

3

Interactions Within Communities

1 Motivate

Bellringer Transparency

 Display the Section Focus Transparency for Section 3. Use the accompanying Transparency Activity Master. L2

ELL

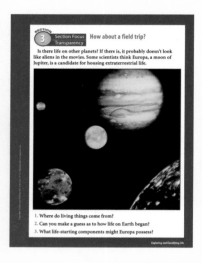

Tie to Prior Knowledge

Have students consider a familiar ecosystem. Ask them to name organisms that make up the community and describe interactions among these organisms.

Interactions Within Communities

As You Read

What You'll Learn
- **Describe** how organisms obtain energy for life.
- **Explain** how organisms interact.
- **Recognize** that every organism occupies a niche.

Vocabulary
producer	commensalism
consumer	parasitism
symbiosis	niche
mutualism	

Why It's Important
How organisms obtain food and meet other needs is critical for their survival.

Obtaining Energy

Just as a car engine needs a constant supply of gasoline, living organisms need a constant supply of energy. The energy that fuels most life on Earth comes from the Sun. Some organisms use the Sun's energy to create energy-rich molecules through the process of photosynthesis. The energy-rich molecules, usually sugars, serve as food. They are made up of different combinations of carbon, hydrogen, and oxygen atoms. Energy is stored in the chemical bonds that hold the atoms of these molecules together. When the molecules break apart—for example, during digestion—the energy in the chemical bonds is released to fuel life processes.

Producers Organisms that use an outside energy source like the Sun to make energy-rich molecules are called **producers.** Most producers contain chlorophyll (KLOR uh fihl), a chemical that is required for photosynthesis. As shown in **Figure 12,** green plants are producers. Some producers do not contain chlorophyll and do not use energy from the Sun. Instead, they make energy-rich molecules through a process called chemosynthesis (kee moh SIHN thuh sus). These organisms usually are found near volcanic vents on the ocean floor. Mineral molecules in the water provide the energy source for chemosynthesis.

 A Magnification: 125×

 B Magnification: 225×

Figure 12
Green plants, including the grasses that surround this pond, are producers. Many microscopic organisms like **A** *Euglena* are producers, as well as **B** simple plantlike organisms called algae.

Section ✓*Assessment* Planner

PORTFOLIO	**CONTENT ASSESSMENT**
Science Journal, p. 23	Section, p. 24
PERFORMANCE ASSESSMENT	Challenge, p. 24
Skill Builder Activities, p. 24	Chapter, pp. 32–33
See page 32 for more options.	

Consumers

Herbivores

Carnivores

Omnivores

Decomposers

Figure 13
Four categories of consumers are shown. *What kind of consumer is a cactus wren? A mushroom?*

Consumers Organisms that cannot make their own energy-rich molecules are called **consumers.** Consumers obtain energy by eating other organisms. **Figure 13** shows the four general categories of consumers. Herbivores are the vegetarians of the world. They include rabbits, deer, and other plant eaters. Carnivores are animals that eat other animals. Frogs and spiders are carnivores that eat insects. Omnivores, including pigs and humans, eat mostly plants and animals. Decomposers, including fungi, bacteria, and earthworms, consume wastes and dead organisms. Decomposers help recycle once-living matter by breaking it down into simple, energy-rich substances. These substances might serve as food for decomposers, be absorbed by plant roots, or be consumed by other organisms.

Chemistry INTEGRATION

Glucose is a nutrient molecule produced during photosynthesis. Look up the chemical structure of glucose and draw it in your Science Journal.

☑ Reading Check *How are producers different from consumers?*

Food Chains Ecology includes the study of how organisms depend on each other for food. A food chain is a simple model of the feeding relationships in an ecosystem. For example, shrubs are food for deer, and deer are food for mountain lions. This food chain is shown in **Figure 14.** What food chain would include you?

Figure 14
Food chains illustrate how consumers obtain energy from other organisms in an ecosystem.

Resource Manager

Chapter Resources Booklet
Transparency Activity, p. 46
Enrichment, p. 32
Directed Reading for Content Mastery, pp. 21, 22

Text Question Answer
Accept any answer that shows a human eating food derived from a plant or animal. For example, in Figure 14, humans might replace the mountain lion, because humans eat venison.

Caption Answer
Figure 13 A cactus wren is an omnivore; a mushroom is a decomposer.

Obtaining Energy

Chemistry INTEGRATION

Energy for life is stored in the bonds of organic molecules such as glucose. A molecule of glucose is made of 6 carbons, 12 hydrogens, and 6 oxygens atoms ($C_6H_{12}O_6$). The structure is as follows.

☑ Reading Check

Answer A producer can make its own energy-rich molecules; a consumer must obtain energy-rich molecules from other organisms.

Use Science Words

Word Origin Types of consumers are described by words derived from Latin. *Vorare* means "to devour," *herba* means "grass," *caro* means "flesh," and *omnis* means "all." Present this information to students and have them use it to explain the terms *herbivore, carnivore,* and *omnivore.*

Discussion

Most humans are omnivores. Are humans suited for this type of diet? Possible responses: Humans have canine teeth, which carnivores have, as well as molars, which herbivores have. Herbivores have long digestive tracts; carnivores have shorter tracts. Humans have digestive tracts of intermediate length.

Symbiotic Relationships

Activity

Bring in stones or pieces of tree bark with lichens growing on them. Have students look at the lichens using hand lenses. Then have them prepare wet-mount slides of lichen pieces and observe them using microscopes. **How do the algae and fungus benefit each other?** Algae make food for the fungus, and the fungus provides a habitat and moisture for the algae. L2 🖼 **Visual-Spatial**

Use an Analogy

Challenge students to describe a human interaction that is analogous to commensalism. Possible example: A person may go through another's trash and find something useful. This is analogous to commensalism because one person benefits, while the other is neither helped nor harmed.

Figure 15
Many examples of symbiotic relationships exist in nature.

A Lichens are a result of mutualism.

B Clown fish and sea anemones have a commensal relationship.

Magnification: 128×

C This roundworm is a parasite that robs nutrients from its host.

Symbiotic Relationships

Not all relationships among organisms involve food. Many organisms live together and share resources in other ways. Any close relationship between species is called **symbiosis.**

Mutualism You may have noticed crusty lichens growing on fences, trees, or rocks. Lichens, like those shown in **Figure 15A,** are made up of an alga or a cyanobacterium that lives within the tissues of a fungus. Through photosynthesis, the cyanobacterium or alga supplies energy to itself and the fungus. The fungus provides a protected space in which the cyanobacterium or alga can live. Both organisms benefit from this association. A symbiotic relationship in which both species benefit is called **mutualism** (MYEW chuh wuh lih zum).

Commensalism If you've ever visited a marine aquarium, you might have seen the ocean organisms shown in **Figure 15B.** The creature with gently waving, tubelike tentacles is a sea anemone. The tentacles contain a mild poison. They capture shrimp, fish, and other small animals that the anemone eats. The striped clown fish can swim among the tentacles without being harmed. The anemone's tentacles protect the clown fish from predators. In this relationship, the clown fish benefits but the sea anemone is not helped or hurt. A symbiotic relationship in which one organism benefits and the other is not affected is called **commensalism** (kuh MEN suh lih zum).

Parasitism Pet cats or dogs sometimes have to be treated for worms. Roundworms, like the one shown in **Figure 15C,** are common in puppies. The roundworm attaches itself to the inside of the puppy's intestine and feeds on nutrients in the puppy's blood. The puppy may have abdominal pain, bloating, and diarrhea. If the infection is severe, the puppy might die. A symbiotic relationship in which one organism benefits but the other is harmed is called **parasitism** (PER uh suh tih zum).

Inclusion Strategies

Learning Disabled Help make the differences between the types of symbiotic relationships more clear by asking students to categorize these examples: a bee gets nectar from a flower and pollinates the flower *(mutualism)*; an orchid, which gets it moisture and nutrients from the air, grows on a tall tree *(commensalism)*; a tick attaches to a deer and sucks its blood *(parasitism)*.

Niches

One habitat might contain hundreds or even thousands of species. Look at the rotting log habitat shown in **Figure 16.** A rotting log in a forest can be home to many species of insects, including termites that eat decaying wood and ants that feed on the termites. Other species that live on or under the rotting log include millipedes, centipedes, spiders, and worms. You might think that competition for resources would make it impossible for so many species to live in the same habitat. However, each species has different requirements for its survival. As a result, each species has its own niche (NIHCH). A **niche** refers to how an organism survives, how it obtains food and shelter, how it finds a mate and cares for its young, and how it avoids danger.

✔ Reading Check *Why does each species have its own niche?*

Special adaptations that improve survival are often part of an organism's niche. Milkweed plants contain a poison that prevents many insects from feeding on them. Monarch butterfly caterpillars have an adaptation that allows them to eat milkweed. Monarchs can take advantage of a food resource that other species cannot use. Milkweed poison also helps protect monarchs from predators. When the caterpillars eat milkweed, they become slightly poisonous. Birds avoid eating monarchs because they learn that the caterpillars and adult butterflies have an awful taste and can make them sick.

Health
INTEGRATION

The poison in milkweed is similar to the drug digitalis. Small amounts of digitalis are used to treat heart ailments in humans, but it is poisonous in large doses. Look up digitalis and explain in your Science Journal how it affects the human body.

Figure 16
Different adaptations enable each species living in this rotting log to have its own niche.
A Termites eat wood. They make tunnels inside the log.
B Millipedes feed on plant matter and find shelter beneath the log. C Wolf spiders capture insects living in and around the log.

E ◆ 23

Niches

Discussion

The term *niche* is sometimes described as an activity that one person is good at, but others find difficult. **How is this similar to the biological definition?** Organisms with a particular niche often have adaptations that give them an advantage in their environment.

Health
INTEGRATION

Digitalis and similar drugs control heart rate. They tend to increase the force but decrease the frequency of heartbeats. Very small doses are used in medicine because larger amounts can cause death.

✔ Reading Check

Answer Each species has different requirements for its survival.

IDENTIFYING Misconceptions

Students may think that plants do not depend on other organisms. Refer to page 6F for teaching strategies that address this misconception.

Resource Manager

Chapter Resources Booklet
 Reinforcement, p. 29
Reading and Writing Skill Activities, p. 49
Cultural Diversity, p. 13

Science Journal

Local Niches Have students identify organisms in local habitats that have different niches. Encourage them to research one organism and to write descriptive paragraphs in their science journals about how the organism survives, obtains food and shelter, finds a mate, cares for young, and avoids danger. [P]

Reteach

What might happen if all insects were eliminated? Possible responses: Other animals that eat insects for food would be in danger of dying if they could not substitute another food source; insects would no longer decompose wastes or once-living materials, allowing wastes to accumulate. Bees and other insects would not pollinate plants, so they wouldn't form fruits and seeds. This would result in less food for people and other animals. L2
LS Naturalist

Challenge

Find the name of a bird or other animal that lives in the area around your school or home. Ask students to research the niche of the animal and suggest reasons that the animal is able to survive there. L3
LS Naturalist

✓ Assessment

Process Have students classify the following organisms based on how each obtains nutrition: spider (carnivore); pig (omnivore); goat (herbivore); fungus (decomposer); frog (carnivore). Use **Performance Assessment in the Science Classroom,** p. 121.

Figure 17
The alligator is a predator. The turtle is its prey.

Predator and Prey When you think of survival in the wild, you might imagine an antelope running away from a lion. An organism's niche includes how it avoids being eaten and how it finds or captures its food. Predators, like the one shown in **Figure 17,** are consumers that capture and eat other consumers. The prey is the organism that is captured by the predator. The presence of predators usually increases the number of different species that can live in an ecosystem. Predators limit the size of prey populations. As a result, food and other resources are less likely to become scarce, and competition between species is reduced.

Cooperation Individual organisms often cooperate in ways that improve survival. For example, a white-tailed deer that detects the presence of wolves or coyotes will alert the other deer in the herd. Many insects, such as ants and honeybees, live in social groups. Different individuals perform different tasks required for the survival of the entire nest. Soldier ants protect workers that go out of the nest to gather food. Worker ants feed and care for ant larvae that hatch from eggs laid by the queen. These cooperative actions improve survival and are a part of the species' niche.

Section 3 Assessment

1. Explain why all consumers ultimately depend on producers for food.
2. Draw a food chain that models the feeding relationships of three species in a community. Choose a food chain other than the one shown in **Figure 14.**
3. Make up two imaginary organisms that have a mutualistic relationship. Give them names and explain how they benefit from the association.
4. What is the difference between a habitat and a niche?
5. **Think Critically** A parasite can obtain food only from a host organism. Most parasites weaken but do not kill their hosts. Why?

Skill Builder Activities

6. **Manipulating Variables and Controls** You are sure that Animal A benefits from a relationship with Plant B, but you are not sure if Plant B benefits, is harmed, or is unaffected by the relationship. Design an experiment to compare how well Plant B grows on its own and when Animal A is present. **For more help, refer to the Science Skill Handbook.**
7. **Using Graphics Software** Use graphics software to make three different food chains. Represent each organism with a shape that resembles it. For example, you could use a leaf shape to represent a plant. Label each shape. **For more help, refer to the Technology Skill Handbook.**

24 ◆ E   CHAPTER 1 Interactions of Life

Answers to Section Assessment

1. Producers can make their own carbohydrates from nonliving materials; other types of organisms cannot do this and must feed on producers, either directly or indirectly.
2. Answers will vary but must begin with a producer; for example, desert broom—hare—coyote.
3. Answers will vary, but both species should benefit from the relationship.
4. The place an organism lives is its habitat. How an organism survives is its niche.
5. If a parasite kills its host, the parasite will also die.
6. Answers will vary but should include a sample of Animal A grown with Plant B. This will be compared to a sample of Plant B grown alone.
7. Answers will vary, but each food chain must begin with a producer.

Activity

Feeding Habits of Planaria

You probably have watched minnows darting about in a stream. It is not as easy to observe organisms that live at the bottom of a stream, beneath rocks, logs, and dead leaves. Countless stream organisms, including insect larvae, worms, and microscopic organisms, live out of your view. One such organism is a type of flatworm called a planarian. In this activity, you will find out about the eating habits of planarians.

What You'll Investigate
What food items do planarians prefer to eat?

Materials
small bowl
planarians (several)
lettuce leaf
raw liver or meat
guppies (several)
pond or stream water
magnifying lens

Goals
■ **Observe** the food preference of planarians.
■ **Infer** what planarians eat in the wild.

Safety Precautions

Procedure
1. Fill the bowl with stream water.
2. Place a lettuce leaf, piece of raw liver, and several guppies in the bowl. Add the planarians. Wash your hands.
3. **Observe** what happens inside the bowl for at least 20 minutes. Do not disturb the bowl or its contents. Use a magnifying lens to look at the planarians.
4. **Record** all of your observations in your Science Journal.

Conclude and Apply
1. Which food did the planarians prefer?
2. **Infer** what planarians might eat when in their natural environment.
3. Based on your observations during this activity, explain what niche planarians might fill in stream ecosystems.
4. **Predict** where in a stream you might find planarians. Use references to find out whether your prediction is correct.

Communicating Your Data

Share your results with other students in your class. Plan an adult-supervised trip with several classmates to a local stream to search for planarians in their native habitat. **For more help, refer to the** Science Skill Handbook.

Purpose Students observe the eating habits of planarians and infer what wild planarians eat. L2 IS **Visual-Spatial**

Process Skills observing, predicting, inferring

Time Required 30 minutes

Safety Precautions Instruct students to handle planarians with care and to wash their hands after the lab.

Teaching Strategies To house the planarians for an extended period of time, change the water of their bowls every other day and keep a small piece of liver in the bowl.

Troubleshooting
- Set up a bowl of planarians to serve as a reference.
- The piece of liver should be about the size of a quarter.
- Tell students to cover their dishes for a few minutes; planaria do not like light.

Answers to Questions
1. liver
2. Most planaria are carnivorous night feeders. They eat protozoans, tiny snails, worms, and dead animals.
3. Although planarians prey on slow-moving animals, they primarily scavenge dead organisms from the bottom of streams.
4. Planarians live in slow-moving or still portions of a stream where dead organisms settle to the stream bottom. They are found beneath rotting leaves or rocks.

Resource Manager

Chapter Resources Booklet
    Activity Worksheets, pp. 5–6, 7–8
    Lab Activities, pp. 9–11, 13–16
Home and Community Involvement, p. 47
Lab Management and Safety, p. 71

Communicating Your Data

Have students write a paragraph describing their results. They can exchange papers with a classmate to see their results.

Assessment

Performance Ask students to infer how their results might have differed had they used tap water instead of stream water. Tap water contains chemicals toxic to soft bodied animals and could kill the planarians. Use **PASC,** p. 89.

Activity

BENCH TESTED

Recognize the Problem

Purpose

Students will test the effect of a change in one environmental factor on the rate of growth of a fruit fly population.

Process Skills

identifying a question, forming hypotheses, testing a hypothesis, identifying and manipulating variables, collecting data, making and using tables, recording data, recording observations, analyzing results, forming operational definitions, evaluating other's data and conclusions, communicating, making and using graphs

Time

two 45–minute periods and once weekly observations for one to two months

Materials

Standard fruit fly culture kits are available from biological supply houses. Possible culture containers include mayonnaise jars or other empty, sanitized food jars.

Safety Precautions

• Students should take care not to release their fruit flies within the school building.

• Used fruit fly culture containers can contain bacteria and mold, and should not be reused for other purposes.

Activity
Design Your Own Experiment

Population Growth in Fruit Flies

Populations can grow at an exponential rate only if the environment provides the right amount of food, shelter, air, moisture, heat, living space, and other factors. You probably have seen fruit flies hovering near ripe bananas or other fruit. Fruit flies are fast-growing organisms often raised in science laboratories. The flies are kept in culture tubes and fed a diet of specially prepared food flakes. Can you improve on this standard growing method to achieve faster population growth?

Recognize the Problem

Will a change in one environmental factor affect the growth of a fruit fly population?

Form a Hypothesis

Based on your reading about fruit flies, state a hypothesis about how changing one environmental factor will affect the rate of growth of a fruit fly population.

Goals

■ **Identify** the environmental factors needed by a population of fruit flies.

■ **Design** an experiment to investigate how a change in one environmental factor affects in any way the size of a fruit fly population.

■ **Observe** and **measure** changes in population size.

Possible Materials

fruit flies
standard fruit fly culture kit
food items (banana, orange peel, or other fruit)
water
heating or cooling source
culture containers
cloth, plastic, or other tops for culture containers
hand lens

Safety Precautions

Data Table:

Fruit Fly Population				
Culture number	Number of Flies			
	Date	Date	Date	Date
1				
2				
3				

Form a Hypothesis

Students' hypotheses should reflect a change in one environmental factor, such as type of food, amount of water, or size of container, and its possible effect on the rate of growth of the fruit fly population. For example: A larger living space will result in a faster-growing fruit fly population.

Test Your Hypothesis

Plan

1. As a group, decide on one environmental factor to investigate. Agree on a hypothesis about how a change in this factor will affect population growth. Decide how you will test your hypothesis, and identify the experimental results that would confirm your hypothesis.

2. **List** the steps you will need to take to test your hypothesis. Describe exactly what you will do. List your materials.

3. **Determine** the method you will use to measure changes in the size of your fruit fly populations.

4. Prepare a data table in your Science Journal to record weekly measurements of your fruit fly populations.

5. Read the entire experiment and make sure all of the steps are in a logical order.

6. **Identify** all constants, variables, and controls in your experiment.

Do

1. Make sure your teacher approves your plan before you start.

2. **Research** the standard method used to raise fruit flies in the laboratory. Use this method as the control in your experiment.

3. Carry out your experiment.

4. **Measure** the growth of your fruit fly populations weekly and record the data in your data table.

Analyze Your Data

1. What were the constants in your experiment? The variables?

2. **Compare** changes in the size of your control population with changes in your experimental population. Which population grew faster?

3. Using the information in your data table, make a line graph that shows how the sizes of your two fruit fly populations changed over time. Use a different colored pencil for each population's line on the graph.

Draw Conclusions

1. Did the results support your hypothesis? Explain.

2. **Compare** the growth of your control and experimental populations. Did either population reach exponential growth? How do you know?

*C*ommunicating

Your Data

Compare the results of your experiment with those of other students in your class. **For more help, refer to the** Science Skill Handbook.

Test Your Hypothesis

Possible Procedures

Provide two equal-sized populations of fruit flies with the same amount of food and moisture and the same temperature, but two different sized containers to test the effect of living area on fruit fly population growth. Make observations of the fly populations over the next one to two months. The life cycle of a fruit fly takes approximately two weeks, so students should see rapid changes in population size.

Teaching Strategy

Most students are familiar with fruit flies "appearing" near ripe fruit. Have students consider the source of these flies. Sometimes the eggs were already present on the fruit; other times flies have used their great sense of smell to locate the ripe fruit.

Expected Outcome

Most results will show that any extreme change from the standard method of maintaining fruit flies will result in a decreased rate of population growth.

Analyze Your Data

1. Answers will vary.
2. Answers will vary.
3. Student graphs will vary. Check students' work.

Error Analysis

Have students compare their results and their hypotheses and explain why differences occurred.

Draw Conclusions

1. Answers will be determined by student's hypotheses.
2. A population shows exponential growth if it increases at a fixed percentage per time period. Student answers will depend on results.

✓*Assessment*

Oral Have students explain the relationship between environmental conditions and population growth in fruit flies. Flies achieve the fastest rate of growth when all the conditions in their environment are at optimal levels. Any change in these conditions will result in a decrease in population growth rates. Use **Performance Assessment in the Science Classroom,** p. 89.

*C*ommunicating

Your Data

Students can make an electronic spreadsheet that allows comparison of data about different environmental factors that affect the rate of growth of the fruit fly population.

TIME

SCIENCE AND HISTORY

Content Background

The election year 2000 raised a number of questions concerning electors in the Electoral College. For perhaps the first time in recent U.S. history, a large number of people began to wonder how electors are chosen and how many are apportioned for each state.

The answer to these questions lies in the process of census taking. The census affects not only the number and distribution of congressional candidates, but also the number of electors to the Electoral College. Each state has as many electors as it has members of Congress, and every state must have at least one representative and two senators. Every 10 years the census results are used to determine the number of congressional seats of each state. The number of U.S. Representatives gained or lost in the year 1990 as a result of the census affected 21 states. For example, California gained seven seats to the 103rd Congress and New York lost three. Regionally, the South and the West gained 15 seats between 1980 and 1990 and the Northeast and the Midwest lost 15. In the year 2000, the Sun belt won 12 seats at the expense of the Rust belt.

Even though the number of Representatives remains at 435, reapportionment of seats to Congress can have significant impact.

Reapportionment of seats within states necessitates redistricting within those states so that the Representatives stand for equal numbers of people in that state.

TIME SCIENCE AND HISTORY

SCIENCE CAN CHANGE THE COURSE OF HISTORY!

YOU CAN COUNT

The Census gives a snapshot of the people of the United States

The doorbell rings and you hear someone at the door say to your mom, "I'm working for the U.S. Census Bureau, doing follow-up interviews. Do you have a few minutes to answer some questions?" What does this person—and the U.S. government—want to know about your family?

Counting people is important to the United States and to many other countries around the world. It helps governments determine the distribution of people in the various regions of a nation. To obtain this information, the government takes a census—a count of how many people are living in their country on a particular day at a particular time, and in a particular place. A census is a snapshot of a country's population. The time at which the count occurs is called the "census moment." Some countries actually close their borders for a day or two so everyone will "sit still" for the census camera at the census moment, as was done in Nigeria in 1992.

Counting on the Count

When the United States government was formed, its founders set up the House of Representatives based on population. Areas with more people had more government representatives, and areas with fewer people had fewer representatives. In 1790, the requirement for a census became part of the Constitution. A census must be taken every ten years so the proper number of representatives for each state can be calculated.

Over the years, the U.S. Census Bureau has added questions to obtain more information than just a popular count. In 1810, questions about business and work were added. In 1850, as more immigrants began coming to the United States, a new question about where people were born was added. In 1880, census takers asked people whether or not they were married. And in 1950, the first computers were used to add up the census results.

 Next, read on to find out more about the census.

 Resources for Teachers and Students

The American Census: A Social History by Margo J. Anderson. Yale University Press, New Haven, CT. 1988.

"The History of Census Tabulation" by Keith S. Reid-Green. *Scientific American* 260 (February 1989): 98-103.

Understanding the Census by Michael R. Lavin. Epic Books, New York. 1996.

Who Counts? The Politics of Census-Taking in Contemporary America by Margo J. Anderson and Stephen E. Fienberg. Russell Sage Foundation, New York. 1999.

ON IT

Growing by the Numbers

Chances are you just blinked your eyes. While you did it, three people were added to the world's population. There, you blinked again—that's another three people! It may seem impossible, but that's how quickly the world's population is growing. It adds up to 184 people every minute, 11,040 every hour, 264,960 every day, and 97 million every year! On October 12, 1999, the official number of people on the planet reached a record 6 billion.

The Short Form

Before 1970, United States census data was collected by field workers. They went door to door to count the number of people living in each household. Since then, the census has been done mostly by mail. People are sent a form they must fill out. The form asks for the number of people living at an address and their names, races, ages, and relationships. Answers to these and other questions are confidential. Census workers visit some homes to check on the accuracy of the information. The census helps the government to figure out how the population is aging. Census data are also important in deciding how to distribute government services and funding.

The 2000 Snapshot

One of the findings of the 2000 Census is that the U.S. population is becoming more equally spread out across age groups. By analyzing the data from the census, officials estimate that by 2020 the population of children, middle-aged people, and senior citizens will be about equal. It's predicted also that there will be more people who are over 100 years old than ever before.

Martha F. Riche researches population changes in the United States. She was also a director of the Census Bureau. Riche thinks that the more equal distribution in age will lead to challenges for the nation. How will we meet the demands of more people who are living longer? Will we need to build more hospitals to care for them? Will more children mean a need to build more schools? Federal, state, and local governments will be using the results of the 2000 Census for years to come as they plan our future.

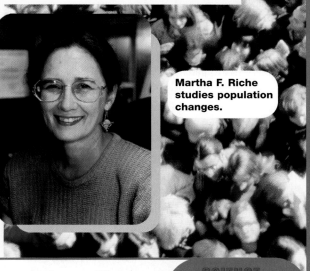

Martha F. Riche studies population changes.

CONNECTIONS Class Census Develop a school census. What questions will you ask? (Don't ask questions that are too personal.) Who will ask them? How will you make sure you counted everyone? Using the results, can you make any predictions about your school's future or its current students?

SCIENCE Online

For more information, visit science.glencoe.com

CONNECTIONS Today, the entire census is taken using a mail-in form. Have students develop a short mail-in form to take a school census. Have groups write questions to include on the forms. Challenge students to design the form so that it is understandable. After the census is taken, have students discuss challenges they encountered.

SCIENCE Online

Internet Addresses

_____

_____

_____

Explore the Glencoe Science Web site at **science.glencoe.com** to find out more about topics in this feature.

Discussion

What do you think accounts for the U.S. population becoming more spread out across age groups? Remind students that from the 1940s through the 1960s there was a sharp increase in the number of babies being born. This created what is popularly known as a "baby boom," which has accounted for the disproportionate number of people in a certain age bracket. Possible answer: The population is becoming more equal in number across age groups because the population in general is declining. People are having smaller families. Seniors are living longer, so their numbers are rising to meet the numbers of middle-aged.

Historical Significance

Explain to students that census data can have a direct affect on electing our President and Congressmen and women. Explain to students that the Electoral College is made up of selected representatives in each state that cast their vote for the President. Tell students that the number of Electoral College votes, not popular votes, elects the President. States with large populations have more electors than do states with small populations. Explain that the number of electors gained or lost in a given state is a direct result of the U.S. Census. Tell students that in the 1990 census, the South and the West gained 15 electors and the Northeast and the Midwest lost 15. Ask students what they think accounts for the shift. Do they think that this shift had an affect on the 2000 election?

Reviewing Main Ideas

Preview

Students can answer the questions in their Science Journals. Discuss the answers as you go through the chapter. **Linguistic**

Review

Students can write their answers, then compare them with those of other students. **Interpersonal**

Reteach

Students can look at the illustrations and describe details that support the main ideas of the chapter. **Visual-Spatial**

Answers to Chapter Review

SECTION 1

1. Yes, because it is part of the upper layer of crust.

SECTION 2

2. Answers may include the availability of food, water, and choice nesting places. Predators can also be a limiting factor.

SECTION 3

4. The monarch caterpillar has an adaptation that allows it to feed on the poisonous milkweed plants. This causes the adult monarch to be poisonous to its predators.

Chapter 1 Study Guide

Reviewing Main Ideas

Section 1 Living Earth

1. Ecology is the study of interactions that take place in the biosphere. *Is ice-covered Antarctica a part of Earth's biosphere? Why or why not?*

2. Populations are made up of all organisms of the same species living in a community.

3. Communities are made up of all the populations of different species of organisms living in one ecosystem.

4. Living and nonliving factors affect an organism's ability to survive in its habitat.

Section 2 Populations

1. Population size can be estimated by counting a sample of a total population.

2. Competition for limiting factors can restrict the size of a population. *What limiting factors might influence the size of a rabbit population?*

3. Population growth is affected by birthrate, death rate, and the movement of individuals into or out of a community.

4. Exponential population growth can occur in environments that provide a species with plenty of food, shelter, and other resources.

Section 3 Interactions Within Communities

1. All life requires energy.

2. Most producers use the Sun's energy to make food in the form of energy-rich molecules. Consumers obtain their food by eating other organisms.

3. Mutualism, commensalism, and parasitism are the three kinds of symbiosis.

4. Every species has its own niche, which includes adaptations for survival. *What adaptations are involved in the relationship between the milkweed plant and the caterpillar of the monarch butterfly?*

FOLDABLES
Reading & Study Skills

After You Read

Under the population tab of your Concept Map Study Fold, write what would happen if there were an increase in the population of your animal.

FOLDABLES
Reading & Study Skills

After You Read

After students have read the chapter and completed the Foldable described in Before You Read, have them do the activity on the student page.

Dinah Zike

Visualizing Main Ideas

Complete the following concept map on communities.

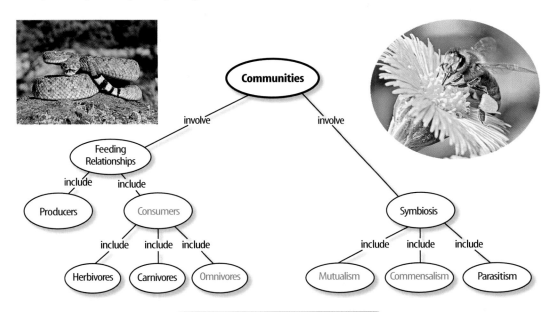

Communities
— involve → Feeding Relationships
— involve → Symbiosis

Feeding Relationships
— include → Producers
— include → Consumers

Consumers
— include → Herbivores
— include → Carnivores
— include → Omnivores

Symbiosis
— include → Mutualism
— include → Commensalism
— include → Parasitism

Vocabulary Review

Vocabulary Words

a. biosphere
b. carrying capacity
c. commensalism
d. community
e. consumer
f. ecology
g. ecosystem
h. habitat

i. limiting factor
j. mutualism
k. niche
l. parasitism
m. population
n. producer
o. symbiosis

THE PRINCETON REVIEW **Study Tip**

Get together with a friend to study. Quiz each other about specific topics from your textbook and class material to prepare for a test.

Using Vocabulary

Explain the difference between the vocabulary words in each of the following sets.

1. niche, habitat

2. mutualism, commensalism

3. limiting factor, carrying capacity

4. biosphere, ecosystem

5. producer, consumer

6. population, ecosystem

7. community, population

8. parasitism, symbiosis

9. ecosystem, ecology

10. parasitism, commensalism

See student page.

Using Vocabulary

1. Habitat is the place an organism lives. Niche refers to adaptations that help an organism survive.

2. Both describe symbiotic relationships. In mutualism both organisms benefit. In commensalism, one organism benefits, and the other neither benefits nor is harmed.

3. Carrying capacity is the largest number of individuals of one species that an ecosystem can support. Limiting factors restrict carrying capacity.

4. An ecosystem is all the living and nonliving components of an area. The biosphere is the part of Earth that supports life. It is made up of many ecosystems.

5. Producers make their own nutrients. Consumers eat producers or other consumers for nutrients.

6. An ecosystem is all the living and nonliving components of an area. A population is all the individuals of one species living in an area.

7. A community is all the different species in an area. A population refers to one species in an area.

8. Symbiosis describes a close relationship between species. Parasitism is a type of symbiosis in which one species benefits and the other species is harmed.

9. An ecosystem is all the living and nonliving components of an area. Ecology is the study of interactions between these components.

10. Both are types of symbiosis. In parasitism, one species benefits, and the other is harmed. In commensalism, one organism benefits, and the other neither benefits nor is harmed.

IDENTIFYING Misconceptions

Assess

Use the assessment as follow-up to page 6F after students have completed the chapter.

Activity After completing the activity in which students find and label interactions outdoors, have students again draw a picture of a natural community. Have students describe the interactions in the picture.

Expected Outcome In this second drawing, students should be able to identify more relationships between organisms than they did in the first drawing. The interactions they depict should include not only predation, but also various types of symbiosis. Students should also recognize that each organism interacts with many other organisms, not just a single predator or prey species.

Checking Concepts

1. A
2. C
3. D
4. D
5. B
6. A
7. C
8. C
9. D
10. A

Thinking Critically

11. It may absorb nutrients from the organism, as does a tapeworm living inside a human's intestine, or it may slowly feed on the tissue of an organism, as does a tick feeding on the blood of a deer.
12. Possible answers: food, water, shelter, space, birth and death rates, immigration, emigration
13. Description of habitat should include where the student lives. Description of niche should include adaptations and behaviors that enhance the student's survival.
14. commensalism
15. Organisms are adapted to feed on different foods, hunt at different times, and nest in different places. Therefore many niches can exist in the same habitat.

Chapter 1 Assessment

Checking Concepts

Choose the word or phrase that best answers the question.

1. Which of the following is a living factor in the environment?
   - **A)** animals
   - **B)** air
   - **C)** sunlight
   - **D)** soil

2. What is made up of all the populations in an area?
   - **A)** niches
   - **B)** habitats
   - **C)** community
   - **D)** ecosystem

3. What does the number of individuals in a population that occupies an area of a specific size describe?
   - **A)** clumping
   - **B)** size
   - **C)** spacing
   - **D)** density

4. Which of the following animals is an example of an herbivore?
   - **A)** wolf
   - **B)** moss
   - **C)** tree
   - **D)** rabbit

5. What term best describes a symbiotic relationship in which one species is helped and the other is harmed?
   - **A)** mutualism
   - **B)** parasitism
   - **C)** commensalism
   - **D)** consumerism

6. Which of the following conditions tends to increase the size of a population?
   - **A)** births exceed deaths
   - **B)** population size exceeds the carrying capacity
   - **C)** movements out of an area exceed movements into the area
   - **D)** severe drought

7. Which of the following is most likely to be a limiting factor in a population of fish living in the shallow water of a large lake?
   - **A)** sunlight
   - **B)** water
   - **C)** food
   - **D)** soil

8. An ecologist wants to know the size of a population of wild daisy plants growing in a meadow. The meadow measures 1,000 m². The ecologist counts 30 daisy plants in a sample area that is 100 m². What is the estimated population of daisies in the entire meadow?
   - **A)** 3
   - **B)** 30
   - **C)** 300
   - **D)** 3,000

9. Which of these organisms is a producer?
   - **A)** mole
   - **B)** owl
   - **C)** whale
   - **D)** oak tree

10. Which pair of words is incorrect?
   - **A)** black bear—carnivore
   - **B)** grasshopper—herbivore
   - **C)** pig—omnivore
   - **D)** lion—carnivore

Thinking Critically

11. Why does a parasite have a harmful effect on the organism it infects?

12. What factors affect carrying capacity?

13. Describe your own habitat and niche.

14. The female cowbird lays eggs in the nest of another bird. The other birds care for and feed the cowbird chicks when they hatch. Which type of symbiosis is this?

15. Explain how several different niches can exist in the same habitat.

Developing Skills

16. **Making Models** Place the following organisms in the correct sequence to model a food chain: grass, snake, mouse, and hawk.

Chapter ✓Assessment Planner

Portfolio Encourage students to place in their portfolios one or two items of what they consider to be their best work. Examples include:
- Activity, p. 10
- Curriculum Connection, p. 15
- Science Journal, p. 23

Performance Additional performance assessments, Performance Task Assessment Lists, and rubrics for evaluating these activities can be found in Glencoe's **Performance Assessment in the Science Classroom.**

17. Predicting Dandelion seeds can float great distances on the wind with the help of white, featherlike attachments. Predict how a dandelion seed's ability to be carried on the wind helps reduce competition among dandelion plants.

18. Classifying Classify the following relationships as parasitism, commensalism, or mutualism: a shark and a remora fish that cleans and eats parasites from the sharks' gills; head lice and a human; a spiny sea urchin and a tiny fish that hides from predators by floating among the sea urchin's spines.

19. Comparing and Contrasting Compare and contrast the diets of omnivores and herbivores. Give examples of each.

20. Making and Using Tables Complete the following table.

Types of Symbiosis		
Organism A	**Organism B**	**Relationship**
Gains	Doesn't gain or lose	Commensalism
Gains	Gains	Mutualism
Gains	Loses	Parasitism

Performance Assessment

21. Poster Use photographs from old magazines to create a poster that shows at least three different food chains. Display your poster for your classmates.

TECHNOLOGY

Go to the Glencoe Science Web site at **science.glencoe.com** or use the **Glencoe Science CD-ROM** for additional chapter assessment.

THE PRINCETON REVIEW — Test Practice

A food web shows how organisms in a particular ecosystem depend on each other for food. The food web below shows how the plants and animals in a grassland ecosystem obtain energy from each other.

Study the picture and answer the following questions.

1. Other organisms also live in this habitat. Which of the following organisms could fill in the blank space in this food web?
A) tree
B) bison
C) alligator
D) hawk

2. Suppose all the snakes were removed from this ecosystem. Which of the following statements represents the most reasonable prediction of what could happen in this ecosystem?
F) The plants would die.
G) The owls would start eating foxes.
H) There would be no more predators to eat the mice.
J) The eagles would start eating more mice.

The Test-Taking Tip was written by The Princeton Review, the nation's leader in test preparation.
1. B
2. J

Developing Skills

16. grass, mouse, snake, hawk
17. Individual seeds are able to float far from the parent plant, which helps reduce population density.
18. mutualism; parasitism; commensalism
19. Both eat plants. Omnivores, such as pigs and humans, eat both plants and animals. Herbivores, such as goats, eat only plants.
20. See student page.

Performance Assessment

21. Posters should show photographs in the correct order of energy flow. All food chains should start with a producer and then move to consumers. Use **Performance Assessment in the Science Classroom**, p. 145.

✓Assessment Resources

📁 Reproducible Masters

Chapter Resources Booklet
Chapter Review, pp. 37–38
Chapter Tests, pp. 39–42
Assessment Transparency Activity, p. 49

Glencoe Science Web site
Interactive Tutor
Chapter Quizzes

Glencoe Technology
- Assessment Transparency
- Interactive CD-ROM Chapter Quizzes
- ExamView Pro Test Bank
- Vocabulary PuzzleMaker Software
- MindJogger Videoquiz DVD/VHS

Section/Objectives	Standards		Activities/Features
Chapter Opener	**National**	**State/Local**	**Explore Activity:** Compare climate differences, p. 35 **Before You Read,** p. 35
	See p. 6T for a Key to Standards.		
Section 1 Abiotic Factors 🕐 2 sessions 📦 1 block 1. **Identify** common abiotic factors in most ecosystems. 2. **List** the components of air that are needed for life. 3. **Explain** how climate influences life in an ecosystem.	National Content Standards: UPC1, A1, C1, C4, D1, F2		**MiniLAB:** Determining Soil Makeup, p. 38 **Math Skills Activity:** Graphing Temperature Versus Elevation, p. 40 **Physics Integration,** p. 41 **Activity:** Humus Farm, p. 43
Section 2 Cycles of Nature 🕐 2 sessions 📦 1 block 1. **Explain** the importance of Earth's water cycle. 2. **Diagram** the carbon cycle. 3. **Recognize** the role of nitrogen in life on Earth.	National Content Standards: UPC1, A1, B1, C1, C4, D1, F2		**MiniLAB:** Comparing Fertilizers, p. 47 **Visualizing the Carbon Cycle,** p. 48 **Science Online,** p. 49
Section 3 Energy Flow 🕐 3 sessions 📦 1.5 blocks 1. **Explain** how organisms produce energy-rich compounds. 2. **Describe** how energy flows through ecosystems. 3. **Recognize** how much energy is available at different levels in a food chain.	National Content Standards: UPC1, A1, B1, B3, C1, C4, D1, F2		**Earth Science Integration,** p. 51 **Activity:** Where does the mass of a plant come from?, pp. 54–55 **Science Stats:** Extreme Climates, pp. 56–57

Activity Materials	Reproducible Resources	Section Assessment	Technology
Explore Activity: globe or world map, weather references	**Chapter Resources Booklet** Foldables Worksheet, p. 17 Directed Reading Overview, p.19 Note-taking Worksheets, pp. 33–34	GLENCOE'S ASSESSMENT ADVANTAGE	
MiniLAB: soil (2 cups), quart jar with lid, water, dishwashing liquid (1 teaspoon), watch or clock, metric ruler **Activity:** widemouth jar, soil, grass clippings or green leaves, water, marker, metric ruler, graduated cylinder	**Chapter Resources Booklet** Transparency Activity, p. 44 MiniLAB, p. 3 Enrichment, p. 30 Reinforcement, p. 27 Directed Reading, p. 20 Lab Activity, pp. 9–12 Activity Worksheet, pp. 5–6 **Cultural Diversity,** p. 33 **Reading and Writing Skill Activities,** p. 3 **Science Inquiry Labs,** p. 7	**Portfolio** Assessment, p. 42 **Performance** MiniLAB, p. 38 Math Skills Activity, p. 40 Skill Builder Activities, p. 42 **Content** Section Assessment, p. 42	Section Focus Transparency Interactive CD-ROM/DVD Guided Reading Audio Program
MiniLAB: labels (and prices) of 3 brands of houseplant fertilizer *Need materials?* Contact Science Kit at 1-800-828-7777 or www.sciencekit.com on the Internet.	**Chapter Resources Booklet** Transparency Activity, p. 45 MiniLAB, p. 4 Enrichment, p. 31 Reinforcement, p. 28 Directed Reading, p. 21 Lab Activity, pp. 13–16 **Science Inquiry Labs,** pp. 29, 39	**Portfolio** Activity, p. 48 **Performance** MiniLAB, p. 47 Skill Builder Activities, p. 49 **Content** Section Assessment, p. 49	Section Focus Transparency Interactive CD-ROM/DVD Guided Reading Audio Program
Activity: 8 oz. plastic or paper cup, potting soil to fill cup, scale or balance, 4 radish seeds, water, paper towels	**Chapter Resources Booklet** Transparency Activity, p. 46 Enrichment, p. 32 Reinforcement, p. 29 Directed Reading, pp. 21, 22 Transparency Activity, pp. 47–48 Activity Worksheet, pp. 7–8 **Lab Management and Safety,** p. 38	**Portfolio** Visual Learning, p. 51 **Performance** Skill Builder Activities, p. 53 **Content** Section Assessment, p. 53	Section Focus Transparency Teaching Transparency Interactive CD-ROM/DVD Guided Reading Audio Program

End of Chapter Assessment

GLENCOE'S ASSESSMENT ADVANTAGE

Blackline Masters	Technology	Professional Series
Chapter Resources Booklet Chapter Review, pp. 37–38 Chapter Tests, pp. 39–42 **Standardized Test Practice by The Princeton Review,** pp. 15–18	MindJogger Videoquiz CD-ROM Explorations and Quizzes Vocabulary Puzzle Makers ExamView Pro Test Bank Interactive Lesson Planner Interactive Teacher's Edition	Performance Assessment in the Science Classroom (PASC)

Transparencies

Section Focus

Section Focus Transparency 1 — A Factory Analogy

If this factory were a cell, it would run 24 hours a day and 7 days a week. Just like a factory, cells use raw materials to produce what's needed. Like a factory, they have a control center, a source of power, and a way to move products and waste.

1. A part of the cell called the nucleus directs what the cell does. What part of the drawing is like the nucleus?
2. Other parts of the cell called mitochondria provide energy for the cell. Identify the part of the drawing similar to the mitochondria.
3. What function do the storage barrels have?

L2

Section Focus Transparency 2 — At Home in the Salt

The Dead Sea has very high salt concentrations, and people have used it as a salt resource since ancient times. But is the Dead Sea really dead? The concentration of salt is too high for most living things, but bacteria like the ones below are able to live in its waters.

1. Why might ancient people have thought the Dead Sea was totally without life?
2. What tool would you use to show there really is life in the Dead Sea?
3. Is the living thing pictured simple or complex? Defend your answer.

L2

Section Focus Transparency 3 — Thanks for sharing!

Sneezing is an involuntary action that aids the body by clearing congestion within the nose. But sneezing also spreads germs, including cold and influenza viruses.

1. How do you feel when you catch a cold?
2. What can you do to limit the spread of viruses?

L2

Assessment

Assessment Transparency — Life's Structure and Function

Directions: Carefully review the diagram and answer the following questions.

1. The chromosomes are located in the ___.
   A cytoplasm
   B vacuoles
   C nucleus
   D nucleolus
2. The scientist performing this experiment wants to study interferon because it may work as a powerful medicine. If the scientist wanted to learn how powerful interferon is, the experiment could be repeated ___.
   F at a higher temperature   H with less interferon
   G at a lower altitude   J with more labels
3. The cell on the far right of the picture will probably soon ___.
   A grow   C move
   B divide   D die

L2

Teaching

Teaching Transparency 1 — Plant and Animal Cells

L2

This is a representation of key blackline masters available in the Teacher Classroom Resources. See Resource Manager boxes within the chapter for additional information.

Key to Teaching Strategies

The following designations will help you decide which activities are appropriate for your students.

L1 Level 1 activities should be appropriate for students with learning difficulties.

L2 Level 2 activities should be within the ability range of all students.

L3 Level 3 activities are designed for above-average students.

ELL ELL activities should be within the ability range of English Language Learners.

COOP LEARN Cooperative Learning activities are designed for small group work.

LS Multiple Learning Styles logos are used throughout to indicate strategies that address different learning styles.

P These strategies represent student products that can be placed into a best-work portfolio.

Hands-on Activities

Activity Worksheets

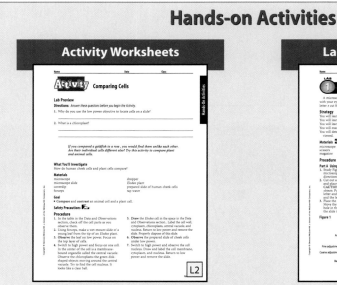

Activity — Comparing Cells

Lab Preview
Directions: Answer these questions before you begin the Activity.
1. Why do you use the low power objective to locate cells on a slide?
2. What is a chloroplast?

L2

Laboratory Activities

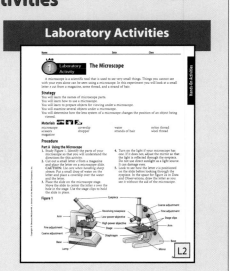

Laboratory Activity 1 — The Microscope

L2

Meeting Different Ability Levels

Content Outline

L2

Reinforcement

L2

Directed Reading

L1

Assessment

Chapter Tests

L2

Enrichment

L3

Spanish Directed Reading

L1

Test Practice Workbook

L2

Chapter Review

L2

Science Content Background

SECTION 1

Abiotic Factors

Importance to Life

Important abiotic factors include air, water, soil, sunlight, temperature, and climate. These factors are interrelated and can vary from environment to environment and over time. Consider temperature, which changes from hour to hour, day to day, season to season, and year to year. Abiotic and biotic factors are not independent. Lack of rainfall can cause a drought in a grassland. The animals that depend on plants for food would find it hard to survive. Many of the factors are predictable and cyclic, but may have extreme variations. Some can be influenced by other factors such as pollution in air, water, and soil.

Fun Fact

According to the *Guinness Book of Records,* the greatest temperature variation in one day in the United States was 100°F. This occurred in Browning, Montana on January 23–24, 1916, when the temperature dropped from 44°F to –56°F.

SECTION 2

Cycles of Nature

Natural Recycling

Matter, in the form of nutrients, moves through the organisms at each trophic level in an ecosystem. But matter cannot be replenished like the energy from sunlight. The atoms of carbon, nitrogen, and other elements that make up the bodies of organisms alive today are the same atoms that have been on Earth since life began. Matter is constantly being recycled.

Water Cycle

The amount of water on Earth remains fairly constant. While some of the water on Earth cycles, much of it is held in oceans or as ice and does not enter the cycle. At a given time, the atmosphere holds about 12,000 cubic kilometers of water, while all the freshwater rivers and lakes hold 120,000 cubic kilometers. Every day about 1,200 cubic kilometers of water evaporates from the ground or transpires from plants and about the same amount falls back to the surface as rain.

Fun Fact

If evaporation did not replenish the water in the atmosphere, it would dry out in ten days.

Nitrogen Cycle

Nitrogen gas makes up about 79 percent of the atmosphere, but cannot be utilized by plants in this form. In addition to fixation in the soil by bacteria, the high energy of lightning and cosmic radiation combines nitrogen with oxygen into usable nitrates that are carried to Earth with precipitation. The nitrogen in fertilizers is artificially fixed in processing plants. Nitrogen, which is taken up directly by plants and incorporated into plant tissue, enters the food web when plants are consumed.

Carbon Cycle

The total amount of carbon available on Earth is about 49,000 metric gigatons (1 metric gigaton equals 10 metric tons). The oceans contain about 71 percent and fossils contain 22 percent of the total carbon available. Six percent is held in dead organic matter or in living organisms. That leaves only one percent available in the atmosphere for circulation. The accelerated greenhouse effect is caused by an increased amount of carbon dioxide in the atmosphere, due largely to the burning of fossil fuels.

SCIENCE *Online*

For additional content background on this topic, go to the Glencoe Science Web site at science.glencoe.com.

SECTION 3

Energy Flow

Food Chains

The law of conservation of energy states that energy cannot be created or destroyed, but can change from one form to another. The energy in an ecosystem is passed from one organism to another through a series of interactions called a food chain. Food chains, food webs and ecological pyramids show how energy moves in only one direction through the trophic levels of an ecosystem and how energy is lost at each transition, from one trophic level to the next. The energy is lost to the environment in the form of heat generated by the body processes of organisms. Although the heat is ultimately lost to the environment, it also serves the purpose of maintaining the body temperature of the organism. Sunlight is the source of all energy, so energy is always being replaced.

Food Webs

Some food webs are terrestrial, some are aquatic, and some are combinations. Two types of food webs are grazing and detrital. Detritivores are organisms such as crabs and earthworms that consume dead or decomposing organic matter. The largest amount of energy passes through detrital food webs.

Fun Fact

Animal muscle yields only about one calorie of work for every four given up as heat.

Fritz Polking/Peter Arnold, Inc.

The Nonliving Environment

Chapter Vocabulary

biotic
abiotic
atmosphere
soil
climate
evaporation
condensation
water cycle
nitrogen fixation
nitrogen cycle
carbon cycle
chemosynthesis
food web
energy pyramid

What do you think?

Science Journal The photograph shows a chloroplast. Chlorophyll within chloroplasts traps energy from the Sun and converts it to carbohydrates. Almost all living things on Earth depend on this process to provide the energy they need to live.

The Nonliving Environment

Could you write a story about what would happen if the Sun stopped shining? Most life on Earth depends on the Sun's energy. In this chapter, you'll learn about how organisms called producers use energy to make food and how other organisms called consumers take in that food. You'll also read about cycles in nature such as the water, carbon, and nitrogen cycles, and many other nonliving factors that affect your life.

What do you think?

Science Journal Look at the picture below with a classmate. Discuss what this might be. Here's a hint: *It's a factory that relies on sunlight for its energy supply.* Write your answer or best guess in your Science Journal.

Theme Connection

Systems and Interactions The ingredients for life are a part of the nonliving environment. Organisms can't exist without interaction with nonliving systems.

Do you live in a dry, sandy region covered with cactus plants or desert scrub? Is your home in the mountains? Does snow fall during the winter? Perhaps you live near the coast, where flowers bloom year-round. Earth has many ecosystems. In this chapter, you'll learn why the nonliving factors in each ecosystem are different. The following activity will get you started.

Compare climate differences

1. Locate your city or town on a globe or world map. Find your latitude. Latitude shows your distance from the equator and is expressed in degrees, minutes, and seconds.

2. Locate another city with the same latitude as your city but on a different continent.

3. Locate a third city with latitude close to the equator.

4. Using references, compare average annual precipitation and average high and low temperatures for all three cities.

Observe
In your Science Journal, hypothesize how latitude affects average temperatures and rainfall.

FOLDABLES
Reading & Study Skills

Before You Read

Making a Cause and Effect Study Fold Make the following Foldable to help you understand the cause and effect relationship of the nonliving environment.

1. Place a sheet of paper in front of you so the long side is at the top. Fold the left and right sides in to divide the paper into thirds. Then fold it in half from left to right. Unfold all the folds.

2. Using the fold lines as a guide, refold the paper into a fan. Unfold all the folds again.

3. Before you read the chapter, draw a picture of a familiar ecosystem on one side of the paper. On the other side, label the folds *Nonliving, Water, Soil, Wind, Temperature,* and *Elevation* as shown.

4. As you read the chapter, write on the folds how each nonliving factor affects the environment you drew.

Nonliving
Water
Soil
Wind
Temperature
Elevation

E ◆ 35

EXPLORE ACTIVITY

Purpose Use the Explore Activity to show students how latitude affects climate. ⎣L2⎦ **Visual-Spatial**

Preparation Obtain reference information that provides climate data for various cities.

Materials world maps or globes, climate reference information

Teaching Strategy Have students compare their findings with other students' findings. Discuss differences and similarities.

Observe

In general, the lower the latitude, the higher the temperature. Rainfall is influenced by many variables, so there was probably no consistent relationship found between latitude and rainfall.

✓Assessment

Performance Give students a map of the United States and ask them to put Phoenix, San Francisco, and Los Angeles in order from lowest average temperature to highest. Use **Performance Assessment in the Science Classroom,** p. 89.

FOLDABLES
Reading & Study Skills

Before You Read

Dinah Zike Study Fold

Purpose Students make and use a Foldable to understand the cause and effect relationship of the nonliving environment. They examine five nonliving aspects of an ecosystem and the effects of these aspects on the environment as a whole.

📁 For additional help, see Foldables Worksheet, p. 17 in **Chapter Resources Booklet,** or go to the Glencoe Science Web site at **science.glencoe.com.** See After You Read in the Study Guide at the end of this chapter.

SECTION

1

Abiotic Factors

1 Motivate

Bellringer Transparency

 Display the Section Focus Transparency for Section 1. Use the accompanying Transparency Activity Master. L2 ELL

Tie to Prior Knowledge

Have students examine a fish tank or a scene from nature. Ask them to identify nonliving things that are important for living things to survive.

SECTION

1

Abiotic Factors

As You Read

What You'll Learn
- **Identify** common abiotic factors in most ecosystems.
- **List** the components of air that are needed for life.
- **Explain** how climate influences life in an ecosystem.

Vocabulary

biotic　　　　soil
abiotic　　　climate
atmosphere

Why It's Important
Knowing how organisms depend on the nonliving world can help humans maintain a healthy environment.

Environmental Factors

Living organisms depend on one another for food and shelter. The leaves of plants provide food and a home for grasshoppers, caterpillars, and other insects. Many birds depend on insects for food. Dead plants and animals decay and become part of the soil. The features of the environment that are alive, or were once alive, are called **biotic** (bi AH tihk) factors. The term *biotic* means "living."

Biotic factors are not the only things in an environment that are important to life. Most plants cannot grow without sunlight, air, water, and soil. Animals cannot survive without air, water, or the warmth that sunlight provides. The nonliving, physical features of the environment are called **abiotic** (ay bi AH tihk) factors. The prefix *a* means "not." The term *abiotic* means "not living." Abiotic factors include air, water, soil, sunlight, temperature, and climate. The abiotic factors in an environment often determine which kinds of organisms can live there. For example, water is an important abiotic factor in the environment, as shown in **Figure 1.**

Figure 1
Abiotic factors—air, water, soil, sunlight, temperature, and climate—influence all life on Earth.

36 ◆ E

Section ✓*Assessment* Planner

PORTFOLIO
Assessment, p. 42
PERFORMANCE ASSESSMENT
Try at Home MiniLAB, p. 38
Math Skills Activity, p. 40
Skill Builder Activities, p. 42
See page 60 for more options.

CONTENT ASSESSMENT
Section, p. 42
Challenge, p. 42
Chapter, pp. 60–61

Air

Air is invisible and plentiful, so it is easily overlooked as an abiotic factor of the environment. The air that surrounds Earth is called the **atmosphere.** Air contains 78 percent nitrogen, 21 percent oxygen, 0.03 percent carbon dioxide, and trace amounts of other gases. Some of these gases provide substances that support life.

Carbon dioxide (CO_2) is required for photosynthesis. Photosynthesis—a series of chemical reactions—uses CO_2, water, and energy from sunlight to produce sugar molecules. Organisms like plants that can use photosynthesis are called producers because they produce their own food. During photosynthesis, oxygen is released into the atmosphere.

When a candle burns, oxygen from the air releases energy from molecules of candle wax. Chemical energy stored in the wax is converted to heat and light energy. In a similar way, cells use oxygen to release the chemical energy stored in sugar molecules. This process is called respiration. Through respiration, cells obtain the energy needed for all life processes. Air-breathing animals aren't the only organisms that need oxygen. Plants, some bacteria, algae, fish, and most other organisms also need oxygen for respiration.

Water

Water is essential to life on Earth. It is a major ingredient of the fluid inside the cells of all organisms. In fact, most organisms are 50 percent to 95 percent water. Respiration, digestion, photosynthesis, and many other important life processes can take place only in the presence of water. As **Figure 2** shows, environments that have plenty of water usually support a greater diversity of and a larger number of organisms than environments that have little water.

Figure 2
Water is an important abiotic factor in deserts and rain forests.

A Life in deserts is limited to species that can survive for long periods without water.

B Thousands of species can live in lush rain forests where rain falls almost every day.

2 Teach

Environmental Factors

Use Science Words

Word Origin Write the words *biotic* and *abiotic* on the board. Ask students to find the meanings of *bio-*, *sphere*, and *a-*. *bio:* life; *sphere:* area; *a:* without, or not

Activity

Have students make a list of the biotic and abiotic factors that would affect the population growth of frogs near a pond. L2 LS **Naturalist**

Air

Quick Demo

Light a candle and explain that oxygen is used to release heat and light energy from the wax. In a similar way, living things use oxygen to release the energy from food. Put a bell jar over the candle and direct students to observe. As the flame goes out, explain that without oxygen, the flame and many organisms cannot obtain the energy they need. LS **Visual-Spatial**

Water

Extension

Refer to a world map of biomes. Have students compare areas of similar latitude that have different biomes. Varying amounts of precipitation is most likely the primary difference between these areas. L2 LS **Visual-Spatial**

Inclusion Strategies

Learning Disabled Ask students to comment on this question: **We can't see air, so how do we know it exists?** A variety of evidence can be discussed. We can feel the air when we move our hands very fast. We can see the effect of air when we blow it into a balloon. L1 LS **Naturalist**

Soil

TRY AT HOME
Mini LAB

Purpose Students investigate the components that make up soil. [L2] [IS] **Kinesthetic**

Materials two cups soil, large jar with lid, water, alum or dishwashing liquid, spoon, metric ruler

Teaching Strategy Review the components of soil before students carry out the activity.

Analysis
1. Clay is likely suspended in the water.
2. Answers will vary. It is likely that silt will form the greatest component.

✓Assessment

Oral Why did you examine the sample at different times? Different-sized particles settle at different rates. Use **Performance Assessment in the Science Classroom,** p. 89.

TRY AT HOME
Mini LAB

Determining Soil Makeup

Procedure
1. Collect 2 cups of **soil.** Remove large pieces of debris and break up clods.
2. Put the soil in a **quart jar or similar container that has a lid.**
3. Fill the container with **water** and add 1 teaspoon of **dishwashing liquid.**
4. Put the lid on tightly and shake the container.
5. After 1 min, measure and record the depth of sand that settled on the bottom.
6. After 2 h, measure and record the depth of silt that settles on top of the sand.
7. After 24 h, measure and record the depth of the layer between the silt and the floating organic matter.

Analysis
1. Clay particles are so small that they can remain suspended in water. Where is the clay in your sample?
2. Is sand, silt, or clay the greatest part of your soil sample?

Figure 3
Photosynthesis requires light. **A** Little sunlight reaches the shady forest floor, so plant growth beneath trees is limited. **B** Sunlight does not reach into deep lake or ocean waters. Photosynthesis can take place only in shallow water or near the water's surface. *How do fish that live at the bottom of the deep ocean obtain energy?*

Soil

Soil is a mixture of mineral and rock particles, the remains of dead organisms, water, and air. It is the topmost layer of Earth's crust, and it supports plant growth. Soil is formed, in part, of rock that has been broken down into tiny particles.

Soil is considered an abiotic factor because most of it is made up of nonliving rock and mineral particles. However, soil also contains living organisms and the decaying remains of dead organisms. Soil life includes bacteria, fungi, insects, and worms. The decaying matter found in soil is called humus. Soils contain different combinations of sand, clay, and humus. The type of soil present in a region has an important influence on the kinds of plant life that grow there.

Sunlight

All life requires energy, and sunlight is the energy source for almost all life on Earth. During photosynthesis, producers convert light energy into chemical energy that is stored in sugar molecules. Consumers are organisms that cannot make their own food. Energy is passed on to consumers when they eat producers or other consumers. As shown in **Figure 3,** photosynthesis cannot take place if light is never available.

LAB DEMONSTRATION

Purpose to determine the amount of humus in soil

Materials Bunsen burner, crucible, topsoil rich in humus, goggles, scale

Preparation Obtain and dry topsoil before class. Explain to students that humus can burn, but the rest of soil cannot.

Procedure Fill a crucible with soil, pour it out, and weigh it. Return soil to the crucible and heat on high for 10 min. Allow to cool. Pour out the soil and reweigh it. Determine the mass of the humus, and its percentage of the original soil.

Expected Outcome Topsoils are 2–15% humus.

✓Assessment

Give students the following measurements and have them calculate the mass and percentage of humus in soil.

initial mass = 10 grams

final mass = 9 grams

mass of humus = 1 gram; 10% of original soil

Figure 4
Temperature is an abiotic factor that can affect an organism's survival.

A The penguin has a thick layer of fat to hold in heat and keep the bird from freezing. These emperor penguins huddle together for added warmth.

B The Arabian camel stores fat only in its hump. This way, the camel loses heat from other parts of its body, which helps it stay cool in the hot desert.

Temperature

Sunlight supplies life on Earth with light energy for photosynthesis and heat energy for warmth. Most organisms can survive only if their body temperatures stay within the range of 0°C to 50°C. Water freezes at 0°C. The penguins in **Figure 4** are adapted for survival in the freezing Antarctic. Camels can survive the hot temperatures of the Arabian Desert because their bodies are adapted for staying cool. The temperature of a region depends in part on the amount of sunlight it receives. The amount of sunlight depends on the land's latitude and elevation.

 Reading Check *What does sunlight provide for life on Earth?*

Latitude In this chapter's Explore Activity, you discovered that temperature is affected by latitude. You found that cities located at latitudes farther from the equator tend to have colder temperatures than cities at latitudes nearer to the equator. As **Figure 5** shows, polar regions receive less of the Sun's energy than equatorial regions. Near the equator, sunlight strikes Earth directly. Near the poles, sunlight strikes Earth at an angle, which spreads the energy over a larger area.

Figure 5
Because Earth is curved, latitudes farther from the equator are colder than latitudes near the equator.

Temperature, continued

Figure 6
The stunted growth of these trees is a result of abiotic factors.

Elevation If you have climbed or driven up a mountain, you probably noticed that the temperature got cooler as you went higher. A region's elevation, or distance above sea level, affects its temperature. Earth's atmosphere acts as insulation that traps the Sun's heat. At higher elevations, the atmosphere is thinner than it is at lower elevations. Air becomes warmer when sunlight heats the air molecules. Because there are fewer air molecules at higher elevations, air temperatures there tend to be cooler.

Figure 6 shows how elevation affects other abiotic conditions, including soil and wind. At higher elevations, trees get shorter and the ground becomes rocky. Above the timberline—the elevation beyond which trees do not grow—plant life is limited to low-growing plants. The tops of some mountains are so cold that no plants can survive. Some mountain peaks are covered with snow year-round.

Math Skills Activity

Graphing Temperature Versus Elevation

Example Problem

You climb a mountain and record the temperature every 1,000 m of elevation. The temperature is 30°C at 304.8 m, 25°C at 609.6 m, 20°C at 914.4 m, 15°C at 1,219.2 m, and 5°C at 1,828.8 m. Make a graph of the data. Use your graph to predict the temperature at an altitude of 2,133.6 m.

Solution

1 *This is what you know:*
The data can be written as ordered pairs (elevation, temperature). The ordered pairs for these data are (304.8, 30), (609.6, 25), (914.4, 20), (1,219.2, 15), (1,828.8, 5).

2 *This is what you want to find:*
Predict the temperature at an elevation of 2,133.6 m.

3 *This is what you need to do:*
Graph the data by plotting elevation on the *x*-axis and temperature on the *y*-axis. Draw a line to connect the data points on your graph.

4 *Predict the temperature at 2,133.6 m:*
Extend the graph line to predict the temperature at 2,133.6 m.

Practice Problem

Temperatures on another mountain are 33°C at sea level, 31°C at 125 m, 29°C at 250 m, and 26°C at 425 m. Graph the data and predict the temperature at 550 m.

For more help, refer to the Math Skill Handbook.

Cultural **Diversity**

Kenyan Runners Many great long-distance runners are from the Kalenjin tribe in a high-altitude area of Kenya. **Why might great runners come from this area?** Possible answers: Because of lower oxygen levels at high altitudes, these Kenyans may have adaptations for increased cardiovascular efficiency; their high-altitude training may help them produce more red blood cells; there may also be social reasons.

☑ Active Reading

Quickwrites This strategy, sometimes called freewrites, lets students use spontaneous writing to discover what they already know. Have students write a list of ideas about a topic, then share these ideas with the class. Next, have students write their ideas without worrying about punctuation, spelling, and grammar. Have students use a Quickwrite to share ideas about abiotic factors.

Climate

In Fairbanks, Alaska, winter temperatures may be as low as −52°C, and more than a meter of snow might fall in one month. In Key West, Florida, snow never falls and winter temperatures rarely dip below 5°C. These two cities have different climates. **Climate** refers to an area's average weather conditions over time, including temperature, rainfall or other precipitation, and wind.

For the majority of living things, temperature and precipitation are the two most important components of climate. The average temperature and rainfall in an area influence the type of life found there. Suppose a region has an average temperature of 25°C and receives an average of less than 25 cm of rain every year. It is likely to be the home of cactus plants and other desert life. A region with similar temperatures that receives more than 300 cm of rain every year is probably a tropical rain forest.

Wind Heat energy from the Sun not only determines temperature, but also is responsible for the wind. The air is made up of molecules of gas. As the temperature increases, the molecules spread farther apart. As a result, warm air is lighter than cold air. Colder air sinks below warmer air and pushes it upward, as shown in **Figure 7.** These motions create air currents that are called wind.

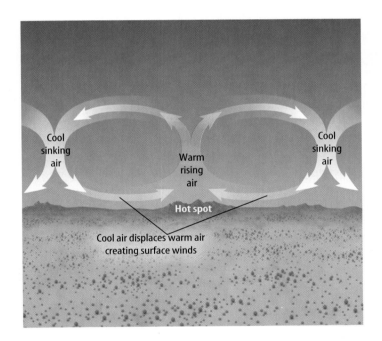

Cool sinking air

Warm rising air

Cool sinking air

Hot spot

Cool air displaces warm air creating surface winds

Physics
INTEGRATION

Gravity pulls the gases of the atmosphere toward Earth's surface. Also, the weight of the air at the top of the atmosphere presses down on the air below it. In your Science Journal, explain why air at sea level is thicker than air at the top of a mountain.

SCIENCE Online

Data Update Visit the Glencoe Science Web site at **science.glencoe.com** to look up recent weather data for your area. In your Science Journal, describe how these weather conditions affect plants or animals that live in your area.

Figure 7
Winds are created when sunlight heats some portions of Earth's surface more than others. In areas that receive more heat, the air becomes warmer and lighter. Cold air sinks beneath the warm air forcing the warm air upward.

Climate

Teacher FYI

Weather refers to the day-to-day atmospheric conditions in an area. Climate takes a long-term view and describes the general weather conditions associated with an area.

Physics
INTEGRATION

There is more air above the air at sea level than the air at the top of a mountain. The taller column of air presses down, making the air at the bottom of the column at sea level thicker.

Quick Demo

Show the rain shadow effect by moving a damp sponge over an imaginary mountain. As it rises up, explain that the air cools and water condenses into rain. Squeeze the sponge to show rain. As air decends on the other side of the moutain, it warms. Any remaining water in the air changes back to water vapor. L2 ELL IS **Visual-Spatial**

SCIENCE Online
Internet Addresses

_____
_____
_____
_____

Explore the Glencoe Science Web site at **science.glencoe.com** to find out more about topics in this section.

Resource Manager

Chapter Resources Booklet
   Enrichment, p. 30
   Reinforcement, p. 27

Reading and Writing Skill Activities, p. 3

Earth Science Critical Thinking/Problem Solving, pp. 6, 22

Inclusion Strategies

Learning Disabled Show a globe and explain that since areas near the equator receive a lot of direct sunshine, they are much warmer than areas toward the poles. As hot air is pushed aloft near the equator, cooler air rushes in to take its place. This causes wind, which is responsible for precipitation patterns. L1 IS **Visual-Spatial**

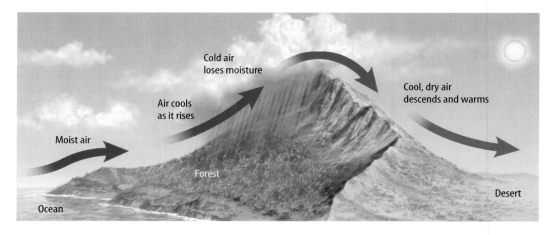

Figure 8
In Washington State, the western side of the Cascade Mountains receives an average of 101 cm of rain each year. The eastern side of the Cascades is in a rain shadow that receives only about 25 cm of rain per year.

The Rain Shadow Effect The presence of mountains can affect rainfall patterns. As **Figure 8** shows, wind blowing toward one side of a mountain is forced upward by the mountain's shape. As the air nears the top of the mountain, it cools. When air cools, the moisture it contains falls as rain or snow. By the time the cool air crosses over the top of the mountain, it has lost most of its moisture. The other side of the mountain range receives much less precipitation. It is not uncommon to find lush forests on one side of a mountain range and desert on the other side.

Section ① Assessment

1. What is the difference between biotic and abiotic factors?
2. What substances in the air are required for life on Earth?
3. Why is soil considered an abiotic factor and a biotic factor?
4. Why is climate an important abiotic factor?
5. **Think Critically** On day 1 of a hiking trip, you walk in shade under tall trees. On day 2, the trees are shorter and farther apart. On day 3, you see small plants but no trees. On day 4, you see snow. What abiotic factors might contribute to these changes?

Skill Builder Activities

6. **Identifying and Manipulating Variables and Controls** Describe an experiment to find out how much water different types of dry soil can hold. **For more help, refer to the** Science Skill Handbook.

7. **Using an Electronic Spreadsheet** Obtain two months of temperature and precipitation data for two cities in your state. Enter the data in a spreadsheet and calculate average daily temperature and rainfall. Use your calculations to compare the two climates. **For more help, refer to the** Technology Skill Handbook.

Answers to Section Assessment

1. Biotic factors are, or once were, living. Abiotic factors are nonliving.
2. carbon dioxide, nitrogen, oxygen
3. While it is mostly nonliving material, there are many things living in soil, as well as decaying organic matter called humus.

4. Climate refers to an area's temperature, amount of precipitation, and wind. These are physical features of the environment that affect the life found there.
5. Changes in elevation, which influence temperature, are probably responsible. This could occur on a mountain, as you reach and surpass the timberline.
6. Answers will vary. Possible answer: Put soil into a funnel. Then, pour measured amounts of water into the funnel until water flows through the soil and comes out the funnel.

7. Spreadsheets should result in average temperature and rainfall for two different cities.

Activity

Humus Farm

Soil contains abiotic factors, including rock particles and minerals. Soil also contains biotic factors, such as bacteria, molds, fungi, worms, insects, and decayed organisms. The crumbly, dark brown soil found in gardens or forests contains a high percentage of humus. Humus is formed primarily from the decayed remains of plants, animals, and animal droppings. It adds essential nutrients to the soil, including nitrogen. In this activity, you will cultivate your own humus.

What You'll Investigate
How does humus form?

Materials
widemouth jar	water
soil	marker
grass clippings	metric ruler
or green leaves	graduated cylinder

Goals
- **Observe** the formation of humus.
- **Observe** biotic factors in the soil.
- **Infer** how humus forms naturally.

Safety Precautions
Wash your hands thoroughly after handling soil, grass clippings, or leaves.

Humus Formation	
Date	**Observations**
	Answers will vary

Procedure

1. Copy the data table below into your Science Journal.
2. Place 4 cm of soil in the jar. Pour 30 mL of water into the jar to moisten the soil.
3. Place 2 cm of grass clippings or green leaves on top of the soil in the jar.
4. Use a marker to mark the height of the grass clippings or green leaves in the jar.
5. Put the jar in a sunny place. Every other day, add 30 mL of water to it. In your Science Journal, write a prediction of what you think will happen in your jar.
6. **Observe** your jar every other day for four weeks. Record your observations in your data table.

Conclude and Apply

1. **Describe** what happened during your investigation.
2. **Infer** how molds and bacteria help the process of humus formation.
3. **Infer** how humus forms on forest floors or in grasslands.

Communicating Your Data

Compare your humus farm with those of your classmates. With several classmates, write a recipe for creating the richest humus. Ask your teacher to post your recipe in the classroom. **For more help, refer to the Science Skill Handbook.**

Purpose Students observe humus formation over several weeks.

Visual-Spatial

Process Skills observing, describing, inferring

Time Required 25 minutes for set-up; 5 minute observation periods every other day for four weeks

Alternate Materials If green leaves are used instead of grass clippings, the leaves must be chopped in order for the activity to work.

Safety Precautions Instruct students to wash their hands when finished.

Teaching Strategy Encourage students to bring in leaf litter to be used in the activity.

Troubleshooting To be certain the humus farms get enough water, assign a person from each group to water the jars every other day.

Answers to Questions
1. Students should first observe the growth of mold in their jar. As the mold and decomposing bacteria break down the clippings or litter, large particles of organic matter will form. As the organic materials decompose, their height will decrease. These particles are the beginning of humus.
2. Molds and bacteria decompose materials into organic particles.
3. Organic materials such as leaves, twigs, or grasses fall to the ground and are decomposed into organic particles.

Resource Manager

Chapter Resources Booklet
   Activity Worksheet, pp. 5–6
Performance Assessment in the Science Classroom, p. 48

Communicating Your Data

Students may want to consult cookbooks to see how the ingredients for recipes are written and arranged.

✓ *Assessment*

Process Ask students to discuss how forest ecosystems would be affected if leaf litter if did not become humus. Use **PASC,** p. 93.

SECTION

2

Cycles in Nature

1 Motivate

Bellringer Transparency

Display the Section Focus Transparency for Section 2. Use the accompanying Transparency Activity Master. L2 ELL

Tie to Prior Knowledge

Most students will have some familiarity with the water cycle. Ask students to explain how water cycles through the environment. Ask them to think of other materials that also cycle.

Teacher FYI

This section deals with how matter changes its form as it cycles through the environment. Matter cycles, but energy does not.

SECTION

2 Cycles in Nature

As You Read

What You'll Learn
- **Explain** the importance of Earth's water cycle.
- **Diagram** the carbon cycle.
- **Recognize** the role of nitrogen in life on Earth.

Vocabulary

evaporation	nitrogen fixation
condensation	nitrogen cycle
water cycle	carbon cycle

Why It's Important
The recycling of matter on Earth demonstrates natural processes.

Figure 9
Water vapor is a gas that is present in the atmosphere.

A Water evaporates after a summer rain.

The Cycles of Matter

Imagine an aquarium tank containing water, fish, snails, plants, algae, and bacteria. The tank is sealed so that only light can enter. Food, water, and air cannot be added. Will the organisms in this environment survive? Through photosynthesis, plants and algae produce their own food. They also supply oxygen to the tank. Fish and snails take in oxygen and eat plants and algae. Wastes from fish and snails fertilize plants and algae. Organisms that die are decomposed by the bacteria. The organisms in this closed environment can survive because the materials are recycled. A constant supply of light energy is the only requirement. Earth's biosphere also contains a fixed amount of water, carbon, nitrogen, oxygen, and other materials required for life. These materials cycle through the environment and are reused by different organisms.

Water Cycle

If you leave a glass of water on a sunny windowsill, the water will disappear. It evaporates. **Evaporation** takes place when liquid water changes into water vapor, which is a gas, and enters the atmosphere, as shown in **Figure 9.** Water evaporates from the surfaces of lakes, streams, puddles, and oceans. Water vapor enters the atmosphere from plant leaves in a process known as transpiration (trans puh RAY shun). Animals release water vapor into the air when they exhale. Water also returns to the environment from animal wastes.

B Water also evaporates from the ocean.

Section ✓Assessment Planner

PORTFOLIO
Activity, p. 48

PERFORMANCE ASSESSMENT
MiniLAB, p. 47
Skill Builder Activities, p. 49
See page 60 for more options.

CONTENT ASSESSMENT
Section, p. 49
Challenge, p. 49
Chapter, pp. 60–61

Transpiration

Precipitation

Condensation

Evaporation

Groundwater

Condensation Water vapor that has been released into the atmosphere eventually comes into contact with colder air. The temperature of the water vapor drops. Over time, the water vapor cools enough to change back into liquid water. The process of changing from a gas to a liquid is called **condensation.** Water vapor condenses on particles of dust in the air, forming tiny droplets. At first, the droplets clump together to form clouds. When they become large and heavy enough, they fall to the ground as rain or other precipitation. As the diagram in **Figure 10** shows, the **water cycle** is a model that describes how water moves from the surface of Earth to the atmosphere and back to the surface again.

Water Use **Table 1** gives data on the amount of water people take from reservoirs, rivers, and lakes for use in households, businesses, agriculture, and power production. These actions can reduce the amount of water that evaporates into the atmosphere. They also can influence how much water returns to the atmosphere by limiting the amount of water available to plants and animals.

Figure 10
The water cycle involves evaporation, condensation, and precipitation. Water molecules can follow several pathways through the water cycle. *How many water cycle pathways can you identify from this diagram?*

Table 1 U.S. Estimated Water Use in 1990		
Water Use	**Millions of Gallons per Day**	**Percent of Total**
Homes and Businesses	39,100	11.5
Industry and Mining	27,800	8.2
Farms and Ranches	141,000	41.5
Electricity Production	131,800	38.6

Science Journal

Water Stories Have students imagine they are molecules of water. They should each make up a story as to how they travel and what they encounter as they go through one complete cycle of the water cycle. L2 IS **Linguistic**

Nitrogen Cycle

Extension

Ask students to use the internet to find photographs of plants with a nitrogen deficiency. Have them describe some symptoms. Possible answers: yellow leaves, stunted growth L2

IS Visual-Spatial

Use an Analogy

What would happen to a student who ate only candy? They would ingest a lot of sugar but not enough protein. Sugar provides energy but no protein to build or repair tissues. In a similar way, if a plant did not have enough nitrogen it could make sugars, but its growth and functioning would be impaired because it could not make enough proteins.

IS Logical-Mathematical

✔ Reading Check

Answer the changing of atmospheric nitrogen into nitrogen compounds that plants and animals can use

Visual Learning

Figure 11 Ask students to use the diagram as a basis for suggesting to farmers two things they can do to increase the nitrogen in their soil. Add chemical fertilizer; add decaying organic matter (compost).

Nitrogen Cycle

The element nitrogen is important to all living things. Nitrogen is a necessary ingredient of proteins. Proteins are required for the life processes that take place in the cells of all organisms. Nitrogen is also an essential part of the DNA of all organisms. Although nitrogen is the most plentiful gas in the atmosphere, most organisms cannot use nitrogen directly from the air. Plants need nitrogen that has been combined with other elements to form nitrogen compounds. Through a process called **nitrogen fixation,** some types of soil bacteria can form the nitrogen compounds that plants need. Plants absorb these nitrogen compounds through their roots. Animals obtain the nitrogen they need by eating plants or other animals. When dead organisms decay, the nitrogen in their bodies returns to the soil or to the atmosphere. This transfer of nitrogen from the atmosphere to the soil, to living organisms, and back to the atmosphere is the **nitrogen cycle,** shown in **Figure 11.**

✔ Reading Check

What is nitrogen fixation?

Figure 11
During the nitrogen cycle, nitrogen gas from the atmosphere is converted to a soil compound that plants can use.

Nitrogen gas is changed into usable compounds by lightning or by nitrogen-fixing bacteria that live on the roots of certain plants.

Plants use nitrogen compounds to build cells.

Animals eat plants. Animal wastes return some nitrogen compounds to the soil.

Animals and plants die and decompose, releasing nitrogen compounds back into the soil.

Inclusion Strategies

Gifted Have students research how ammonia wastes are converted to less toxic forms by bacteria in aquariums. Ammonia is oxidized by bacteria to form nitrates and nitrites. L3 **IS Naturalist**

Learning Disabled Help students realize that as plants grow, they use minerals from the soil. As plants die or drop leaves, these minerals are restored. In farming, however, the nutrients are taken away from the soil. If this is ongoing, the soil will become less fertile. In organic farming, humus and animal wastes are added to the soil to restore fertility. Other farmers also use chemical fertilizers. L1 **IS Naturalist**

Figure 12
Nitrogen fixation is important to plant growth.

A Soybeans can help restore nitrogen to the soil.

B The swollen nodules on the roots of the soybean plants contain colonies of nitrogen-fixing bacteria.

C The bacteria depend on the plant for food. The plant depends on the bacteria to form the nitrogen compounds the plant needs.

Magnification: 1,000×

Soil Nitrogen Human activities can affect the part of the nitrogen cycle that takes place in the soil. If a farmer grows a crop, such as corn or wheat, most of the plant material is taken away when the crop is harvested. The plants are not left in the field to decay and return their nitrogen compounds to the soil. If these nitrogen compounds are not replaced, the soil could become infertile. You might have noticed that adding fertilizer to soil can make plants grow greener, bushier, or taller. Most fertilizers contain the kinds of nitrogen compounds that plants need for growth. Fertilizers can be used to replace soil nitrogen in crop fields, lawns, and gardens. Compost and animal manure also contain nitrogen compounds that plants can use. They also can be added to soil to improve fertility.

Another method farmers use to replace soil nitrogen is to grow nitrogen-fixing crops. Most nitrogen-fixing bacteria live on or in the roots of certain plants. Some plants, such as peas, clover, and beans including the soybeans shown in **Figure 12,** have roots with swollen nodules that contain nitrogen-fixing bacteria. These bacteria supply nitrogen compounds to the soybean plants and add nitrogen compounds to the soil.

Mini LAB

Comparing Fertilizers

Procedure
1. Examine the three numbers (e.g., 5-10-5) on the **labels of three brands of houseplant fertilizer.** The numbers indicate the percentages of nitrogen, phosphorus, and potassium, respectively, that the product contains.
2. Compare the prices of the three brands of fertilizer.
3. Compare the amount of each brand needed to fertilize a typical houseplant.

Analysis
1. Which brand has the highest percentage of nitrogen?
2. Which brand is the most expensive source of nitrogen? The least expensive?

Mini LAB

Purpose Students compare the nutrient amounts in different fertilizer brands. L2

IS Kinesthetic

Materials labels and pricing information for three different brands of fertilizer

Teaching Strategy Have students ask their parents if they can bring from home fertilizers that have price tags on them.

Analysis
1. Answers will vary; the nitrogen percentage is listed first on the label.
2. Answers will vary depending on brands examined.

✓ Assessment

Performance Give students the following information. Brand Q is 5-2-6 and Brand R is 10-4-1. **Which would be the better fertilizer for soil that has adequate amounts of nitrogen and phosphorous but that is low in potassium?** Brand Q Use **Performance Assessment in the Science Classroom,** p. 99.

Resource Manager

Chapter Resources Booklet
    MiniLAB, p. 4
    Lab Activity, pp. 13–16
Science Inquiry Labs, pp. 29, 39
Physical Science Critical Thinking/Problem Solving, pp. 12, 17

Cultural Diversity

Beans Nitrogen-fixing legumes are so important in traditional agriculture that the food they produce has become part of many cultures. Ask students to recall dishes they eat at home that are made from beans. L2

Visualizing the Carbon Cycle

Have students examine the pictures and read the captions. Then ask the following questions.

What activities release carbon dioxide into the atmosphere? The burning of fossil fuels, the decomposition of carbon-containing molecules by decomposers, and the break down of sugar molecules in plants by other organisms releases carbon dioxide into the atmosphere.

Why is this process called a cycle? Possible answer: Plants use carbon dioxide from the atmosphere to make sugars. The plants then are consumed by other organisms and the carbon dioxide is released back into the atmosphere as a waste product.

Activity

Have students make their own diagram of the carbon cycle, without looking at this page, and label each part.
IS **Visual-Spatial**

Extension

Have students review or research photosynthesis and how plants use carbon dioxide to make food. Then have them write a report on how photosynthesis ties into the carbon cycle.
IS **Naturalist**

Figure 13

Carbon—in the form of different kinds of carbon-containing molecules—moves through an endless cycle. The diagram below shows several stages of the carbon cycle. It begins when plants and algae remove carbon from the environment during photosynthesis. This carbon returns to the atmosphere via several carbon-cycle pathways.

A Air contains carbon in the form of carbon dioxide gas. Plants and algae use carbon dioxide to make sugars, which are energy-rich, carbon-containing compounds.

B Organisms break down sugar molecules made by plants and algae to obtain energy for life and growth. Carbon dioxide is released as a waste.

C Burning fossil fuels and wood releases carbon dioxide into the atmosphere.

D When organisms die, their carbon-containing molecules become part of the soil. The molecules are broken down by fungi, bacteria, and other decomposers. During this decay process, carbon dioxide is released into the air.

E Under certain conditions, the remains of some dead organisms may gradually be changed into fossil fuels such as coal, gas, and oil. These carbon compounds are energy-rich.

48 ◆ E   **CHAPTER 2** The Nonliving Environment

Resource Manager

Chapter Resources Booklet
   Enrichment, p. 31
   Reinforcement, p. 28
Life Science Critical Thinking/Problem Solving, pp. 12, 22

Inclusion Strategies

Learning Disabled Have students work in groups to prepare a concept map that describes the carbon cycle. Include terms such as *consumers, photosynthesis, respiration,* and *producers.* L2 ELL
COOP LEARN **IS** **Visual-Spatial**

The Carbon Cycle

Carbon atoms are found in the molecules that make up living organisms. Carbon is an important part of soil humus, which is formed when dead organisms decay, and it is found in the atmosphere as carbon dioxide gas (CO_2). The **carbon cycle** describes how carbon molecules move between the living and nonliving world, as shown in **Figure 13.**

The carbon cycle begins when producers remove CO_2 from the air during photosynthesis. They use CO_2, water, and sunlight to produce energy-rich sugar molecules. Energy is released from these molecules during respiration—the chemical process that provides energy for cells. Respiration uses oxygen and releases CO_2. Photosynthesis uses CO_2 and releases oxygen. These two processes help recycle carbon on Earth.

✔ Reading Check *How does carbon dioxide enter the atmosphere?*

Human activities also release CO_2 into the atmosphere. Fossil fuels such as gasoline, coal, and heating oil are the remains of organisms that lived millions of years ago. These fuels are made of energy-rich, carbon-based molecules. When people burn these fuels, CO_2 is released into the atmosphere as a waste product. People also use wood for building and for fuel. Trees that are harvested for these purposes no longer remove CO_2 from the atmosphere during photosynthesis. The amount of CO_2 in the atmosphere is increasing. Extra CO_2 could trap more heat from the Sun and cause average temperatures on Earth to rise.

SCIENCE Online

Research Visit the Glencoe Science Web site at **science.glencoe.com** for the chemical equations that describe photosynthesis and respiration. In your Science Journal, write these equations and use them to explain how respiration is the reverse of photosynthesis.

Section 2 Assessment

1. Describe the water cycle.
2. Explain how respiration can be considered the reverse of photosynthesis.
3. How might burning fossil fuels affect the composition of gases in the atmosphere?
4. Why do plants, animals, and other organisms need nitrogen?
5. **Think Critically** Most chemical fertilizers contain nitrogen, phosphorus, and potassium. Why don't they contain carbon? How do plants obtain carbon?

Skill Builder Activities

6. **Identifying and Manipulating Variables and Controls** Describe an experiment that would determine whether extra carbon dioxide enhances the growth of tomato plants. **For more help, refer to the** Science Skill Handbook.
7. **Communicating** Pretend you are a carbon molecule. Write a fictional account of your travels from the atmosphere, through at least two organisms, and back to the atmosphere. **For more help, refer to the** Science Skill Handbook.

The Carbon Cycle

SCIENCE Online
Internet Addresses

_____
_____
_____

Explore the Glencoe Science Web site at **science.glencoe.com** to find out more about topics in this section.

✔ Reading Check

Answer as a by product of respiration

③ Assess

Reteach

Ask students to explain the different paths water vapor, carbon, and nitrogen in the air would follow before they could enter a plant. L2 IS **Naturalist**

Challenge

Suppose you covered all the bodies of water on Earth with oil. **How would this affect the water cycle?** Possible answers: water could not evaporate; the water cycle would be disrupted; a drought may result.

Portfolio Have students draw a diagram of the nitrogen cycle. Use **Performance Assessment in the Science Classroom,** p. 127.

Answers to Section Assessment

1. Cycles should include evaporation, condensation, and precipitation.
2. Respiration usually requires oxygen to break down substances and to obtain energy. The process releases CO_2 and water vapor. Photosynthesis requires CO_2, water, and light energy to make sugars. The process gives off oxygen as a waste.
3. It could result in an increase in the concentration of carbon dioxide.
4. to make amino acids for proteins and nucleic acids
5. Plants can get carbon from the atmosphere. Carbon is also found in humus.
6. Answers will vary, but should include one group with normal CO_2 and one with extra CO_2. An operational definition of the growth of the tomato plants should be given, along with plans for taking measurements.
7. Answers will vary, but the first step should be photosynthesis.

SECTION

Energy Flow

1 Motivate

Bellringer Transparency

Display the Section Focus Transparency for Section 3. Use the accompanying Transparency Activity Master. L2
ELL

Tie to Prior Knowledge

Students may have seen athletes "hit the wall." Ask why this happens, and if they have ever "run out of energy." Explain that energy is necessary to fuel life.

SECTION

Energy Flow

As You Read

What You'll Learn

- **Explain** how organisms produce energy-rich compounds.
- **Describe** how energy flows through ecosystems.
- **Recognize** how much energy is available at different levels in a food chain.

Vocabulary
chemosynthesis   energy pyramid
food web

Why It's Important
All living things, including people, need a constant supply of energy.

Figure 14
A Chemicals in the water that flows from hydrothermal vents provide bacteria with a source of energy. **B** The bacterial producers use this energy to make nutrients through the process of chemosynthesis. Consumers, such as tubeworms, feed on the bacteria.

B

Magnification: 38,000×

Converting Energy

All living things are made of matter, and all living things need energy. Matter and energy move through the natural world in different ways. Matter can be recycled over and over again. The recycling of matter requires energy. Energy is not recycled, but it is converted from one form to another. The conversion of energy is important to all life on Earth.

Photosynthesis During photosynthesis, producers convert light energy into the chemical energy in sugar molecules. Some of these sugar molecules are broken down as energy is needed. Others are used to build complex carbohydrate molecules that become part of the producer's body. Fats and proteins also contain stored energy.

Chemosynthesis Not all producers rely on light for energy. During the 1970s, scientists exploring the ocean floor were amazed to find communities teeming with life. These communities were at a depth of almost 3.2 km and living in total darkness. They were found near powerful hydrothermal vents like the one shown in **Figure 14**.

A

Section ✔Assessment Planner

PORTFOLIO
Activity, p. 51
PERFORMANCE ASSESSMENT
Skill Builder Activities, p. 53
See page 60 for more options.

CONTENT ASSESSMENT
Section, p. 53
Challenge, p. 53
Chapter, pp. 60–61

Hydrothermal Vents A hydrothermal vent is a deep crack in the ocean floor through which the heat of molten magma can escape. The water from hydrothermal vents is extremely hot from contact with molten rock that lies deep in Earth's crust.

Because no sunlight reaches these deep ocean regions, plants or algae cannot grow there. How do the organisms living in this community obtain energy? Scientists learned that the hot water contains nutrients such as sulfur molecules that bacteria use to produce their own food. The production of energy-rich nutrient molecules from chemicals is called **chemosynthesis** (kee moh SIN thuh sus). Consumers living in the hydrothermal vent communities rely on chemosynthetic bacteria for nutrients and energy. Chemosynthesis and photosynthesis allow producers to make their own energy-rich molecules.

✓ **Reading Check** *What is chemosynthesis?*

Energy Transfer

Energy can be converted from one form to another. It also can be transferred from one organism to another. Consumers cannot make their own food. Instead, they obtain energy by eating producers or other consumers. This way, energy stored in the molecules of one organism is transferred to another organism. At the same time, the matter that makes up those molecules is transferred from one organism to another. Throughout nature, energy and matter move from organism to organism when one organism becomes food for another organism.

Food Chains A food chain is a way of showing how matter and energy pass from one organism to another. Producers—plants, algae, and other organisms that are capable of photosynthesis or chemosynthesis—are always the first step in a food chain. Animals that consume producers such as herbivores are the second step. Carnivores and omnivores—animals that eat other consumers—are the third and higher steps of food chains. One example of a food chain is shown in **Figure 15.**

Earth Science
INTEGRATION

The first hydrothermal vent community discovered was found along the Galápagos rift zone. A rift zone forms where two plates of Earth's crust are spreading apart. In your Science Journal, describe the energy source that heats the water in the hydrothermal vents of the Galápagos rift zone.

Figure 15
In this food chain, grasses are producers, marmots are herbivores that eat the grasses, and grizzly bears are consumers that eat marmots. The arrows show the direction in which matter and energy flow.

---

2 Teach

Converting Energy

Earth Science
INTEGRATION

The source of heat in the vents is geothermal energy.

✓ **Reading Check**

Answer Chemosynthesis is the production of energy-rich food molecules from chemical energy.

Energy Transfer

Discussion
What do the arrows in food chains represent? the flow of matter and energy from one organism to another Ask students to generate other food chains. Answers will vary.

Activity
Have students make a food chain for a deep sea community. Food chains should be similar to that of a simple aquatic system, except that chemosynthetic bacteria will replace aquatic plants as producers. L2
🅺 **Visual-Spatial** P

Resource Manager

Chapter Resources Booklet
Transparency Activity, p. 46
Directed Reading for Content Mastery, pp. 21, 22
Transparency Activity, pp. 47–48
Mathematics Skill Activities, p. 9

Inclusion Strategies

Learning Disabled Have students who understand the concepts of producer and consumer work with students who are having difficulty. Have partners group the terms *producer, photosynthesis, plants, bacteria, chemosynthesis, consumer,* and *animal.* L1 COOP LEARN 🅺 **Interpersonal**

Energy Transfer,
continued

Visual Learning___

Figure 16 Have students design three different food chains based on the food web. Then have students assess the impact on other organisms if one organism from the food web were removed. The impact varies, depending upon many factors, including whether or not the organism is a keystone species. Regardless of this, however, the entire community would be affected, as the diversity and balance of the ecosystem would be disturbed.

Energy Pyramids

Make a Model

Find a grasshopper or cricket and weigh it. Then have students collect ten times the weight of the insect in grass. For example, if the insect weighs 1 g, they should gather 10 g of grass. Place the insect on top of the pile of grass to make a model of a biomass pyramid.
L1 **IS** **Logical-Mathematical**

Use an Analogy

Help students understand why so much energy is lost from one level to another. If they raised a cat from a kitten, ask them to imagine how much food the cat has eaten in its life. It is far more than the weight of the cat. Most of the food was used for energy. If a coyote ate their cat, it would not get all the food the cat ate, just the caloric value of the cat.

Food Webs A forest community includes many feeding relationships. These relationships can be too complex to show with a food chain. For example, grizzly bears eat many different organisms, including berries, insects, chipmunks, and fish. Berries are eaten by bears, birds, insects, and other animals. A bear carcass might be eaten by wolves, birds, or insects. A **food web** is a model that shows all the possible feeding relationships among the organisms in a community. A food web is made up of many different food chains, as shown in **Figure 16.**

Energy Pyramids

Food chains usually have at least three links, but rarely more than five. This limit exists because the amount of available energy is reduced as you move from one level to the next in a food chain. Imagine a grass plant that absorbs energy from the Sun. The plant uses some of this energy to grow and produce seeds. Some of the energy is stored in the seeds.

Figure 16
Compared to a food chain, a food web provides a more complete model of the feeding relationships in a community.

Teacher **FYI**
The law of conservation of energy states that energy is not created or destroyed, but only converted into other forms of energy. In most ecosystems the energy starts as light energy, which is converted through photosynthesis into chemical energy.

Inclusion Strategies
Visually Impaired Obtain or make a pyramid-shaped object. Allow students to handle the model to identify its shape. Explain that the model depicts the relative amount of energy available as one moves up a food chain.
IS **Kinesthetic**

Available Energy When a mouse eats grass seeds, energy stored in the seeds is transferred to the mouse. However, most of the energy the plant absorbed from the Sun was used for the plant's growth. Much less energy is stored in the seeds eaten by the mouse. The mouse uses much of the energy remaining in the seeds for its own life processes, including respiration, digestion, and growth. A hawk that eats the mouse obtains even less energy.

The same thing happens at every feeding level of a food chain. The amount of available energy is reduced from one feeding level to another. An **energy pyramid,** like the one in **Figure 17,** shows the amount of energy available at each feeding level in an ecosystem. The bottom layer of the pyramid, which represents all of the producers, is the first feeding level. It is the largest level because it contains the most energy and the largest number of organisms. As you move up the pyramid, each level becomes smaller. Only about ten percent of the energy available at each feeding level of an energy pyramid is transferred to the next higher level.

Carnivores

Herbivores

Producers

Figure 17
This energy pyramid shows that each feeding level contains less energy than the level below it. *What would happen if the hawks and snakes outnumbered the rabbits and mice in this ecosystem?*

 Reading Check *Why does the first feeding level of an energy pyramid contain the most energy?*

Caption Answer

Figure 17 Less energy would be available to hawks and snakes. Eventually they would begin to die off until a balance was achieved.

☑ **Reading Check**

Answer because little energy has been lost in maintaining body systems

3 Assess

Reteach

Write the word *humans* on the board. Have students write the names of all the animals we eat below this word. Below this write all the plants that we eat or that are eaten by the animals we eat. Connect lines to make food chains. Then draw more lines to show a food web. L1
LS **Visual-Spatial**

Challenge

Ask students to research the following organisms and design a food web that shows their relationships: *corn, rabbit, hawk, grass, wheat, rat, fox, human,* and *cow.*

☑ **Assessment**

Performance Use the overhead projector to project a scene from nature. Help students identify the organisms in the picture. Then have them design food chains based on the picture and their knowledge of the organisms. Use **Performance Assessment in the Science Classroom,** p. 127.

Section 3 Assessment

1. Compare and contrast photosynthesis and chemosynthesis.

2. Explain how your three favorite foods provide you with energy from the Sun.

3. What is the difference between a food web and an energy pyramid?

4. Why is there a limit to the number of links in a food chain?

5. **Think Critically** Use your knowledge of food chains and the energy pyramid to explain why the number of mice in a grassland ecosystem is greater than the number of hawks.

Skill Builder Activities

6. **Classifying** Classify each species as photosynthetic or chemosynthetic: *Red hattus* uses red light to make its food; *Selen dion* makes food if the element selenium is present. **For more help, refer to the** Science Skill Handbook.

7. **Solving One-Step Equations** A forest has 24,055,000 kilocalories (kcals) of producers, 2,515,000 kcals of herbivores, and 235,000 kcals of carnivores. How much energy is lost between producers and herbivores? Between herbivores and carnivores? **For more help, refer to the** Math Skill Handbook.

SECTION 3 Energy Flow **E ◆ 53**

Answers to Section Assessment

1. Both involve nutrient production; photosynthesis uses energy from the Sun to produce nutrients, while chemosynthesis uses energy from chemicals.

2. All of the foods we eat provide us with energy from the Sun, either directly (producers) or indirectly (consumers).

3. A food web shows the path of energy and matter in an ecosystem. An energy pyramid shows the amount of energy available at each level.

4. because a significant amount of energy is lost at each level

5. Hawks eat mice. For the mice to support the hawk population, there must be far more energy at the mouse level than at the hawk level. Since mice are smaller than hawks, this means that there must be many more mice than hawks.

6. *Red hattus* is photosynthetic; *Selen dion* is chemosynthetic.

7. producers and herbivores: 21,540,000 kcal; herbivores and carnivores: 2,280,000 kcal

Activity

BENCH TESTED

What You'll Investigate

Purpose

Students perform a variation of Johannes Baptista Van Helmont's famous experiment to determine if plants get their mass from the soil. L2 **Logical-Mathematical**

Process Skills

observing, measuring, predicting, interpreting data, using numbers

Time Required

45 minutes to set up; three weeks for the plants to grow; 1 hour for the final measurements, calculations, and cleanup

Safety Precautions

Caution students to wash their hands after handling plants and soil.

Activity

Where does the mass of a plant come from?

An enormous oak tree starts out as a tiny acorn. The acorn sprouts in dark, moist soil. Roots grow down through the soil. Its stem and leaves grow up toward the light and air. Year after year, the tree grows taller, its trunk grows thicker, and its roots grow deeper. It becomes a towering oak that produces thousands of acorns of its own. An oak tree has much more mass than an acorn. Where does this mass come from? The soil? The air? In this activity, you'll find out by conducting an experiment with radish plants.

What You'll Investigate

Does all of the matter in a radish plant come from the soil?

Goals

■ **Measure** the mass of soil before and after radish plants have been grown in it.
■ **Measure** the mass of radish plants grown in the soil.
■ **Analyze** the data to determine whether the mass gained by the plants equals the mass lost by the soil.

Materials

8-oz plastic or paper cup
potting soil to fill cup
scale or balance
radish seed (4)
water
paper towels

Safety Precautions 🥽 🧤

54 ◆ E

Inclusion Strategies

Learning Disabled Help students understand the purpose of the investigation. Hand students a piece of two-by-four lumber so they can feel how heavy it is. Ask them where the weight of the tree came from. The weight came from the food the tree utilized to build its body.

Resource Manager

Chapter Resources Booklet
  Activity Worksheet, pp. 7–8
Lab Management and Safety, p. 38

Procedure

1. Copy the data table into your Science Journal.
2. Fill the cup with dry soil.
3. Find the mass of the cup of soil and record this value in your data table.
4. Moisten the soil in the cup. Plant four radish seeds 2 cm deep in the soil. Space the seeds an equal distance apart. Wash your hands.
5. Add water to keep the soil barely moist as the seeds sprout and grow.
6. When the plants have developed four to six true leaves, usually after two to three weeks, carefully remove the plants from the soil. Gently brush the soil off the roots. Make sure all the soil remains in the cup.
7. Spread the plants out on a paper towel. Place the plants and the cup of soil in a warm area to dry out.

8. When the plants are dry, measure their mass and record this value in your data table. Write this number with a plus sign in the Gain or Loss column.
9. When the soil is dry, find the mass of the cup of soil. Record this value in your data table. Subtract the End mass from the Start mass and record this number with a minus sign in the Gain or Loss column.

Sample Data

Mass of Soil and Radish Plants			
	Start	End	Gain (+) or Loss (−)
Mass of dry soil and cup	75.8 g	75.7 g	0.1 g −
Mass of dried radish plants	0 g	2.1 g	2.1 g +

Conclude and Apply

1. In the early 1600s, a Belgian scientist named J. B. van Helmont conducted this experiment with a willow tree. What is the advantage of using radishes instead of a tree?
2. How much mass was gained or lost by the soil? By the radish plants?
3. Did the mass of the plants come completely from the soil? How do you know?

4. If all of the mass gained by the plants did not come from the soil, where could it have come from?

Communicating Your Data

Compare your conclusions with those of other students in your class. **For more help, refer to the** Science Skill Handbook.

Procedure

Teaching Strategy

Prior to getting results, ask students if most of the mass gained by the radish plants will come from the soil. If they don't think it will come from the soil, ask where they think it will come from.

Expected Outcome

The radish plants' mass gain will be more than the soil's mass loss.

Conclude and Apply

1. Radishes grow faster and use less space. You can get a quantitative amount of mass gained and lost.
2. Answers will vary, but the soil will have a very small mass loss and the plants will have a much larger mass gain.
3. No, because the mass loss of the soil is smaller than the mass gain of the plants.
4. Answers will vary, but should include carbon dioxide from the air and water from the soil.

Error Analysis

Some errors may occur because the plants and soil are not completely dry. However, this usually does not affect the conclusion.

Assessment

Content Pretend that you grew a willow tree for five years like Van Helmont. Write down how much mass the tree might have gained and how much mass the soil might have lost. Use **Performance Assessment in the Science Classroom,** p. 89.

Communicating Your Data

Have students post their data tables on a bulletin board for other students to see.

Science Stats

Content Background

The term *climate* refers to the average weather of a region over a period of time. Earth has a huge variety of climates and the climate of any region can change over time. The following list explains the main influences on the climate of a region.

1. Wind, which distributes moisture and heat
2. Distance of the region from the equator, which determines how much solar radiation reaches the area
3. Presence of large bodies of water, which decrease temperature variation in the surrounding regions
4. Altitude, which affects the temperature
5. Presence of mountains and other surface features, which influence cloud formation and precipitation

Discussion

What type of weather would you expect the south pole to have while it is pointed away from the Sun? Students should infer that the South Pole would have low temperatures and cold weather during the time it is pointed away from the Sun.

Activity

Have students work as a class to record and graph daily high and low temperatures each day for a month.

IS Logical-Mathematical

Science Stats

Extreme Climates

Did you know...

2,896 cm

... The greatest snowfall in one year occurred at Mount Baker in Washington State. Approximately 2,896 cm of snow fell on Mount Baker during the 1998-99 12-month snowfall season. That's enough snow to bury an eight-story building.

... The hottest climate in the United States is found in Death Valley, California. In July 1913, Death Valley reached approximately 57°C. This is the hottest officially recognized temperature on Earth. As a comparison, a comfortable room temperature is about 20°C.

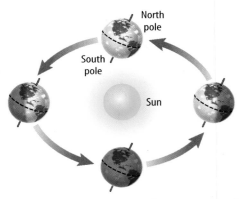

North pole

South pole

Sun

... The record for the lowest temperature was set in Antarctica in 1983. The temperature was a frigid −89°C. As a comparison, the temperature of your freezer at home is about −15°C.

... The south pole receives sunshine for less than 50 percent of the days in a year. Because Earth is tilted, the south pole is pointed away from the Sun for about half the year and receives very little during that time.

SCIENCE *Online*
Internet Addresses
_____
_____
_____
_____

Explore the Glencoe Science Web site at **science.glencoe.com** to find out more about topics in this feature.

... The fastest tornado winds have been measured at a speed of about 512 km/h. That's faster than the blades of some helicopters, which can rotate at about 450 km/h.

Lowest Average Annual Rainfall

Highest Average Annual Rainfall

Do the Math

1. Look at the graph above. How many years of average south pole precipitation would it take to equal a single year of average precipitation in Lloro, Colombia?
2. What is the difference in degrees Celsius between the world record low temperature and the world record high temperature?
3. What was the average monthly snowfall at Mount Baker during the 1998-99 snowfall season?

Go Further

Go to **science.glencoe.com** and find out the average monthly rainfall in a tropical rain forest. Make a line graph to show how the amount of precipitation changes during the 12 months of the year.

Do the Math

Teaching Strategies

- Remind students to use the label on each graph to determine the value represented by each bar. Also remind students to include the unit (years) with their answer.
- Use a number line to demonstrate the relative position of −89°C and +57°C. Remind students that the difference between these two values will be larger than either of the numbers.
- Inform students that the snowfall season on Mount Baker is 12 months long. The average monthly snowfall can be calculated by dividing the total snowfall by 12.

Answers

1. approximately 650 years
2. 146°C
3. 241.3 cm

Go Further

Have students add lines to their graphs to represent the average monthly rainfall in your area. Compare the amount of precipitation received in your location to that received in a tropical rain forest. Ask students to predict how the local environment would change if the amount of precipitation increased.

Visual Learning

Lowest Average Annual Rainfall, Highest Average Annual Rainfall Have each student choose one location represented on each graph and use the annual rainfall number to calculate an average monthly rainfall number for each location. Then, have students cut a strip of paper the same height as the average amount of monthly rainfall in each of the locations they have chosen. Use the paper strips for comparison. **LS Visual-Spatial**

Chapter 2 Study Guide

Reviewing Main Ideas

Preview

Students can answer the questions in their Science Journals. Discuss the answers as you go through the chapter. **IS Linguistic**

Review

Students can write their answers, then compare them with those of other students. **IS Interpersonal**

Reteach

Students can look at the illustrations and describe details that support the main ideas of the chapter. **IS Visual-Spatial**

Answers to Chapter Review

SECTION 1

1. Possible answers: proper temperatures, sufficient water and oxygen, sunlight and soil minerals for trees to make nuts

SECTION 2

1. They produce oxygen as a waste product of photosynthesis.

SECTION 3

1. through photosynthesis
5. Most of the apple's energy is converted into energy for your life functions.

Reviewing Main Ideas

Section 1   Abiotic Factors

1. Abiotic factors include air, water, soil, sunlight, temperature, and climate. *What abiotic factors are required for this squirrel's survival? Explain.*

2. The availability of water and light influences where life exists on Earth.

3. Soil and climate have an important influence on the types of organisms that can survive in different environments.

4. High latitudes and elevations generally have lower average temperatures.

Section 2   Cycles in Nature

1. Matter is limited on Earth and is recycled through the environment. *How do green plants help recycle oxygen?*

2. The water cycle involves evaporation, condensation, and precipitation.

3. The carbon cycle involves photosynthesis and respiration.

4. Nitrogen in the form of soil compounds enters plants which are then consumed by other organisms.

Section 3   Energy Flow

1. Producers make energy-rich molecules through photosynthesis or chemosynthesis. *How do seaweeds in shallow water obtain energy?*

2. When organisms feed on other organisms, they obtain matter and energy.

3. Matter can be recycled, but energy cannot.

4. Food webs are models of the complex feeding relationships in communities.

5. Available energy decreases as you go to higher feeding levels in an energy pyramid. *What happens to most of the energy in an apple that you eat?*

FOLDABLES
Reading & Study Skills

After You Read

Find a student who drew a different ecosystem on their Cause and Effect Study Fold. Then, compare and contrast the information on your two Foldables.

FOLDABLES
Reading & Study Skills

After You Read

After students have read the chapter and completed the Foldable described in Before You Read, have them do the activity on the student page.

Dinah Zike

Visualizing Main Ideas

This diagram shows photosynthesis in a leaf. Fill in the blank lines with the terms light, carbon dioxide, *and* oxygen.

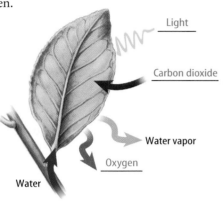

Light

Carbon dioxide

Water vapor

Oxygen

Water

Vocabulary Review

Vocabulary Words

a. abiotic
b. atmosphere
c. biotic
d. carbon cycle
e. chemosynthesis
f. climate
g. condensation
h. energy pyramid

i. evaporation
j. food web
k. nitrogen cycle
l. nitrogen fixation
m. soil
n. water cycle

THE PRINCETON REVIEW **Study Tip**

Write out the full questions and answers to end-of-chapter quizzes, not just the answers. This will help you form complete responses to important questions.

Using Vocabulary

Which vocabulary word best corresponds to each of the following events?

1. A liquid changes to a gas.

2. Some types of bacteria form nitrogen compounds in the soil.

3. Decaying plants add nitrogen to the soil.

4. Chemical energy is used to make energy-rich molecules.

5. Decaying plants add carbon to the soil.

6. A gas changes to a liquid.

7. Water flows downhill into a stream. The stream flows into a lake, and water evaporates from the lake.

8. Burning coal and exhaust from automobiles release carbon into the air.

CHAPTER STUDY GUIDE E ◆ 59

Chapter ② Study Guide

Visualizing Main Ideas

See student page.

Vocabulary Review

Using Vocabulary

1. evaporation
2. nitrogen fixation
3. nitrogen cycle
4. chemosynthesis
5. carbon cycle
6. condensation
7. water cycle
8. carbon cycle

Checking Concepts

1. B
2. B
3. A
4. D
5. A
6. A
7. B
8. B
9. A
10. C

Thinking Critically

11. The country should grow corn and other vegetables for the people to eat. If they grow corn to feed cattle, most of the energy of the corn will be lost.

12. Webs show complex interactions rather than the simple interactions of a chain.

13. Yes; nitrogen is an important component of DNA.

14. In the mature forest, the tall trees block most of the sunlight from reaching the floor. There is therefore little plant growth, making it easy to walk.

15. As the air blows over the mountains from the ocean on the west side, it cools and loses moisture. Thus there is a forest on one side, but a desert on the other.

Chapter 2 Assessment

Checking Concepts

Choose the word or phrase that best answers the question.

1. Which of the following is an abiotic factor?
   A) penguins   C) soil bacteria
   B) rain   D) redwood trees

2. Which group makes up the largest level of an energy pyramid?
   A) herbivores   C) decomposers
   B) producers   D) carnivores

3. You climb up the western slope of the Cascade Mountains and down the eastern side. Which of the following weather changes do you observe?
   A) Warm and wet changes to cold and wet, then cold and dry, then warm and dry.
   B) Cold and wet changes to warm and wet, then warm and dry, then cold and dry.
   C) Warm and wet changes to cold and wet, then cold and dry, then warm and wet.
   D) Warm and dry changes to cold and dry, then warm and dry, then cold and dry.

4. Which of the following applies to latitudes farther from the equator?
   A) higher elevations
   B) higher temperatures
   C) higher precipitation levels
   D) lower temperatures

5. Water vapor forming droplets that form clouds directly involves which process?
   A) condensation C) evaporation
   B) respiration   D) transpiration

6. Which one of the following components of air is least necessary for life on Earth?
   A) argon   C) carbon dioxide
   B) nitrogen   D) oxygen

7. What do plants make that requires nitrogen?
   A) sugars   C) fats
   B) proteins   D) carbohydrates

8. Which of the following processes removes carbon dioxide from the air?
   A) condensation C) burning
   B) photosynthesis D) respiration

9. Earth receives a constant supply of which of the following items?
   A) light energy C) nitrogen
   B) carbon   D) water

10. Which of these is an energy source for chemosynthesis?
   A) sunlight   C) sulfur molecules
   B) moonlight   D) carnivores

Thinking Critically

11. A country has many starving people. Should they grow vegetables and corn to eat, or should they grow corn to feed cattle so they can eat beef? Explain.

12. Why is a food web a better model than a food chain?

13. Do bacteria need nitrogen? Why or why not?

14. It is often easier to walk through an old, mature forest of tall trees than through a young forest that is full of small trees. Why?

15. The Inyo Mountains are located in central California. Explain why giant sequoia trees grow on the west side of the mountains and Death Valley, a desert, is on the east side.

Developing Skills

16. **Classifying** Classify each of the following environmental concerns according to the cycle it affects—carbon, nitrogen, or water.
   a. algal blooms caused by excess fertilizer
   b. acid rain damage to pine trees
   c. the unnatural warming of Earth

Chapter ✓Assessment Planner

Portfolio Encourage students to place in their portfolios one or two items of what they consider to be their best work. Examples include:
- Assessment, p. 42
- Activity, p. 48
- Activity, p. 51

Performance Additional performance assessments, Performance Task Assessment Lists, and rubrics for evaluating these activities can be found in Glencoe's **Performance Assessment in the Science Classroom.**

17. Recognizing Cause and Effect A lake in Kenya has been taken over by a floating weed. What could you do to determine if nitrogen fertilizer runoff from farms is causing the problem?

18. Making and Using Graphs Abiotic factors, such as climate, cause populations to move from place to place. Make a bar graph of the following migration distances.

Mighty Migrators	
Species	**Distance (km)**
Desert locust	4,800
Caribou	800
Green turtle	1,900
Arctic tern	35,000
Gray whale	19,000

19. Forming Hypotheses For each hectare of land, ecologists found 10,000 kcals of producers, 10,000 kcals of herbivores, and 2,000 kcals of carnivores. Suggest a reason why producer and herbivore levels are equal.

20. Concept Mapping Draw a food web of these organisms: *caterpillars and rabbits eat grasses, raccoons eat rabbits and mice, mice eat grass seeds,* and *birds eat caterpillars.*

Performance Assessment

21. Poster Use magazine photographs to make a visual representation of the water cycle.

TECHNOLOGY

 Go to the Glencoe Science Web site at **science.glencoe.com** or use the **Glencoe Science CD-ROM** for additional chapter assessment.

 Test Practice

Food chains model how energy is transferred from one organism to another organism in the environment. The diagram below shows a food chain that includes aquatic plants and animals and a land animal.

Study the diagram and answer the following questions.

1. Which of the following statements is true based on the order of the food chain shown above?
A) Algae eat plankton.
B) Plankton eat salmon.
C) Herring eat plankton.
D) Salmon eat algae.

2. If the supply of salmon were suddenly depleted, the numbers of which of the following might also be depleted?
F) algae   **H)** herring
G) plankton   **J)** eagles

 Test Practice

The Test-Taking Tip was written by The Princeton Review, the nation's leader in test preparation.
1. C
2. J

Developing Skills

16. a. nitrogen cycle
b. water cycle
c. carbon cycle
17. Possible answer: Ask farmers to restrict their use of nitrogen fertilizer and see if this clears up the lake.
18. From highest bar to lowest: Arctic tern, gray whale, desert locust, green turtle, caribou
19. Reasons may include a poor growth year for plants or a very good year for herbivore reproduction.
20. Check student food webs to ensure correct relationships are in place.

Performance Assessment

21. Posters will vary, but should show how the cycle continues. Use **PASC**, p. 145.

✓Assessment Resources

📁 **Reproducible Masters**

Chapter Resources Booklet
Chapter Review, pp. 37–38
Chapter Tests, pp. 39–42
Assessment Transparency Activity, p. 49

Glencoe Science Web site
Interactive Tutor
Chapter Quizzes

Glencoe Technology
🔦 Assessment Transparency
💿 Interactive CD-ROM Chapter Quizzes
💿 ExamView Pro Test Bank
💿 Vocabulary PuzzleMaker Software
📼 MindJogger Videoquiz DVD/VHS

Section/Objectives	Standards		Activities/Features
Chapter Opener	**National**	**State/Local**	**Explore Activity:** Infer the origin of houseplants, p. 63 **Before You Read,** p. 63
	See p. 6T for a Key to Standards.		
Section 1 How Ecosystems Change ⏱ 2 sessions 📦 1 block 1. **Explain** how ecosystems change over time. 2. **Describe** how new communities begin in areas without life. 3. **Compare** pioneer communities and climax communities.	National Content Standards: UCP1, UCP3, C4, F2		**Science Online,** p. 65 **Visualizing Secondary Succession,** p. 66
Section 2 Biomes ⏱ 2 sessions 📦 1 block 1. **Explain** how climate influences land environments. 2. **Identify** seven biomes of Earth. 3. **Describe** the adaptations of organisms found in each biome.	National Content Standards: UCP1, A1, C4, C5		**MiniLAB:** Modeling Rain Forest Leaves, p. 72 **Earth Science Integration,** p. 74 **Activity:** Studying a Land Ecosystem, p. 76
Section 3 Aquatic Ecosystems ⏱ 3 sessions 📦 1.5 blocks 1. **Compare** flowing freshwater and standing freshwater ecosystems. 2. **Identify** and describe important saltwater ecosystems. 3. **Identify** problems that affect aquatic ecosystems.	National Content Standards: UCP1, A1, C4, C5, F2, G1		**MiniLAB:** Modeling Freshwater Environments, p. 78 **Chemistry Integration,** p. 79 **Math Skills Activity,** p.80 **Science Online,** p. 81 **Activity:** Exploring Wetlands, pp. 84–85 **Science and Society:** Helping Nature Help Itself, pp. 86–87

NATIONAL GEOGRAPHIC

Teacher's Corner

PRODUCTS AVAILABLE FROM GLENCOE
To order call 1-800-334-7344:
CD-ROM
NGS PictureShow: Looking at Ecosystems
Poster
Water

Transparency Set
NGS PicturePack: Looking at Ecosystems
Videodiscs
STV: Habitats; STV: Water

PRODUCTS AVAILABLE FROM NATIONAL GEOGRAPHIC SOCIETY
To order call 1-800-368-2728:
Videos
The Living Ocean; Water: A Celebration; Water: A Precious Resource

Activity Materials	Reproducible Resources	Section Assessment	Technology
Explore Activity: houseplant	**Chapter Resources Booklet** Foldables Worksheet, p. 15 Directed Reading Overview, p. 17 Note-taking Worksheets, pp. 31–32	*GLENCOE'S* **ASSESSMENT** *ADVANTAGE*	
Need materials? Contact Science Kit at 1-800-828-7777 or www.sciencekit.com on the Internet.	**Chapter Resources Booklet** Transparency Activity, p. 42 Enrichment, p. 28 Reinforcement, p. 25 Directed Reading, p. 18 Lab Activity, pp. 9–10	**Portfolio** Visual Learning, p. 66 **Performance** Skill Builder Activities, p. 67 **Content** Section Assessment, p. 67	✎ Section Focus Transparency 💿 Interactive CD-ROM/DVD 🎧 Guided Reading Audio Program
MiniLAB: poster board, metric ruler, scissors, sink, water **Activity:** graph paper, thermometer, hand lens, notebook, binoculars, field guides, compass	**Chapter Resources Booklet** MiniLAB, p. 3 Transparency Activity, p. 43 Enrichment, p. 29 Reinforcement, p. 26 Directed Reading, p. 19 Activity Worksheet, pp. 5–6 **Reading and Writing Skill Activities,** p. 1	**Portfolio** Assessment, p. 75 **Performance** MiniLAB, p. 72 Skill Builder Activities, p. 75 **Content** Section Assessment, p. 75	✎ Section Focus Transparency 💿 Interactive CD-ROM/DVD 🎧 Guided Reading Audio Program
MiniLAB: pond sediment or debris; pond plants, water, and organisms; clear plastic container with lid; net; hand lens **Activity:** Internet sites or reference sources on wetlands	**Chapter Resources Booklet** MiniLAB, p. 4 Transparency Activity, p. 44 Enrichment, p. 30 Reinforcement, p. 27 Directed Reading, pp. 19, 20 Activity Worksheet, pp. 7–8 Lab Activity, pp. 11–14 Transparency Activity, pp. 45–46 **Lab Management and Safety,** p. 37	**Portfolio** Science Journal, p. 80 **Performance** MiniLAB, p. 78 Math Skills Activity, p. 80 Skill Builder Activities, p. 83 **Content** Section Assessment, p. 83	✎ Section Focus Transparency ✎ Teaching Transparency 💿 Interactive CD-ROM/DVD 🎧 Guided Reading Audio Program

GLENCOE'S ASSESSMENT *ADVANTAGE*
End of Chapter Assessment

Blackline Masters	Technology	Professional Series
Chapter Resources Booklet Chapter Review, pp. 35–36 Chapter Tests, pp. 37–40 **Standardized Test Practice by The Princeton Review,** pp. 19–22	▭ MindJogger Videoquiz 💿 CD-ROM Explorations and Quizzes 💿 Vocabulary Puzzle Makers 💿 ExamView Pro Test Bank 💿 Interactive Lesson Planner 💿 Interactive Teacher's Edition	Performance Assessment in the Science Classroom (PASC)

Transparencies

Section Focus

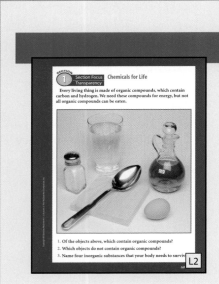

SECTION 1 Section Focus Transparency — Chemicals for Life

Every living thing is made of organic compounds, which contain carbon and hydrogen. We need these compounds for energy, but not all organic compounds can be eaten.

1. Of the objects above, which contain organic compounds?
2. Which objects do not contain organic compounds?
3. Name four inorganic substances that your body needs to survive.

L2

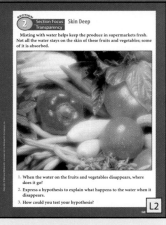

SECTION 2 Section Focus Transparency — Skin Deep

Misting with water helps keep the produce in supermarkets fresh. Not all the water stays on the skin of these fruits and vegetables; some of it is absorbed.

1. When the water on the fruits and vegetables disappears, where does it go?
2. Express a hypothesis to explain what happens to the water when it disappears.
3. How could you test your hypothesis?

L2

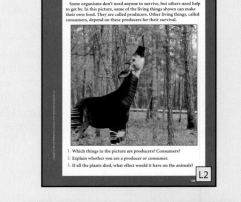

SECTION 3 Section Focus Transparency — What's for dinner?

Some organisms don't need anyone to survive, but others need help to get by. In this picture, some of the living things shown can make their own food. They are called producers. Other living things, called consumers, depend on these producers for their survival.

1. Which things in the picture are producers? Consumers?
2. Explain whether you are a producer or consumer.
3. If all the plants died, what effect would it have on the animals?

L2

This is a representation of key blackline masters available in the Teacher Classroom Resources. See Resource Manager boxes within the chapter for additional information.

Key to Teaching Strategies

The following designations will help you decide which activities are appropriate for your students.

L1 Level 1 activities should be appropriate for students with learning difficulties.

L2 Level 2 activities should be within the ability range of all students.

L3 Level 3 activities are designed for above-average students.

ELL ELL activities should be within the ability range of English Language Learners.

COOP LEARN Cooperative Learning activities are designed for small group work.

LS Multiple Learning Styles logos are used throughout to indicate strategies that address different learning styles.

P These strategies represent student products that can be placed into a best-work portfolio.

Assessment

Assessment Transparency — Cell Processes

Directions: Carefully review the diagrams and answer the following questions.

1. Which of the following questions would best be addressed by the experiment shown above?
   A Can salt float in water?
   B What is the membrane's permeability?
   C Does salt dissolve in water?
   D What compounds are found in salt?
2. This experiment probably relies on ____.
   F osmosis   H friction
   G endocytosis   J exocytosis
3. If the water and salt could cross the membrane equally, the water would ____.
   A increase on the left   C equalize
   B increase on the right   D collapse the membrane

L2

Teaching

SECTION 1 Teaching Transparency — Organic Compounds

L2

Hands-on Activities

Activity Worksheets

Activity — Observing Osmosis

L2

Laboratory Activities

Laboratory Activity — Diffusion

L2

Meeting Different Ability Levels

Content Outline

Reinforcement

Directed Reading

Assessment

Chapter Tests

Enrichment

Spanish Directed Reading

Test Practice Workbook

Chapter Review

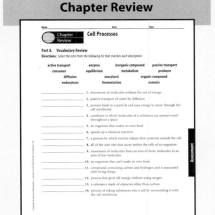

Science Content Background

SECTION 1

How Ecosystems Change
Defining Ecosystems

A system is a group of parts that work together to form a functioning whole. Some common examples of systems include cars, watches, and digestive systems. An ecosystem is a group of organisms interacting with each other and the environment through a flow of energy and cycling of matter. It is the interdependence of all the parts that makes the whole a system.

Student Misconception

Ecosystems consist of only a few interactions among living things in an area.

Refer to the facing page for teaching strategies to address this misconception. Refer to pages 64–67 for content related to this topic.

SECTION 2

Biomes
Tundra

The tundra receives less energy from the Sun than does any other biome. The Sun's energy is dispersed over a greater area at higher latitudes. The Sun's rays lose much of their energy because they must travel diagonally through the atmosphere.

Desert

Desert covers less than 5% of North America. The North American deserts are the Mojave, Sonoran, Great Basin, and Chihuahuan. Temperatures in the desert undergo drastic changes over a 24-hour period. Daytime temperatures can be 30°C higher than nighttime readings. These fluctuations occur because of the lack of heat-retaining moisture in the desert air.

SECTION 3

Aquatic Ecosystems
Nutrients in Aquatic Ecosystems

In aquatic ecosystems, nutrients tend to sink below the light zone where many organisms cannot use them. In the ocean, the process that moves the bottom water with its valuable nutrients up to the surface is called an upwelling. In an upwelling, winds and currents work together near the continental shelf. The winds carry water away from land. Bottom water with its nutrients is pulled up into the photic zone to replace water that has moved out to sea. Upwellings occur in only a few places, such as along the coast of Peru.

SCIENCE *Online*

For additional content background on this topic, go to the Glencoe Science Web site at science.glencoe.com.

Kevin & Cat Sweeney/DRK Photo

IDENTIFYING **Misconceptions**

Find Out What Students Think

Students may think that . . .

- **Systems only exist as parts of an organism or process.**

- **Ecosystems consist of only a few interactions among living things in an area.**

Students often do not understand the nature of systems in general, and they understand even less about the specific aspects of an ecosystem. Students may have learned that some things are called systems or ecosystems, but they may not be aware that ecosystems consist of parts, subsystems, and many interactions between biotic and abiotic factors.

Discussion

Show a photo of a bicycle, or bring in a bicycle for students to examine. Have students describe what they see. It is likely that students will respond that they see a bike. Point out that although there is one bicycle functioning as a whole unit, the bicycle consists of many components such as wheels, seat, chain, pedals, and so on. If any one of these components is removed, the bicycle will not function properly. The individual parts work together to do what a bicycle is supposed to do. In addition, in order for the bike to function, it needs an input of energy from a rider. Like a bicycle, an ecosystem is made up of many components, both abiotic (nonliving) and biotic (living), and it receives energy in the form of light and heat from the Sun.

Promote Understanding

Activity

Have students make a terrarium or display a completed terrarium.

- Discuss the biotic (living) and abiotic (nonliving) factors included in the terrarium, such as plants, insects, light, water, soil, and air.

- Have students diagram connections between the components. Then relate these connections to the flow of energy and cycling of materials. **What do you think would happen if one of the components of the terrarium were removed?** Explain that if a component such as light were removed, the plants would not be able to photosynthesize. Have students

discuss the long-term effects of this event. The plants would die, the insects that eat the plants would not have food, and so on.

- Emphasize that the removal of light would cause the ecosystem to function improperly. Underscore this idea, using a diagram of the flow of energy and cycling of materials in the terrarium.

  As an extension, have students choose another component of the terrarium and discuss how its removal would affect all other components of the terrarium.

Assess

After completing the chapter, see *Identifying Misconceptions* in the Study Guide.

Ecosystems

Chapter Vocabulary

succession
pioneer species
climax community
biome
tundra
taiga
desert
temperate deciduous forest
temperate rain forest
tropical rain forest
grassland
wetland
coral reef
intertidal zone
estuary

What do you think?

Science Journal Lava covers the soil on land, forming a rock layer. Lichens grow on the rock, gradually breaking it down and starting the process of primary succession.

CHAPTER

Ecosystems

During the summer of 2000, wildfires burned out of control in Montana and other western states. Can this Montana hillside recover from the forest fire? Can the animals that lived here before the fire adapt to the changed environment? How is the forest in this picture different from a rain forest in South America? In this chapter, you will learn about the different ecosystems that exist on Earth. You also will learn how ecosystems change and how plants and animals adapt to those changes.

What do you think?

Science Journal Look at the picture below with a classmate. Discuss what this might be or what is happening. Here's a hint: *It is the first step in creating land.* Write your answer or best guess in your Science Journal.

Theme Connection

Stability and Change Ecosystems change in ways that can be predicted. In the process of succession, each community affects the environment, often producing conditions that result in the community's replacement.

The plants growing in your classroom or home may not look like the same types of plants that you find growing outside. Where do indoor plants come from? Many indoor plants don't grow well outside in most North American climates. Do the activity below to determine what type of climate most houseplants thrive in.

Infer the origin of houseplants

1. Examine a healthy houseplant in your classroom or home.
2. Describe the environmental conditions found in your classroom or home. For example, is the air humid or dry? Are temperatures warm and nearly constant?
3. Using observations from step 1 and descriptions from step 2, hypothesize about the natural environment of the plants in your classroom or home.

Observe

In your Science Journal, record the observations that led to your hypothesis. How would you design an experiment to test your hypothesis?

Before You Read

FOLDABLES
Reading & Study Skills

Making a Main Ideas Study Fold A main idea consists of the major concepts or topics talked about in a chapter. Before you read the chapter, make the following Foldable to help you understand succession, or the gradual change in plants and animals over time.

1. Place a sheet of paper in front of you so the long side is at the top. Fold the paper in half from the left side to the right side. Fold top to bottom but do not crease and unfold.
2. Turn the paper so the fold is at the top and label *Primary Succession* and *Secondary Succession* across the front of the paper, as shown. Draw an arrow down from each and then label *Climax Communities,* as shown. Circle all four labels.
3. Through the top thickness of paper, cut along the middle fold line to form two tabs as shown.
4. As you read the chapter, define terms and collect information under the tabs.

How Ecosystems Change

1 Motivate.

Bellringer Transparency

Display the Section Focus Transparency for Section 1. Use the accompanying Transparency Activity Master. L2

ELL

Tie to Prior Knowledge

Relate the idea of succession to examples found in the local environment. For example, there may be abandoned lots or farm fields showing succession. Many communities are allowing roadside grass areas to revert back to their natural states.

How Ecosystems Change

As You Read

***What* You'll Learn**
- **Explain** how ecosystems change over time.
- **Describe** how new communities begin in areas without life.
- **Compare** pioneer communities and climax communities.

Vocabulary
succession
pioneer species
climax community

***Why* It's Important**
Understanding how ecosystems change can help you predict what can happen to the land around you in the years to come.

Ecological Succession

What would happen if the lawn at your home were never cut? The grass would get longer, as in **Figure 1**, and soon it would look like a meadow. Later, larger plants would grow from seeds brought to the area by animals or wind. Then, trees might sprout. In fact, in 20 years or less you wouldn't be able to tell that the land was once a mowed lawn. An ecologist can tell you what type of ecosystem your lawn would become. If it would become a forest, they can tell you how long it would take and predict the type of trees that would grow there. **Succession** refers to the normal, gradual changes that occur in the types of species that live in an area. Succession occurs differently in different places around the world.

Primary Succession As lava flows from the mouth of a volcano, it is so hot that it destroys everything in its path. When it cools, lava forms new land composed of rock. It is hard to imagine that this land eventually could become a forest or grassland someday.

The process of succession that begins in a place without any soil is called primary succession. It starts with the arrival of living things such as lichens (LI kunz). These living things, called **pioneer species,** do not need soil to survive. They survive drought, extreme heat and cold, and other harsh conditions and start the soil-building process.

Figure 1
Open areas that are not maintained will become overgrown with grasses and shrubs as succession begins.

Section ✓*Assessment* Planner

PORTFOLIO ASSESSMENT
Visual Learning, p. 66
PERFORMANCE ASSESSMENT
Skill Builder Activities, p. 67
See page 90 for more options.

CONTENT ASSESSMENT
Section, p. 67
Challenge, p. 67
Chapter, pp. 90–91

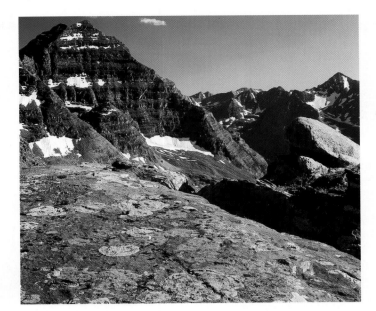

Figure 2
Lichens, like these in Colorado, are fragile and take many years to grow. They often cling to bare rock where many other organisms can't survive. *How do lichens form soil?*

New Soil During primary succession, shown in **Figure 2,** soil begins to form as lichens and the forces of weather and erosion help break down rocks into smaller pieces. When lichens die, they decay, adding small amounts of organic matter to the rock. Plants such as mosses and ferns can grow in this new soil. Eventually, these plants die, adding more organic material. The soil layer thickens, and grasses, wildflowers, and other plants begin to take over. When these plants die, they add more nutrients to the soil. This buildup is enough to support the growth of shrubs and trees. All the while, insects, small birds, and mammals have begun to move in. What was once bare rock now supports a variety of life.

Secondary Succession What happens when a fire, such as the one in **Figure 3,** destroys a forest or when a building is torn down in a city? After a forest fire, not much is left except dead trees and ash-covered soil. After the rubble of a building is removed, all that remains is bare soil. However, these places do not remain lifeless for long. The soil already contains the seeds of weeds, grasses, and trees. More seeds are carried to the area by wind and birds. Other wildlife may move in. Succession that begins in a place that already has soil and was once the home of living organisms is called secondary succession. Because soil already is present, secondary succession occurs faster and has different pioneer species than primary succession does.

 Reading Check *Which type of succession starts without soil?*

SCIENCE *Online*

Data Update Visit the Glencoe Science Web site at **science.glencoe.com** to learn how forests in the western United States are recovering from the wildfires of 2000. Communicate to your class what you learn.

Ecological Succession

Caption Answer

Figure 2 Lichens help to break down rocks into smaller pieces. When lichens die, they decay, adding small amounts of organic material to the soil.

Teacher FYI

The small size of lichens and mosses makes them successful in the harsh environments typical of primary succession. Fast reproduction is a characteristic of secondary pioneers. These plants, which often pop up in gardens, are usually called weeds.

SCIENCE *Online*

Internet Addresses

_____

_____

_____

Explore the Glencoe Science Web site at **science.glencoe.com** to find out more about topics in this section.

Reading Check

Answer primary succession

Resource Manager

Chapter Resources Booklet
  Transparency Activity, p. 42
  Note-taking Worksheets, pp. 31–33
  Directed Reading for Content Mastery, pp. 17, 18

Curriculum Connection

History As the eastern United States was settled by Europeans, large tracts of forest were converted into farmland. With increasing industrialization, many of the farms were abandoned and the land reverted back into forests. Ask students to determine the past extent of the eastern forests and draw a map of this region.

NATIONAL GEOGRAPHIC

Visualizing Secondary Succession

Have students examine the pictures and read the captions. Then ask the following questions.

What characteristics would make a seed likely to survive a fire? A seed that is surrounded by a thick seed coat is more likely to survive a fire than one with a thin seed coat.

As succession proceeds, what changes will occur in the population of plants found on the forest floor? At first, plants that need lots of sunlight can live on the forest floor, because there are no tall trees to block the sunlight. As trees grow and mature there will be less sunlight penetrating to the forest floor, so species that require less light will be found.

Activity

Have the students work in teams to write song lyrics that describe secondary succession. Students can write lyrics that fit any melody they know and enjoy. The steps of secondary succession should be clearly and accurately described in the lyrics.

Extension

Have students research in detail the current state of the areas of Yellowstone Park that burned in 1988. Students should share their findings with the class.

Figure 3

In the summer of 1988, wind-driven flames like those shown in the background photo swept through Yellowstone National Park, scorching nearly a million acres. The Yellowstone fire was one of the worst forest fires in United States history. The images on this page show secondary succession— the process of ecological regeneration—triggered by the fire.

▶ After the fire, burned timber and blackened soil seemed to be all that remained. However, the fire didn't destroy the seeds that were protected under the soil.

◀ Within weeks, grasses and other plants were beginning to grow in the burned areas. Ecological succession was underway.

▶ Many burned areas in the park opened new plots for stands of trees. This picture shows young lodgepole pines in August 1999. The forest habitat of America's oldest national park is gradually being restored through secondary succession.

66 ◆ E CHAPTER 3

Visual Learning

Figure 3 Have students make an outline of the stages in secondary succession that are shown. Then, have them go back and fill in any stages that aren't shown.

Resource Manager

Chapter Resources Booklet
Enrichment, p. 28
Reinforcement, p. 25
Lab Activity, pp. 9–10

Figure 4
This beech-maple forest is an example of a climax community.

Climax Communities A community that has reached a stable stage of ecological succession is called a **climax community.** It is a combination of plants and animals that use the available resources most efficiently. The beech-maple forest shown in **Figure 4** is an example of a community that has reached the end of succession. Diversity and balance are maintained in a climax community because as trees die, they provide nutrients for new communities of organisms. Physical disturbances, such as fire, also are important in maintaining balance in a climax community.

Primary succession begins in areas with no life at all. It can take hundreds or even thousands of years to develop into a climax community. Secondary succession is usually a shorter process, but it still may take a century or more.

Section Assessment

1. What is ecological succession?
2. Explain the difference between primary and secondary succession.
3. What is the difference between pioneer and climax communities?
4. After a climax community is established in an area, explain how long it can survive there.
5. **Think Critically** What kind of succession will take place on an abandoned, unpaved country road? Why?

Skill Builder Activities

6. **Concept Mapping** Show the sequence of events in primary succession. Include the term *climax community.* **For more help, refer to the** Science Skill Handbook.
7. **Solving One-Step Equations** A tombstone etched with 1802 as the date of death has a lichen on it that is 6 cm in diameter. Assuming that the lichen started to grow in 1802, calculate the average yearly growth of the lichen. **For more help, refer to the** Math Skill Handbook.

IDENTIFYING Misconceptions

Students may think that ecosystems consist of only a few interactions among living things in an area. Refer to page 62F for teaching strategies that address this misconception.

3 Assess

Reteach

Arrange the stages of succession for a forest community out of sequence in a diagram. Photocopy the diagram and have students use numbers to put the pictures in the proper sequence.
L2 IS **Logical-Mathematical**

Challenge

Managers of some protected wildlife areas do not put out natural fires; sometimes they even do controlled burns. **Why is this done?** Controlled burns promote succession so that there are a variety of plants and animals in the ecosystem. In addition, these burns minimize tinder build-up so that naturally-occurring fires do not get out of control.

Assessment

Content Have students write a paragraph identifying how each of the following is undergoing succession: a cornfield after a flood, the area around a volcanic eruption, and a newly formed sandbar in a river. Use **Performance Assessment in the Science Classroom,** p. 159.

SECTION

2 Biomes

1 Motivate

Bellringer Transparency

Display the Section Focus Transparency for Section 2. Use the accompanying Transparency Activity Master. L2 ELI

Tie to Prior Knowledge

Choose a biome that students are likely to have some knowledge about, such as deserts or tropical rain forests. Have students make a list of organisms that live in that biome and the biome in which they live. Then have students hypothesize why different plants and animals live in these different biomes.

SECTION

2 Biomes

As You Read

What You'll Learn
- **Explain** how climate influences land environments.
- **Identify** seven biomes of Earth.
- **Describe** the adaptations of organisms found in each biome.

Vocabulary
biome
tundra
taiga
desert

temperate deciduous forest
temperate rain forest
tropical rain forest
grassland

Why It's Important
Resources that you need to survive are found in a variety of biomes.

Figure 5
The land portion of Earth can be divided into seven biomes.

Factors That Affect Biomes

Does a desert in Arizona have anything in common with a desert in Africa? Both have heat, little rain, poor soil, water-conserving plants with thorns, and lizards. Even widely separated regions of the world can have similar biomes because they have similar climates. Climate is the average weather pattern in an area over a long period of time. The two most important climatic factors that affect life in an area are temperature and precipitation.

Major Biomes

Large geographic areas that have similar climates and ecosystems are called **biomes** (BI ohmz). Seven common types of biomes are mapped in **Figure 5.** Areas with similar climates produce similar climax communities. Tropical rain forests are climax communities found near the equator, where temperatures are warm and rainfall is plentiful. Coniferous forests grow where winter temperatures are cold and rainfall is moderate.

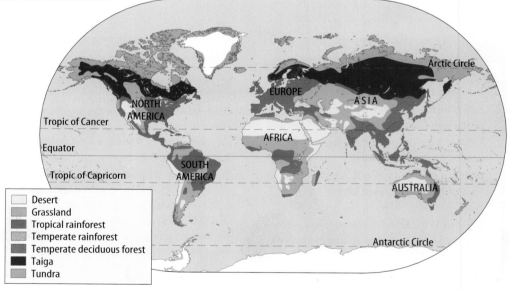

- Desert
- Grassland
- Tropical rainforest
- Temperate rainforest
- Temperate deciduous forest
- Taiga
- Tundra

Section ✔Assessment Planner

PORTFOLIO
Assessment, p. 75
PERFORMANCE ASSESSMENT
Try at Home MiniLAB, p. 72
Skill Builder Activities, p. 75
See page 90 for more options.

CONTENT ASSESSMENT
Section, p. 75
Challenge, p. 75
Chapter, pp. 90–91

Tundra At latitudes just south of the north pole lies a biome that receives little precipitation but is covered with ice most of the year. The **tundra** is a cold, dry, treeless region, sometimes called a cold desert. Precipitation averages less than 25 cm per year. Winters can be six to nine months long. For some of these months, when the Sun never appears above the horizon, the land is dark 24 hours a day. The average temperature of the tundra is about −12°C. For a few days during the short, cold summer, the Sun is always visible. Only the top few inches of soil thaw in the summer. Below the thawed surface is a layer of permanently frozen soil called permafrost, shown in **Figure 6.** Tundra soil has few nutrients because the cold temperatures slow the process of decomposition.

Tundra Life Tundra plants are adapted to drought and cold. They include mosses, grasses, and small shrubs, as seen in **Figure 7.** Many lichens grow on the tundra. During the summer, mosquitoes, blackflies, and other biting insects fill the air. Migratory birds such as ducks, geese, shorebirds, and songbirds nest on the tundra during the summer. Other inhabitants include hawks, snowy owls, and willow grouse. Mice, voles, lemmings, arctic hares, caribou, reindeer, and musk oxen also are found there.

People are concerned about overgrazing by animals on the tundra. Fences, roads, and pipelines have disrupted the migratory routes of some animals and forced them to stay in a limited area. Because the growing season is so short, plants and other vegetation can take decades to recover from damage.

Figure 6
This permafrost in Alaska is covered by soil that freezes in the winter and thaws in the summer. *What types of problems might this cause for people living in this area?*

Figure 7
A Lichens, mosses, grasses, and small shrubs thrive on the tundra. **B** Ptarmigan live on the tundra. In winter, their feathers turn white. Extra feathers on their feet keep them warm and prevent them from sinking into the snow.

Resource Manager

Chapter Resources Booklet
Transparency Activity, p. 43
Enrichment, p. 29
Reading and Writing Skill Activities, p. 1

Cultural **Diversity**

Inuit Life Have students research the Inuit who live in the Arctic tundra and report on how they have adapted to the harsh climate.
L2 **LS** **Linguistic**

2 Teach

Factors That Affect Biomes

Quick Demo
Use a globe and flashlight to show why some winter days in the tundra have 24 hours of darkness and some summer days have 24 hours of light.

Major Biomes

Caption Answer
Figure 6 Permafrost makes it impossible to farm the land.

Discussion
Would you prefer to live in a house with ten acres of land in the tundra or in a small apartment in New York City? Have students defend their responses.

Teacher **FYI**
Limited light and heat, and a short growing season are factors that limit producer growth in the tundra. Lichen species here grow extremely slowly—only 1/6 cm per year. It can take 40 years for lichens to recover from damage caused by a passing herd of caribou.

Fun Fact
The nose botfly has unique adaptations for surviving the cold winter. It lays its eggs in the nose of a caribou. The maggots emerge and travel to the caribou's throat where they are kept warm. In the spring, caribou cough the maggots up. The maggots pupate and then become flies.

Major Biomes, continued

Use Science Words

Word Origin "Taiga" comes from the Russian word *taiga*, which means "swampy forest." Ask students why this is a good description of the taiga biome. The taiga is a cold forest region that is warmer and wetter than the tundra.

IDENTIFYING Misconceptions

Students may think that the location of a particular biome on Earth is permanent. They may not realize that changes in climate have affected the locations of biomes and probably will continue to do so in the future.

Quick Demo

Cut strips of paper of appropriate length to represent the amount of precipitation in centimeters for each biome. Tape these to the board as you discuss the biomes. Start with a strip of paper that represents the amount of rainfall in your area.

Figure 8
A The taiga is dominated by cone-bearing evergreen trees.
B The lynx has broad, heavily furred feet that act like snowshoes to prevent it from sinking in the snow.

Taiga South of the tundra—between latitudes 50°N and 60°N and stretching across Canada, northern Europe, and Asia—is the world's largest biome. The **taiga** (TI guh), shown in **Figure 8,** is a cold, forest region dominated by cone-bearing evergreen trees. Although the winter is long and cold, the taiga is warmer and wetter than the tundra. Precipitation is mostly snow and averages 35 cm to 100 cm each year.

Most soils of the taiga thaw completely during the summer, making it possible for trees to grow. However, permafrost is present in the extreme northern regions of the taiga. The forests of the taiga might be so dense that little sunlight penetrates the trees to reach the forest floor. However, some lichens and mosses do grow on the forest floor. Moose, lynx, shrews, bears, and foxes are some of the animals that live in the taiga.

Temperate Deciduous Forest Temperate regions usually have four distinct seasons each year. Annual precipitation ranges from about 75 cm to 150 cm and is distributed throughout the year. Temperatures range from below freezing during the winter to 30°C or more during the warmest days of summer.

Figure 9
A The leaves on trees in deciduous forests change color in autumn.
B White-tailed deer are found in deciduous forests. They feed on a variety of plants and nuts.

Science Journal

Metric Measurements Students should become familiar with metric measurements, such as those used in this section for temperature. Have them convert the following Celsius temperatures to Fahrenheit:

10°C (50°F); 0°C (32°F); 20°C (68°F); 30°C (86°F)

Inclusion Strategies

Learning Disabled A concept map of "The Forests of the World" may help students visualize the relationship between taiga, temperate deciduous forest, temperate rain forest, and tropical rain forest. L1 **Visual-Spatial**

Temperate Forest Life Many evergreen trees grow in the temperate regions of the world. However, most of the temperate forests in Europe and North America are dominated by climax communities of deciduous trees, which lose their leaves every autumn. These forests, like the one in **Figure 9,** are called **temperate deciduous forests.** In the United States, most of them are located east of the Mississippi River.

When European settlers first came to America, they cut trees to create farmland and to supply wood. As forests were cut, organisms lost their habitats. When agriculture shifted from the eastern to the midwestern and western states, secondary succession began, and trees eventually returned to some areas. Now, nearly as many trees grow in the New England states as did before the American Revolutionary War. Many trees are located in smaller patches. Yet, the recovery of large forests such as those in the Adirondack Mountains in New York State shows that succession is possible.

Temperate Rain Forest New Zealand, southern Chile, and the Pacific Northwest of the United States are some of the places where **temperate rain forests,** shown in **Figure 10,** are found. The average temperature of a temperate rain forest ranges from 9°C to 12°C. Precipitation ranges from 200 cm to 400 cm per year.

Trees with needlelike leaves dominate these forests, including the Douglas fir, western red cedar, and spruce. Many grow to great heights. Animals of the temperate rain forest include the black bear, cougar, bobcat, endangered northern spotted owl, and threatened marbled murrelet. Many species of amphibians also inhabit the temperate rain forest, including salamanders.

The logging industry in the Northwest provides jobs for many people. However, it also removes large parts of the temperate rain forest and destroys the habitat of many organisms. Many logging companies now are required to replant trees to replace the ones they cut down. Also, some rain forest areas are protected as national parks and forests.

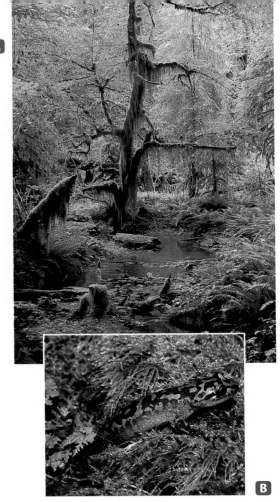

Figure 10
A In the Olympic rain forest in Washington State, mosses and lichens blanket the ground and hang from the trees. **B** Wet areas are perfect habitats for amphibians like this Pacific giant salamander.

Make a Model

Have students:
(a) use long wooden dowels representing trees to show how the land in the Northeastern United States looked before European settlers,
(b) remove the dowels and put up short dowel fences and black paper roads to represent how the land looked when it was made into farms,
(c) return many of the long dowels but keep the fences and roads to show the return of trees. Make the point that although trees are present, many animals are restricted in their movement.

Teacher FYI

The spotted owl is an endangered species that lives in old-growth temperate rain forests. These forests are over 100 years old. Clear-cutting the forest and planting new trees destroys the necessary habitat of these birds.

Resource Manager

Chapter Resources Booklet
Directed Reading for Content Mastery, p. 19
Earth Science Critical Thinking/Problem Solving, p. 6

Inclusion Strategies

Gifted Six common land biomes are presented in this chapter. Students may be assigned other biomes to research, such as tidal wetlands, extreme deserts, bogs, chapparal, continental slope, temperate oceans, tropic savannahs, or coastal arctic tundra. Have them present their findings to the class as posters or other visuals.
 Visual-Spatial

Major Biomes, continued

TRY AT HOME Mini LAB

Purpose Students observe rain forest leaves, analyze their structures, and relate leaf structure to leaf function. [L2]

[LS] Kinesthetic

Materials poster board, pencil, scissors, sink, water, spray bottle

Teaching Strategy Show students philodendron or ficus leaves so they can see real drip tips.

Analysis
1. the leaf with the drip tip
2. Removing water from the leaf's surface prohibits growth of mosses, fungi, or other moisture-loving organisms.

✔Assessment

Process Ask students how they could perform a similar experiment but obtain quantitative results. Answers should involve the measurement of the amount of water falling off the leaves using a graduated cylinder. Use **PASC,** p. 105.

✔ Reading Check

Answer forest floor, understory, canopy, emergents

TRY AT HOME Mini LAB

Modeling Rain Forest Leaves

Procedure
1. Draw an oval leaf about 10 cm long on a piece of **poster board.** Cut it out.
2. Draw a second leaf the same size but make the end pointed. This is called a drip tip. Cut this leaf out.
3. Lay a leaf on each of your hands over a **sink.** Point the drip tip away from you. Tilt your hands down but do not allow the leaves to fall off.
4. Have someone gently spray **water** on the leaves and observe what happens.

Analysis
1. From which leaf does water drain faster?
2. Infer why it is an advantage for a leaf to get rid of water quickly in a rain forest.

Figure 11
Tropical rain forests are lush environments that contain such a large variety of species that many have not been discovered.

Tropical Rain Forest Warm temperatures, wet weather, and lush plant growth are found in **tropical rain forests.** These forests are warm because they are near the equator. The average temperature, about 25°C, doesn't vary much between night and day. Most tropical rain forests receive at least 200 cm of rain annually. Some receive as much as 600 cm of rain each year.

Tropical rain forests, like the one in **Figure 11,** are home to an astonishing variety of organisms. They are the most biologically diverse places in the world. For example, one tree in a South American rain forest might contain more species of ants than exist in all of the British Isles.

Tropical Rain Forest Life Different animals and plants live in different parts of the rain forest. Scientists divide the rain forest into zones based on the types of plants and animals that live there, just as a library separates books about different topics onto separate shelves. The zones are as follows: forest floor, understory, canopy, and emergents, as shown in **Figure 12.** These zones often blend together, but their existence allows many organisms to live in the tropical rain forest.

✔ Reading Check
What are the four zones of a tropical rain forest?

Although tropical rain forests support a huge variety of organisms, the soil of the rain forest contains few nutrients. The soil is poor because of the high number of organisms that live in the soil and because of erosion by water. Any dead leaves or vegetation are consumed quickly.

🔧 LAB DEMONSTRATION

Purpose to show the stabilizing effect of buttress roots on rain forest trees

Materials paper towel tubes, scissors, tape, trough with thin layer of sand

Preparation Cut out four buttresses (which resemble rocket fins) from two paper towel tubes, and tape them to one tube.

Procedure Nutrients are near the surface in rain forest soils, so tree roots don't go very deep. When trees grow to reach light, stability problems often occur. Put two paper towel tubes (one with buttresses, one without) 1 cm into the sand. Blow on the tubes to see which falls first.

Expected Outcome The tube without buttresses will fall first.

✔Assessment

Why do buttresses make trees more stable? They give the trees a wider base. **Why would a rain forest tree be more likely to have buttresses than a temperate forest tree?** Rain forest tree roots do not penetrate the soil as deeply.

Human Impact Farmers that live in tropical areas clear the land to farm and to sell the valuable wood. After a few years, the crops use up the nutrients in the soil, and the farmers must clear more land. As a result, tropical rain forest habitats are being destroyed. Through education, people are realizing the value and potential value of preserving the species of the rain forest. In some areas, logging is prohibited. In other areas, farmers are taught new methods of farming so they do not have to clear rain forest lands continually.

Field GUIDE

Is where you live like a tropical rain forest or some other biome? To find out more about biomes, see the Biome Field Guide at the back of the book.

Use an Analogy

The layers of a rain forest are comparable to the shelves of a library. Just as the shelves provide more space for books, the layers of the rain forest provide more niches for supporting life. This is one of the reasons rain forests are biologically diverse.

Activity

Have students make charts of the main features of the three major zones of the tropical rain forest: the canopy, understory, and forest floor. L2 IS **Naturalist**

Extension

Certain human diseases, such as malaria and yellow fever, are common among human populations living in tropical areas. Have students research tropical diseases and identify misconceptions of the cause of each disease. L3

Figure 12
Emergents These giant trees are much higher than the average canopy tree. Birds such as the macaw and insects are found here.

Canopy The canopy includes the upper parts of the trees. It's full of life—insects, birds, reptiles, and mammals.

Understory This dark, cool environment is under the canopy leaves but above the ground. Many insects, reptiles, and amphibians live in the understory.

Forest Floor The forest floor is full of life. Many insects and the largest mammals in the rain forest generally live here.

E ◆ 73

Visual Learning

Figure 12 Ask students to explain how conditions above the canopy differ from conditions below the canopy. much more sun and wind above the canopy, darker and more humid below the canopy

Major Biomes, continued

Areas with heavy agriculture in the Southwest are the most likely to be affected by desertification in the United States. Changes in climate and human activities also contribute to desertification, which is the loss of productivity of land in arid or semi-arid areas.

✔ Reading Check

Answer because of lack of water

IDENTIFYING Misconceptions

A common idea about deserts is that they are hot, dry places. While this is true of the majority of deserts, there are some cold deserts such as Patagonia in Argentina. Cold deserts are usually caused by their remoteness from the coast, or by mountains that block moist coastal winds. The largest cold desert is in central Asia.

Fun Fact

At one time, the grassland biome covered nearly half of the land on Earth. Today, most of the grassland is used by humans for growing crops, raising animals, and housing.

Earth Science
INTEGRATION

When vegetation is removed from soil in areas that receive little rain, the dry, unprotected surface can be blown away. If the soil remains bare, a desert might form. This process is called desertification. Look on a map and hypothesize about which areas of the United States are most likely to become deserts.

Figure 13
A Desert plants, like these in the Sonoran Desert, are adapted for survival in the extreme conditions of the desert biome. **B** The giant hairy scorpion found in some deserts has a venomous sting.

Desert The driest biome on Earth is the **desert.** Deserts receive less than 25 cm of rain each year and support little plant life. Some desert areas receive no rain for years. When rain does come, it quickly drains away. Any water that remains on the ground evaporates rapidly.

Most deserts, like the one in **Figure 13,** are covered with a thin, sandy, or gravelly soil that contains little organic matter. Due to the lack of water, desert plants are spaced far apart and much of the ground is bare. Barren, windblown sand dunes are characteristics of the driest deserts.

✔ Reading Check   *Why is much of a desert bare ground?*

Desert Life Desert plants are adapted for survival in the extreme dryness and hot and cold temperatures of this biome. Cactus plants are probably the most familiar desert plants of the western hemisphere. Desert animals also have adaptations that help them survive the extreme conditions. Some, like the kangaroo rat, never need to drink water. They get all the moisture they need from the breakdown of food during digestion. Most animals are active only during the night, late afternoon, or early morning when temperatures are less extreme. Few large animals are found in the desert.

In order to provide water for desert cities, rivers and streams have been diverted. When this happens, wildlife tends to move closer to cities in their search for food and water. Education about desert environments has led to an awareness of the impact of human activities. As a result, large areas of desert have been set aside as national parks and wilderness areas to protect desert habitats.

Cultural Diversity

Biomes and Dress Discuss how the dress of people in different areas is influenced by the biome in which they live. For example, Arabic people may wear long robes to shield themselves from the desert heat. Inuits may dress in animal skins to insulate themselves from the cold. Encourage interested students to present a show of "Biome Fashions Around the World."
COOP LEARN

Resource Manager

Chapter Resources Booklet
    Reinforcement, p. 26
    Activity Worksheet, pp. 5–6

Grasslands Temperate and tropical regions that receive between 25 cm and 75 cm of precipitation each year and are dominated by climax communities of grasses are called **grasslands.** Most grasslands have a dry season, when little or no rain falls. This lack of moisture prevents the development of forests. Grasslands are found in many places around the world, and they have a variety of names. The prairies and plains of North America, the steppes of Asia, the savannas of Africa shown in **Figure 14,** and the pampas of South America are types of grasslands.

Grasslands Life The most noticeable animals in grassland biomes are usually mammals that graze on the stems, leaves, and seeds of grass plants. Kangaroos graze in the grasslands of Australia. In Africa, communities of animals such as wildebeests, impalas, and zebras thrive in the savannas.

Grasslands are perfect for growing many crops such as wheat, rye, oats, barley, and corn. Grasslands also are used to raise cattle and sheep. However, overgrazing can result in the death of grasses and the loss of valuable topsoil from erosion. Most farmers and ranchers take precautions to prevent the loss of valuable habitats and soil.

Figure 14
Animals such as zebras and wildebeests feed on the grasses of the savannas in Africa.

Section ② Assessment

1. Which two biomes are the driest?
2. Compare and contrast tundra organisms and desert organisms.
3. What is the biggest climatic difference between a temperate rain forest and a tropical rain forest?
4. Why does the soil of tropical rain forests make poor farmland?
5. **Think Critically** If you climb a mountain in Arizona, you might reach an area where the trees resemble the taiga trees in northern Canada. Why would a taiga forest exist in Arizona?

Skill Builder Activities

6. **Recording Observations** Animals have adaptations that help them survive in their environments. Make a list of animals that live in your area, and record the physical or behavioral adaptations that help them survive. **For more help, refer to the** Science Skill Handbook.

7. **Using a Database** Create a database of information about Earth's biomes. Include data about *temperature range, annual precipitation, limiting factors,* and *descriptions of climax communities.* **For more help, refer to the** Technology Skill Handbook.

3 Assess

Reteach
Make a table showing precipitation, temperature, common plants, and common animals for each biome. Have students identify the name of each biome described. L2 ELL **Naturalist**

Challenge
Have students draw a four-organism food chain for any five of the six biomes presented in this section. L3
 Logical-Mathematical

✓ Assessment

Portfolio Have each student write a story with one of the biomes in this section as the setting. The plot should revolve around an organism that lives in the biome they chose and its interactions with other organisms and the environment. Students can take turns reading their stories to the class. Use **Performance Assessment in the Science Classroom,** p. 155. P

Answers to Section Assessment

1. desert and tundra
2. Tundra organisms are adapted to survive cold and drought. Desert organisms are adapted to survive extreme dryness, hot and cold temperatures, and little water.
3. Tropical rain forests are warmer (have a higher average temperature) than temperate rain forests, and tend to have more precipitation.
4. The majority of available nutrients in the rainforest are in the biomass of the plants and trees, not in the soil. When trees are cut down, nutrients go with them leaving behind very nutrient-poor soil that is easily eroded in the next big rain.
5. Temperatures cool with increased elevation, so places with higher altitude in warm areas can resemble the taiga.
6. Answers will vary but should include adaptations to survive conditions including cold or heat, humidity or dryness, and land or aquatic environments.
7. Databases should include information on the taiga, tundra, desert, temperate deciduous forest, temperate rain forest, tropical rain forest and grassland biomes.

Activity

Purpose Students conduct a study of an ecosystem and determine how the living things interact with each other and the environment. L2 IS **Intrapersonal**

Process Skills observing, classifying, communicating, defining operationally, recognizing cause and effect, predicting

Time Required 50 minutes for setup, four weeks to make observations

Teaching Strategies

- Arrange for students to check out binoculars, field guides, and other useful materials from the science classroom and library.
- Approve the ecosystems chosen by the students before they begin their observations.
- Offer students a set time each day to discuss any problems they may have concerning their method of study.

Answers to Questions

1. Populations would be affected by changes in temperature, water, or other abiotic factors. The entire ecosystem could be disrupted.
2. Other populations could be affected.
3. Possible hypotheses: competition for available resources could make one population extinct or forced away; students may hypothesize about results from favorable or unfavorable interactions among the populations in response to the introduction of a new population.

Activity

Studying a Land Ecosystem

An ecological study includes observation and analysis of organisms and the physical features of the environment.

What You'll Investigate
How do you study an ecosystem?

Materials

graph paper   binoculars
thermometer   pencil
hand lens   field guides
notebook   compass

Goals

- **Observe** biotic factors and abiotic factors of an ecosystem.
- **Analyze** the relationships among organisms and their environment.

Safety Precautions

Procedure

1. Choose a portion of an ecosystem near your school or home to study. You might choose a decaying log, a pond, a forest area in a park, a garden, or even a crack in the sidewalk.
2. Determine the boundaries of your study area.
3. Using a tape measure and graph paper, make a map of your area. Determine north.
4. **Record** your observations in a table similar to the one shown on this page.
5. **Observe** the organisms in your study area. Use field guides to identify them. Use a hand lens to study small organisms and binoculars to study animals you can't get near. Look for evidence (such as tracks or feathers) of organisms you do not see.

Environmental Observations		
Date		
Time of Day		
Temperature	Answers	will vary.
Organisms Observed		
Comments		

6. Use a thermometer to measure the air temperature in your study area. Record this information in the table.
7. Visit your study area as many times as you can and at different times of the day for one week. At each visit, make the same measurements and record all observations. Note how the living and nonliving parts of the ecosystem interact.

Conclude and Apply

1. **Predict** what might happen if one or more abiotic factors were changed suddenly.
2. What might happen if one or more populations of plants or animals were removed from the area?
3. Form a hypothesis about the effect that a new population of organisms might have on your ecosystem.

Communicating Your Data

Make a poster of your data. Then compare your data with those of other students in your class. **For more help, refer to the** Science Skill Handbook.

Assessment

Performance Have students alter the ecosystem in a way that is not harmful. Have them observe how foreign materials affect the behavior of living things in the ecosystem. Use **PASC,** p. 97.

Communicating Your Data

You may choose to display the best student posters along one wall. Allow volunteers to present their poster and data to the class in a short presentation.

Aquatic Ecosystems

Freshwater Ecosystems

In a land environment, temperature and precipitation are the most important factors that determine which species can survive. In aquatic environments, water temperature, the amount of sunlight present, and the amounts of dissolved oxygen and salt in the water are important. Earth's freshwater ecosystems include flowing water such as rivers and streams and standing water such as lakes, ponds, and wetlands.

Rivers and Streams Flowing freshwater environments vary from small, gurgling brooks to large, slow-moving rivers. Currents can quickly wash loose particles downstream, leaving a rocky or gravelly bottom. As the water tumbles and splashes, as shown in **Figure 15,** air from the atmosphere mixes in. The faster a stream flows, the clearer its water tends to be and the higher its oxygen content is.

Most nutrients that support life in flowing-water ecosystems are washed into the water from land. In areas where the water movement slows, such as in the pools of streams or in large rivers, debris settles to the bottom. These environments tend to have higher nutrient levels and more plant growth. They contain organisms that are not as well adapted to swiftly flowing water, such as freshwater mussels, minnows, and leeches.

As You Read

***What* You'll Learn**
- **Compare** flowing freshwater and standing freshwater ecosystems.
- **Identify** and describe important saltwater ecosystems.
- **Identify** problems that affect aquatic ecosystems.

Vocabulary

wetland	intertidal zone
coral reef	estuary

***Why* It's Important**
All of the life processes in your body depend on water.

Figure 15
Streams like this one are high in oxygen because of the swift, tumbling water. *Where do most nutrients in streams come from?*

---

1 Motivate

Bellringer Transparency

 Display the Section Focus Transparency for Section 3. Use the accompanying Transparency Activity Master. L2 ELL

Tie to Prior Knowledge

Most students have some experience with water environments. Have them explain what body of water they observed and which organisms live there.

Caption Answer

Figure 15 They are washed into the stream from the land.

Resource Manager

Chapter Resources Booklet
Transparency Activity, p. 44

Mathematics Skill Activities, p. 9

Section ✓Assessment Planner

PORTFOLIO
Science Journal, p. 80
PERFORMANCE ASSESSMENT
MiniLAB, p. 78
Math Skills Activity, p. 80
Skill Builder Activities, p. 83
See page 90 for more options.

CONTENT ASSESSMENT
Section, p. 83
Challenge, p. 83
Chapter, pp. 90–91

Freshwater Ecosystems

Mini LAB

Purpose Students observe a freshwater ecosystem. L2

Naturalist

Materials clear plastic container, material from the bottom of a pond, pond organisms, net, pond water, hand lens

Teaching Strategy Make sure students don't disturb the container excessively while observing, as sediment stirred up will make observations difficult.

Safety Precaution Make sure to get permission from the land owner or appropriate authorities before collecting samples from the pond.

Analysis

Students' paragraphs will vary depending on organisms obtained.

Assessment

Oral Have students use their observations from the Mini-LAB to identify adaptations of the organisms. Use **PASC**, p. 89.

Mini LAB

Modeling Freshwater Environments

Procedure

1. Obtain a sample of **pond sediment or debris, plants, water, and organisms** from your teacher.
2. Cover the bottom of a **clear, plastic container** with about 2 cm of the debris.
3. Add one or two plants to the container.
4. Carefully pour pond water into the container until it is about two-thirds full.
5. Use a **net** to add several organisms to the water. Seal the container.
6. Using a **hand lens**, observe as many organisms as possible. Record your observations. Return your sample to its original habitat.

Analysis

Write a short paragraph describing the organisms in your sample. How did the organisms interact with each other?

Human Impact People use rivers and streams for many activities. Once regarded as a free place to dump sewage and other pollutants, many people now recognize the damage this causes. Treating sewage and restricting pollutants have led to an improvement in the water quality in some rivers.

Lakes and Ponds When a low place in the land fills with rainwater, snowmelt, or water from an overflowing stream, a lake or pond might form. Pond water hardly moves at all. It contains more plant growth than flowing-water environments contain.

Lakes, such as the one in **Figure 16A,** are larger and deeper than ponds. They have more open water because most plant growth is limited to shallow areas along the shoreline. In fact, organisms found in the warm, sunlit waters of the shorelines often are similar to those found in ponds. If you were to dive to the bottom, you would discover few, if any, plants or algae growing. Colder temperatures and lower light levels limit the types of organisms that can live in deep lake waters. Floating in the warm, sunlit waters near the surface of freshwater lakes and ponds are microscopic algae, plants, and other organisms known as plankton.

A pond, shown in **Figure 16B,** is a small, shallow body of water. Because ponds are shallow, they are filled with animal and plant life. Sunlight usually penetrates to the bottom. The warm, sunlit water promotes the growth of plants and algae. In fact, many ponds are filled almost completely with plant material, so the only clear, open water is at the center. Because of the lush growth in pond environments, they tend to be high in nutrients.

Figure 16
A The population of organisms in the shallow water of lakes is high. Fewer types of organisms live in the deeper water.
B Ponds contain more vegetation than lakes.

Inclusion Strategies

Physically Challenged If students have difficulty with manual dexterity in the MiniLAB, mount the magnifying glass on a ring stand. Have them look through the magnifying glass and slowly move the plastic container.

Resource Manager

Chapter Resources Booklet
   Enrichment, p. 30
   MiniLAB, p. 4
Home and Community Involvement, p. 45

Figure 17
Life in the Florida Everglades was threatened due to pollution, drought, and draining of the water. Conservation efforts are being made in an attempt to preserve this ecosystem.

Water Pollution Human activities can harm freshwater environments. Fertilizer-filled runoff from farms and lawns, as well as sewage dumped into the water, can lead to excessive growth of algae and plants in lakes and ponds. The growth and decay of these organisms reduces the oxygen level in the water, which makes it difficult for some organisms to survive. To prevent problems, sewage is treated before it is released. People also are being educated about problems associated with polluting lakes and ponds. Fines and penalties are issued to people caught polluting waterways. These controls have led to the recovery of many freshwater ecosystems.

Wetlands As the name suggests, **wetlands,** shown in **Figure 17,** are regions that are wet for all or most of a year. They are found in regions that lie between solid land and water. Other names for wetlands include swamps, bogs, and fens. Some people refer to wetlands as biological supermarkets. They are fertile ecosystems, but only plants that are adapted to waterlogged soil survive there. Wetland animals include beavers, muskrats, alligators, and the endangered bog turtle. Many migratory bird populations use wetlands as breeding grounds.

✔ **Reading Check** *Where are wetlands found?*

Wetlands once were considered to be useless, disease-ridden places. Many were drained and destroyed to make roads, farmland, shopping centers, and housing developments. Only recently have people begun to understand the importance of wetlands. Products that come from wetlands, including fish, shellfish, cranberries, and plants, are valuable resources. Now many developers are restoring wetlands, and in most states access to land through wetlands is prohibited.

Chemistry INTEGRATION

Osmosis is the movement of water molecules through a membrane from an area where there are more of them to an area where there are fewer of them. The blood of a freshwater fish is saltier than the lake water is. Explain in your Science Journal whether fish in a lake tend to absorb water or lose water through osmosis.

Chemistry INTEGRATION

Because the fish has saltier blood than the surrounding water, water tends to move into the fish by osmosis. Freshwater fish are covered with scales and a mucous secretion that slows the movement of water into their tissues. The kidneys of these fish are adapted to filter out excess water, and they excrete large amounts of dilute urine.

Teacher FYI

Slow-moving rivers and standing lakes and ponds are easily polluted because less dissolved oxygen is in the water to break down the pollutants, and no currents wash pollutants away.

✔ **Reading Check**

Answer in regions that lie between solid land and water

Curriculum Connection

History Have students research the Seminole people of Florida and how they survived attacks by the United States Army by hiding in the Everglades. [L2]

Inclusion Strategies

Visually Impaired Have a small shallow container represent a pond and a larger container represent a lake. Form a "V" with a plastic sheet. Incline the V at a steep angle, and pour water down it to represent a stream. Hold the V at a slighter angle, and pour a greater volume of water down it. This represents a river. Have students put their hands into the four conditions to feel the differences.

Saltwater Ecosystems

Quick Demo

Float identical corks in freshwater and salt water. Students should observe that the cork in salt water floats higher than the one in freshwater. Explain that this occurs because salt water is denser than freshwater.

Make a Model

Ask students to use clay, colored water, or other materials to show the mixing of freshwater and salt water when a river and ocean combine to form an estuary.

Activity

From a science supply company, purchase kits that measure the dissolved oxygen in water. Compare different bodies of water such as lakes, streams, and oceans. L3 IS **Naturalist**

Math Skills Activity

National Math Standards

Correlation to Mathematics Objectives

1, 2, 4, 6, 9

Answers to Practice Problems

1. $(78°F − 32) / 1.8 = 25.6°C$
2. $(12°C × 1.8) + 32 = 53.6°F$
   $(23°C × 1.8) + 32 = 73.4°F$
   $73.4°F − 53.6°F = 19.8°F$

Saltwater Ecosystems

About 95 percent of the water on the surface of Earth contains high concentrations of various salts. The amount of dissolved salts in water is called salinity. Saltwater ecosystems include oceans, seas, a few inland lakes, such as the Great Salt Lake in Utah, coastal inlets, and estuaries.

Math Skills Activity

Calculating Temperatures

Organisms that live around hydrothermal vents in the ocean deal with temperatures that range from 1.7°C to 371°C. You have probably seen temperatures measured in degrees Celsius (°C) and degrees Fahrenheit (°F). Which one are you familiar with? If you know the temperature in one system, you can convert it to the other.

Example Problem

You have a Fahrenheit thermometer and measure the water temperature of a pond at 59°F. What is that temperature in degrees Celsius?

Solution

1 *This is what you know:*
   water temperature in degrees Fahrenheit = 59°F

2 *This is what you want to find:*
   water temperature in degrees Celsius

3 *This is the equation you need to use:*
   $(°C × 1.8) + 32 = °F$

4 *Solve the equations for degrees Celsius, and then substitute the known value:*
   $°C = (°F − 32)/1.8$
   $°C = (59°F − 32)/1.8 = 15°C$

Check your answer by substituting the Celsius temperature back into the original equation. Do you calculate the Fahrenheit temperature that was given?

Practice Problems

1. The thermometer outside your classroom reads 78°F. What is the temperature in degrees Celsius?

2. If lake water was 12°C in October and 23°C in May, what is the difference in degrees Fahrenheit?

For more help, refer to the Math Skill Handbook.

Science Journal

Marine Biomes Have students compare estuaries and oceans. As part of this comparison, ask students to focus on living and nonliving factors associated with each ecosystem. Have them write a paragraph about each biome in their Science Journals. P

Resource Manager

Chapter Resources Booklet

Directed Reading for Content Mastery, pp. 19, 20

Transparency Activity, pp. 45–46

Science Inquiry Labs, p. 37

Open Oceans Life abounds in the open ocean. Scientists divide the ocean into different life zones, based on the depth to which sunlight penetrates the water. The lighted zone of the ocean is the upper 200 m or so. It is the home of the plankton that make up the foundation of the food chain in the open ocean. Below about 200 m is the dark zone of the ocean. Animals living in this region feed on material that floats down from the lighted zone, or they feed on each other. A few organisms are able to produce their own food.

Coral Reefs One of the most diverse ecosystems in the world is the **coral reef.** Coral reefs are formed over long periods of time from the calcium carbonate shells secreted by animals called corals. When corals die, their shells remain. The shell deposits form reefs such as the Great Barrier Reef off the coast of Australia, shown in **Figure 18.**

Reefs do not adapt well to long-term stress. Runoff from fields, sewage, and increased sedimentation from cleared land harm reef ecosystems. Organizations like the Environmental Protection Agency have developed management plans to protect the diversity of coral reefs. These plans treat a coral reef as a system that includes all the areas that surround the reef. Keeping the areas around reefs healthy will result in a healthy environment for the coral reef ecosystem.

SCIENCE Online

Research Visit the Glencoe Science Web site at **science.glencoe.com** for more information about coral reefs. Communicate to your class what you learn.

SCIENCE Online
Internet Addresses

_____
_____
_____
_____

Explore the Glencoe Science Web site at **science.glencoe.com** to find out more about topics in this section.

IDENTIFYING Misconceptions

Students may think that sea anemones and the coral in coral reefs are plants rather than animals. Help them realize that they are animals that feed on small organisms in the water.

Quick Demo

Bring in a piece of coral such as those used in saltwater aquariums. Explain that this is the calcium carbonate skeleton left behind by the once-living coral.

Figure 18
A The lighter areas around this island are part of the Great Barrier Reef. It comprises about 3,000 reefs and around 900 islands. **B** Reefs contain colorful fish and a large variety of other organisms.

SECTION 3   Aquatic Ecosystems   **E ◆ 81**

✔ **Active Reading**

Jigsaw In this collaborative learning technique, individuals become experts on a portion of a text and share their expertise with a small group, called their home group. Everyone shares responsibility for learning the assigned reading. Assign each person in each home group an expert number (1 through 5, for example). Have students gather into the expert groups that correspond to the number they were assigned. Have them read, discuss, and master chapter concepts, and determine how best to teach them to their home groups. Have students return to their home groups and share the content they learned in their expert groups. Have students use the Jigsaw strategy with the text on aquatic ecosystems.

Fun Fact

The largest tides occur when the Earth, Sun, and Moon are in line. This is when the combined gravities of the Sun and Moon have their greatest effect on Earth's waters.

Visual Learning

Figure 19 Explain that sea stars have special adaptions that enable them to inhabit the intertidal zone. One of these adaptations is the presence of numerous small tube feet under each arm, which allow the sea star to resist being swept away by the tide.

Figure 19
As the tide recedes, small pools of seawater are left behind. These pools contain a variety of organisms such as sea stars and periwinkles.

Earth Science INTEGRATION

Seashores All of Earth's landmasses are bordered by ocean water. The shallow waters along the world's coastlines contain a variety of saltwater ecosystems, all of which are influenced by the tides and by the action of waves. The gravitational pull of the Sun and Moon on Earth causes the tides to rise and fall each day. The height of the tides varies according to the phases of the Moon, the season, and the slope of the shoreline. The **intertidal zone** is the portion of the shoreline that is covered with water at high tide and exposed to the air during low tide. Organisms that live in the intertidal zone, such as those in **Figure 19,** must be adapted to dramatic changes in temperature, moisture, and salinity and must be able to withstand the force of wave action.

Estuaries Almost every river on Earth eventually flows into an ocean. The area where a river meets an ocean and contains a mixture of freshwater and salt water is called an **estuary** (ES chuh wer ee). Other names for estuaries include bays, lagoons, harbors, inlets, and sounds. They are located near coastlines and border the land. Salinity in estuaries changes with the amount of freshwater brought in by rivers and streams, and with the amount of salt water pushed inland by the ocean tides.

Estuaries, shown in **Figure 20,** are extremely fertile, productive environments because freshwater streams bring in tons of nutrients washed from inland soils. Therefore, nutrient levels in estuaries are higher than in freshwater ecosystems or other saltwater ecosystems.

82 ◆ E   CHAPTER 3 Ecosystems

Curriculum Connection

Geography Have students locate Australia on a globe and then identify the location of the Great Barrier Reef. [L1] [IS] **Visual-Spatial**

Resource Manager

Chapter Resources Booklet
    Reinforcement, p. 27

Cultural Diversity, p. 7

Earth Science Critical Thinking/Problem
    Solving, p. 1

Figure 20
The Chesapeake Bay is an estuary rich in resources. Fish and shrimp are harvested by commercial fishing boats. *What other resources can be found in estuaries?*

Caption Answer
Figure 20 crabs, clams, oysters

Reading Check

Answer algae, grasses, shrimp, crabs, clams, oysters, snails, worms, fish

Estuary Life Organisms found in estuaries include many species of algae, salt-tolerant grasses, shrimp, crabs, clams, oysters, snails, worms, and fish. Estuaries also serve as important nurseries for many species of ocean fish. They provide much of the seafood consumed by humans.

Reading Check *What types of organisms live in estuaries?*

3 Assess

Reteach

Write on the chalkboard or on an overhead transparency a description of the three major ocean ecosystems. Have students identify each one. [L2]
IS Naturalist

Challenge

Ask students to make up a story about a molecule of water in a cloud falling to Earth as a raindrop. Direct students to have it pass through three aquatic ecosystems before it evaporates and begins the process again. [L3]

 Section **3** **Assessment**

1. What are the similarities and differences between a lake and a stream?

2. Compare and contrast the dark zone of the ocean with the forest floor of a tropical rain forest. What living or nonliving factors affect these areas?

3. Why do you find few plants at the bottom of deep lakes?

4. What adaptations are necessary for organisms that live in the intertidal zone?

5. **Think Critically** Why do few plants grow in a swift-flowing mountain stream?

Skill Builder Activities

6. **Concept Mapping** Make an events chain concept map of these ecosystems from least salty to most salty: *lake, open ocean, estuary,* and *stream.* **For more help, refer to the** Science Skill Handbook.

7. **Communicating** Wetlands trap and slowly release rain, snow, and groundwater. Describe in your Science Journal what might happen to a town located on a floodplain if nearby wetlands are destroyed. **For more help, refer to the** Science Skill Handbook.

Assessment

Process Assess students' abilities to compare and contrast by having them compare the salinity of rivers, estuaries, and the open ocean. Responses can be written in their Science Journal. Rivers have lower salinity than oceans. The amount of salt in an estuary varies, but they contain more salt than rivers, and less than oceans. Use **Performance Assessment in the Science Classroom,** p. 175.

Answers to Section Assessment

1. Both contain freshwater. A lake has standing water, low oxygen levels, and rich plant growth in shallow water. A stream has swift-moving water, high oxygen levels, and a rocky bottom with little plant life.

2. Both contain scavengers and decomposers; both are affected by temperature and lack of light. The dark zone is a cold envrionment, and the rain forest is warm.

3. Cold temperatures and low light levels limit the types of organisms that can grow there.

4. Such organisms must be able to adapt to drastic changes in temperature, moisture, and salinity; they must be able to withstand wave motion.

5. Possible answer: The water washes away the soil. Plants would be uprooted and washed downstream.

6. stream, lake, estuary, open ocean

7. The town would flood much more often.

Activity

BENCH TESTED

Recognize the Problem

Internet

Students will use Internet sites that can be accessed through the Glencoe Science Web site at **science.glencoe.com**. They will investigate wetlands regions and their unique role in our environment.

Non-Internet Sources

Collect pamphlets from a variety of wetlands conservancy groups.

Time Required

three days to five days

Preparation

Internet Access the Glencoe Science Web site at **science. glencoe.com** to run through the steps that the students will follow.

Non-Internet Organize printed materials by wetlands regions.

Form a Hypothesis

Possible Hypothesis

Students will identify a specific wetlands region and describe the plants and animals native to that environment. For example, a specific wetlands area may be the only regional location for a particular species of endangered animal.

Activity *Use the Internet*

Exploring Wetlands

Wetlands, such as the one shown below, are an important part of the environment. These fertile ecosystems support unique plants and animals that can only survive in wetland conditions. The more you understand the importance of wetlands, the more you can do to preserve and protect them.

Recognize the Problem

Why are wetlands an important part of the ecosystem?

Form a Hypothesis

Why do wetlands need to be protected? What laws are in place to protect wetlands? Form a hypothesis about why wetlands should be protected.

Goals

- **Identify** wetland regions in the United States.
- **Describe** the significance of the wetland ecosystem.
- **Identify** plant and animal species native to a wetland region.
- **Identify** strategies for supporting the preservation of wetlands.

Data Source

SCIENCE *Online* Visit the Glencoe Science Web site at **science.glencoe.com** to get more information about wetland environments and for data collected by other students.

Resource Manager

Chapter Resources Booklet
   Activity Worksheet, pp. 7–8
   Lab Activity, pp. 11–14
Lab Management and Safety, p. 37

SCIENCE *Online*

Internet Addresses

_____

_____

_____

_____

Explore the Glencoe Science Web site at **science.glencoe.com** to find out more about topics in this activity.

Test Your Hypothesis

Plan

1. Determine where some major wetlands are located in the United States.

2. Select one wetland area to study in depth. Where is it located? Is it classified as a marsh, bog, or something else?

3. What role does this ecosystem play in the overall ecology of the area?

4. Find out about the plants and animals that live in the wetland environment you are researching.

5. In most cases, there are federal laws to protect the environment. Additional state and local laws are specific to the area. Investigate what laws protect the wetland you are studying.

Do

1. Make sure your teacher approves your plan before you start.

2. Perform the investigation.

3. Go to the Glencoe Science Web site at **science.glencoe.com** to post your data.

Analyze Your Data

1. **Describe** the wetland area you have researched. What region of the United States is it located in? What other ecological factors are found in that region?

2. What laws protect the wetland you are investigating? How long have the laws been in place?

3. What plants and animals are native to the wetland area you are researching? Are those plants and animals found in other parts of the region or the United States? What adaptations do the plants and animals have that help them survive in a wetland environment?

Draw Conclusions

1. Are all wetlands the same?

2. What is the ecological significance of the wetland area that you studied for that region of the country?

3. Why should wetland environments be protected?

4. What can people do to support the continued preservation of wetland environments in the United States?

*C*ommunicating
Your Data

SCIENCE *Online* Find this *Use the Internet* activity on the Glencoe Science Web site at **science. glencoe.com** and **post** your data in the table provided. **Review** other students' data to learn about other wetland environments in the United States.

Test Your Hypothesis

Teaching Strategies Remind students to investigate how the amount of wetlands areas has decreased over the last 25 years, and how that has made an impact on native plants and animals.

Analyze Your Data

Answers will be based on the students' individual research.

Draw Conclusions

1. Wetlands regions are not all the same. Depending on where they are located, one area may have different species of plants than another.

2. Answers will vary. Remind students to think about the plants and animals that live in that wetlands region and if those species are found elsewhere.

3. Answers will vary. Students should investigate the amount of open space in that region.

4. Answers will vary. Have students find out about conservancy groups and their work to preserve wetlands regions.

✓Assessment

Portfolio Have students make a wetlands field guide for the area they investigated. Include maps and pictures. Have them describe how to support wetlands preservation. Use **Performance Assessment in the Science Classroom,** p. 129.

*C*ommunicating
Your Data

Have students organize their field guides with section names. Suggest Native Animals and Maps to help them arrange their information.

Content Background

The idea of using wetlands to process municipal wastewater was first conceived in the 1970s. Wetlands are flat, low-lying areas where water collects and saturates the soil. The conditions provide habitat for various plants like cattails and bulrushes. The low flow rates prolong contact between the water and plants enabling the roots and trapped microorganisms to remove pollutants and organic matter.

Since natural wetlands provide wildlife habitat and help control river flooding, many are being restored. A constructed wetland mimics the action of a natural marsh. The primary difference is the separation of the natural subsoil from the wetland soil by a concrete trough or layer of heavy clay. This substructure prevents polluted inflow from leaching into the soil before the wetland has processed it. The troughs are filled with sand and soil, then planted with appropriate wetland vegetation. Inflow volume, local climate and degree of pre-processing of the wastewater determine the size and nature of a constructed wetland.

In arid and water-intensive agricultural areas, the aim of wetlands water treatment is to enable the direct reuse of the outflow. Most constructed wetlands in the U.S. are in the South and West where the warm climate ensures year round plant growth, but there are experimental wetland projects in the northern U.S. and southern Canada.

Helping Nature

Pebbles were added to the Corrales wetlands to help with drainage.

When you wash your hands or flush the toilet, you probably don't think much about where the wastewater goes. In most places, it eventually ends up being processed in a traditional sewage-treatment facility. But a handful of places are experimenting with a new method that processes wastewater by creating wetlands. Wetlands, such as swamps or marshes, are home to filtering plants, such as cattails, and sewage-eating bacteria.

In 1996, school officials at the Corrales Elementary School in the city of Albuquerque, New Mexico, faced a big problem. The old wastewater-treatment system had failed.

Replacing it was going to cost a lot of money. The school officials came up with an alternative plan. Instead of constructing a new sewage-treatment plant, they decided to create a natural wetlands system. The wetlands system could do the job less expensively, while protecting the environment. Today, this wetlands efficiently converts polluted water into cleaner water that's good for the environment. U.S. government officials are closely watching this alternative sewage-treatment system to see how successful it is. So far, so good! And if it continues to work well, other communities may start creating wetlands to filter their sewage.

86

Resources for Teachers and Students

Constructed Wetlands in the Sustainable Landscape by Craig S. Campbell and Michael H. Ogden. New York, NY: John Wiley & Sons, 1999.

"Nothing Goes to Waste in Arcata's Teeming Marshes." D. Stewart. *Smithsonian*, Vol. 21. 1990.

University of South Alabama, Department of Civil Engineering Mobile, Alabama 36688-0002

US Department of Agriculture National Agricultural Library Water Quality Information Center 10301 Baltimore Avenue, Beltsville, MD 20705

Creating Wetlands to Purify Wastewater

Help Itself

Water irises grew in the wetlands, less than a year after planting.

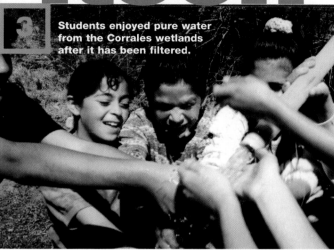

Students enjoyed pure water from the Corrales wetlands after it has been filtered.

How Wetlands Work

Wetlands filter water through the actions of the plants and microorganisms that live there. When plants absorb water into their roots, some, such as cattails, also take up pollutants. The plants convert the pollutants to forms that are not dangerous. At the same time, bacteria and other microorganisms are filtering water as they feed. Water does not move quickly through wetlands, so the organisms have plenty of time to do their work. The wetlands built at Corrales Elementary is called a "constructed" wetlands.

That is a wetlands built by people to filter small amounts of pollutants. In many places, constructed wetlands are better at cleaning wastewater than sewers or septic systems.

From Sewage to Flowers

Nancy Griego, a wetlands plant expert, planted a variety of colorful plants that bloom at different times of the year. A local official said, "School classes are taking field trips to the wetlands to learn what plants do as part of the environment. It's become a real educational asset."

CONNECTIONS Visit and Observe Visit a wetlands. Create a field journal of your observations. Sketch pictures of the plants and animals you see. BONUS: Use a field guide to help identify the wildlife you see. If you don't live near a wetlands, use resources to research wetlands environments.

SCIENCE Online For more information, visit science.glencoe.com

Discussion

Have students research wastewater treatment, both municipal and individual septic systems. **Under what circumstances might wetlands be a better option?** Possible answer: In arid regions where ground water is depleted by well drilling and irrigation and low-lying areas where high water tables compromise standard leach fields. **Are there any instances of natural wetlands being used for wastewater treatment?** Possible answer: Arcata, California

Activity

Research or visit your local sewer treatment plant to find out how wastewater is handled in your community. Help students conduct a survey to determine how much wastewater their school produces. Based on the results of their research, discuss the appropriateness of wetlands treatment for the school and the community.

Investigate the Issue

Wastewater is only one product of sewage treatment. Wetlands, both natural and constructed, can effectively process only second or third stage water. The solid waste is removed in the primary stage or a septic tank. Students can research methods of dealing with "sludge." Present the findings in a graph format and discuss the implications of their data.

CONNECTIONS Lead a discussion on how a constructed wetland benefits wildlife. In coastal areas the discussion may include the importance of marshes to the ocean food chain. Near river systems the effect on wildlife can be discussed in light of the flood control function of wetlands. Discuss how the decline in total wetland acreage can affect the food chain in general.

SCIENCE Online

Internet Addresses

_____

_____

_____

Explore the Glencoe Science Web site at **science.glencoe.com** to find out more about topics in this feature.

Chapter 3 Study Guide

Reviewing Main Ideas

Preview

Students can answer the questions in their Science Journals. Discuss the answers as you go through the chapter. **LS Linguistic**

Review

Students can write their answers, then compare them with those of other students. **LS Interpersonal**

Reteach

Students can look at the illustrations and describe details that support the main ideas of the chapter. **LS Visual-Spatial**

Answers to Chapter Review

SECTION 1
3. secondary succession

SECTION 2
2. taiga

SECTION 3
3. The shell deposits of coral provide shelter for a wide range of organisms on and around a coral reef.

Reviewing Main Ideas

Section 1 How Ecosystems Change

1. Ecological succession is the gradual change from one community to another.

2. Primary succession occurs in a place where no soil exists. It begins with organisms that make up a pioneer community.

3. Secondary succession begins in a place that has soil and was once the home of living organisms. *What type of succession is occurring here?*

4. A community that has reached the final stage of ecological succession is called a climax community.

Section 2 Biomes

1. Temperature and precipitation determine the climate of a region.

2. Large geographic areas with similar climax communities are called biomes. *What type of biome is shown in the photo to the right?*

3. Earth's land biomes include tundra, taiga, temperate deciduous forest, temperate rain forest, tropical rain forest, grassland, and desert.

Section 3 Aquatic Ecosystems

1. Freshwater ecosystems include flowing water, such as streams and rivers, and standing water such as lakes, ponds, and wetlands.

2. Wetlands are land areas that are covered with water most of the year. They are found in regions that lie between solid land and water.

3. Saltwater ecosystems include estuaries, seashores, coral reefs, a few inland lakes, and the deep ocean. *Why are coral reefs, like this one, rich in biodiversity?*

4. Estuaries are important transitional zones between freshwater and saltwater environments. They are extremely fertile, and provide much of the seafood consumed by humans.

FOLDABLES Reading & Study Skills

After You Read

To help review succession, use the Main Ideas Study Fold that you made at the beginning of this chapter. Which type of succession starts with bare rock?

FOLDABLES Reading & Study Skills

After You Read

After students have read the chapter and completed the Foldable described in Before You Read, have them do the activity on the student page.

Dinah Zike

Visualizing Main Ideas

Fill in the circles of the concept map showing land biomes.

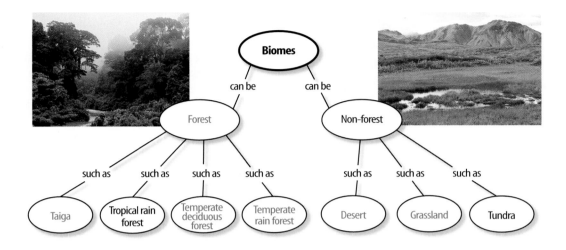

Biomes

can be — Forest

can be — Non-forest

Forest — such as: Taiga, Tropical rain forest, Temperate deciduous forest, Temperate rain forest

Non-forest — such as: Desert, Grassland, Tundra

Vocabulary Review

Vocabulary Words

a. biome
b. climax community
c. coral reef
d. desert
e. estuary
f. grassland
g. intertidal zone
h. pioneer species
i. succession
j. taiga
k. temperate deciduous forest
l. temperate rain forest
m. tropical rain forest
n. tundra
o. wetland

THE PRINCETON REVIEW **Study Tip**

Pay attention to the chapter's illustrations. Try to figure out exactly what main point the picture is trying to stress.

Using Vocabulary

Each of the following sentences is false. Make the sentence true by replacing the underlined word with the correct vocabulary word.

1. <u>Biome</u> refers to the normal changes in the types of species that live in communities.

2. A <u>pioneer species</u> is a group of organisms found in the final stage of succession.

3. Cone-bearing trees are found in the <u>temperate rain forest</u>.

4. The average temperature in <u>tropical rain forests</u> is between 9°C and 12°C.

5. <u>Taigas</u> are the most biologically diverse places in the world.

6. An <u>intertidal zone</u> is an area where freshwater meets the ocean.

Visualizing Main Ideas

See student page.

Vocabulary Review

Using Vocabulary

1. Succession
2. climax community
3. taiga
4. temperate rain forests
5. Tropical rain forests
6. estuary

◆ **IDENTIFYING** **Misconceptions**

Assess

Use the assessment as follow-up to page 62F after students have completed the chapter.

Discussion Ask students to think of components that go into a particular ecosystem, such as a marine or forest ecosystem. Have them draw connections between the components. Have the students pick a few components to remove. Ask students to explain what happens to the flow of energy and/or cycling of materials if these components are removed. While removing some components, depending on what they are, may not cause the system to collapse, it may not be able to function optimally without them.

Chapter 3 Assessment

Checking Concepts

1. B
2. B
3. B
4. C
5. C
6. B
7. A
8. B
9. B
10. B

Thinking Critically

11. The temperate deciduous forest contains more nutrients in its soil because there is less rainfall to wash away the nutrients.

12. These plants grow under the canopy so they do not need a lot of light, they thrive in moderate temperatures, and they are perennials.

13. After a fire burns away the existing plant life, these seeds are ready to germinate in an environment without much competition.

14. It is likely that the grassy meadow is experiencing succession toward an oak-maple forest. The presence of the forest suggests that this climate and land is appropriate for the growth of forests.

15. The tundra soil is thin above the permafrost. Roots cannot penetrate deeply, so plants are small. The growing season is also short.

Chapter 3 Assessment

Checking Concepts

Choose the word or phrase that best answers the question.

1. What are tundra and desert examples of?
   - **A)** ecosystems
   - **B)** biomes
   - **C)** habitats
   - **D)** communities

2. What is a treeless, cold, dry biome called?
   - **A)** taiga
   - **B)** tundra
   - **C)** coral reef
   - **D)** grassland

3. Where would organisms that are adapted to live in freshwater and salt water be found?
   - **A)** lake
   - **B)** estuary
   - **C)** open ocean
   - **D)** intertidal zone

4. Which biome contains the largest number of species?
   - **A)** taiga
   - **B)** temperate deciduous forest
   - **C)** tropical rain forest
   - **D)** grassland

5. Which biome contains mostly frozen soil called permafrost?
   - **A)** taiga
   - **B)** temperate rain forest
   - **C)** tundra
   - **D)** temperate deciduous forest

6. A new island is formed from a volcanic eruption. Which species probably would be the first to grow and survive?
   - **A)** oak trees
   - **B)** lichens
   - **C)** grasses
   - **D)** ferns

7. What would the changes in communities that take place on a recently formed volcanic island best be described as?
   - **A)** primary succession
   - **B)** secondary succession
   - **C)** tertiary succession
   - **D)** magma

8. What is the end result of succession?
   - **A)** pioneer community
   - **B)** climax community
   - **C)** limiting factor
   - **D)** permafrost

9. Which of the following aquatic ecosystems would have the lowest salinity?
   - **A)** estuaries
   - **B)** rivers
   - **C)** coral reefs
   - **D)** open oceans

10. Which ecosystem would experience the most drastic changes in a 24-hour period?
    - **A)** open ocean
    - **B)** intertidal zone
    - **C)** lake
    - **D)** coral reef

Thinking Critically

11. In most cases, would a sample from a temperate deciduous forest contain more or less nutrient-rich soil than a sample from a tropical rain forest? Explain.

12. Why do many tropical rain forest plants make good houseplants?

13. Some plant seeds need fire in order to germinate. Explain how this gives these plants an advantage in secondary succession.

14. A grassy meadow borders a beech-maple forest. Is one of these ecosystems undergoing succession? Why?

15. Why are tundra plants usually small?

Developing Skills

16. **Concept Mapping** Make a network-tree concept map for water environments. Include these terms: *saltwater ecosystems, freshwater ecosystems, intertidal zone, lighted zone, dark zone, lake, pond, coral reef, river, stream, flowing water,* and *standing water.*

17. **Comparing and Contrasting** Compare and contrast the adaptations of organisms living in the tundra with those living in the taiga.

Chapter ✓*Assessment* Planner

Portfolio Encourage students to place in their portfolios one or two items of what they consider to be their best work. Examples include:
- Visual Learning, p. 750
- Assessment, p. 759
- Science Journal, p. 764

Performance Additional performance assessments, Performance Task Assessment Lists, and rubrics for evaluating these activities can be found in Glencoe's **Performance Assessment in the Science Classroom.**

18. Forming Hypotheses Make a hypothesis about what would happen to succession in a pond if the pond owner removed all the cattails and reeds from around the pond edges every summer.

19. Recognizing Cause and Effect Devastating fires, like the one in Yellowstone National Park in 1988, cause many changes to the land. Determine the effect of a fire on an area that has reached its climax community.

20. Making and Using Graphs Make a graph of the amount of rainfall per year in each biome. Which type of graph is best suited to display the data?

Rainfall Amounts

Biome	Rainfall/Year (cm)
Tundra	25
Taiga	50
Temperate rain forest	200
Tropical rain forest	400
Grassland	35
Temperate deciduous forest	150
Desert	25

Performance Assessment

21. Oral Presentation Research a biome that was not covered in this chapter. Find out about the climate, where it is located, and which organisms live there. Present this information to your class.

TECHNOLOGY

Go to the Glencoe Science Web site at **science.glencoe.com** or use the **Glencoe Science CD-ROM** for additional chapter assessment.

THE PRINCETON REVIEW — Test Practice

Each biome around the world contains many different groups of organisms that are unique to that biome. Plants and animals from two different biomes have been drawn in separate boxes below.

A   **B**

Study the pictures above and answer the following questions.

1. The animals in Box B are different from the animals in Box A because the animals in Box B have adaptations that _____ .
A) allow them to survive during heavy rainfall
B) allow them to reproduce asexually and sexually
C) allow them to conserve water
D) allow them to maintain a constant internal temperature

2. Which of the following organisms could complete the group shown in Box B?
F) palm tree
G) salamander
H) fish
J) snake

THE PRINCETON REVIEW — Test Practice

The Test-Taking Tip was written by The Princeton Review, the nation's leader in test preparation.
1. C
2. J

Developing Skills

16. Students should separate water ecosystems into salt water and freshwater. Salt water ecosystems: intertidal zone, lighted zone, dark zone, coral reefs; freshwater ecosystems: lakes and ponds (which contain standing water), rivers and streams (which contain flowing water).

17. Tundra plants are short, unlike the plants of the taiga. Tundra animals need thick fur and other adaptations for extreme cold.

18. Possible answers: (a) succession will slow, (b) succession will stop, or (c) the natural spreading of cattails and reeds toward the center of the pond will be prevented.

19. The area will begin the process of secondary succession with annual plants and grasses.

20. Students should make a bar graph with the biomes across the bottom and amounts of rainfall indicated on the side.

Performance Assessment

21. Answers will vary but should contain a description and example of other biomes, such as tallgrass prairies. Use **Performance Assessment in the Science Classroom**, p. 143.

✓Assessment Resources

 Reproducible Masters

Chapter Resources Booklet
Chapter Review, pp. 35–36
Chapter Tests, pp. 37–40
Assessment Transparency Activity, p. 47

Glencoe Science Web site
Interactive Tutor
Chapter Quizzes

Glencoe Technology
🖱 Assessment Transparency
💿 Interactive CD-ROM Chapter Quizzes
💿 ExamView Pro Test Bank
💿 Vocabulary PuzzleMaker Software
📼 MindJogger Videoquiz DVD/VHS

Section/Objectives	Standards		Activities/Features
Chapter Opener	**National**	**State/Local**	**Explore Activity:** Model topsoil loss, p. 93
	See p. 6T for a Key to Standards.		**Before You Read,** p. 93
Section 1 Resources 🕐 2 sessions 📦 1 block 1. **Compare** renewable and nonrenewable resources. 2. **List** uses of fossil fuels. 3. **Identify** alternatives to fossil fuel use.	National Content Standards: UCP2, A1, F2, F4, F5		**MiniLAB:** Observing Mineral Mining Effects, p. 96 **Physics Integration,** p. 97 **Visualizing Solar Energy,** p. 101
Section 2 Pollution 🕐 2 sessions 📦 1 block 1. **Describe** types of air pollution. 2. **Identify** causes of water pollution. 3. **Explain** methods that can be used to prevent erosion.	National Content Standards: UCP2, A1, E2, F1, F2, F4, F5		**MiniLAB:** Measuring Acid Rain, p. 103 **Science Online,** p. 104 **Health Integration,** p. 106 **Activity:** The Greenhouse Effect, p. 111
Section 3 The Three Rs of Conservation 🕐 3 sessions 📦 1.5 blocks 1. **Recognize** ways you can reduce your use of natural resources. 2. **Explain** how you can reuse resources to promote conservation. 3. **Describe** how many materials can be recycled.	National Content Standards: UCP2, A1, E2, F2, F4, F5, G1		**Science Online,** p. 114 **Problem-Solving Activity:** What items are you recycling at home?, p. 114 **Activity:** Solar Cooking, pp. 116–117 **Science and Language Arts:** Beauty Plagiarized, pp. 118–119

NATIONAL GEOGRAPHIC

Teacher's Corner

PRODUCTS AVAILABLE FROM GLENCOE
To order call 1-800-334-7344:
Posters: *Energy, Ozone, Pollution, Vanishing Wildlife*

PRODUCTS AVAILABLE FROM NATIONAL GEOGRAPHIC SOCIETY
To order call 1-800-368-2728:

Books: *National Geographic Book of Mammals; The Company We Keep: America's Endangered Species; There's Still Time: The Success of the Endangered Species Act*
Videos: *America's Endangered Species: Don't Say Goodbye; Endangered*

Animals: Suvivors on the Brink; Energy: The Fuels and Man; Energy: The Problems and the Future; Investigating Global Warming; Ozone: Protecting the Invisible Shield; Pollution: World at Risk; Power of Water; Recycling: The Endless Cycle

Activity Materials	Reproducible Resources	Section Assessment	Technology
Explore Activity: moist sand, potting soil, plastic basin or aluminum-foil baking pan, moss, water, spray bottle, beaker	**Chapter Resources Booklet** Foldables Worksheet, p. 17 Directed Reading Overview, p. 19 Note-taking Worksheets, pp. 33–35	*GLENCOE'S ASSESSMENT ADVANTAGE*	
MiniLAB: chocolate chip cookie, paper plate, toothpick *Need materials? Contact Science Kit at 1-800-828-7777 or www.sciencekit.com on the Internet.*	**Chapter Resources Booklet** Transparency Activity, p. 44 MiniLAB, p. 3 Enrichment, p. 30 Reinforcement, p. 27 Directed Reading, p. 20 **Cultural Diversity,** p. 41 **Mathematics Skill Activities,** p. 9	**Portfolio** Physics Integration, p. 97 **Performance** MiniLAB, p. 96 Skill Builder Activities, p. 100 **Content** Section Assessment, p. 100	Section Focus Transparency Interactive CD-ROM/DVD Guided Reading Audio Program
MiniLAB: cup, rainwater, pH indicator paper, tap water, distilled water **Activity:** 1–L clear plastic soft-drink bottle with top cut off and label removed (2), 2 thermometers, potting soil, masking tape, plastic wrap, rubber band, lamp with 100-W lightbulb, watch or clock with second hand	**Chapter Resources Booklet** Transparency Activity, p. 45 MiniLAB, p. 4 Enrichment, p. 31 Reinforcement, p. 28 Directed Reading, p. 21 Activity Worksheet, pp. 5–6 Lab Activity, pp. 9–12 Transparency Activity, pp. 47–48	**Portfolio** Assessment, p. 100 **Performance** MiniLAB, p. 103 Skill Builder Activities, p. 110 **Content** Section Assessment, p. 110	Section Focus Transparency Teaching Transparency Interactive CD-ROM/DVD Guided Reading Audio Program
Activity: poster board, cardboard boxes, aluminum foil, string, wire coat hangers, clear plastic sheets, black cookware, thermometer, stopwatch, glue, tape, scissors	**Chapter Resources Booklet** Transparency Activity, p. 46 Enrichment, p. 32 Reinforcement, p. 29 Directed Reading, pp. 21, 22 Activity Worksheet, pp. 7–8 Lab Activity, pp. 13–16 **Lab Management and Safety,** p. 37	**Portfolio** Challenge, p. 115 **Performance** Problem-Solving Activity, p. 114 Skill Builder Activities, p. 115 **Content** Section Assessment, p. 115	Section Focus Transparency Interactive CD-ROM/DVD Guided Reading Audio Program

End of Chapter Assessment

GLENCOE'S ASSESSMENT ADVANTAGE

Blackline Masters	Technology	Professional Series
Chapter Resources Booklet Chapter Review, pp. 37–38 Chapter Tests, pp. 39–42 **Standardized Test Practice by The Princeton Review,** pp. 23–26	MindJogger Videoquiz CD-ROM Explorations and Quizzes Vocabulary Puzzle Makers ExamView Pro Test Bank Interactive Lesson Planner Interactive Teacher's Edition	Performance Assessment in the Science Classroom (PASC)

Transparencies

Section Focus

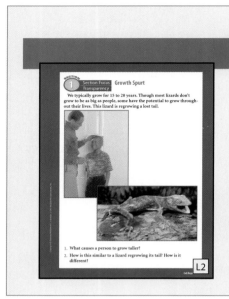

Section Focus Transparency 1 — Growth Spurt

We typically grow for 15 to 20 years. Though most lizards don't grow to be as big as people, some have the potential to grow throughout their lives. This lizard is regrowing a lost tail.

1. What causes a person to grow taller?
2. How is this similar to a lizard regrowing its tail? How is it different?

L2

Section Focus Transparency 2 — I think he has your eyes.

The Santa Gertrudis bull flourishes in the arid plains of Texas. The King Ranch developed the Santa Gertrudis by cross-breeding Brahman cattle with Shorthorns. As you can see, the Santa Gertrudis inherited characteristics from both of its parents.

1. Why might ranchers have wanted to cross-breed Brahmans and Shorthorns?
2. Which of the Santa Gertrudis' traits can you identify in the Brahman and the Shorthorn?

L2

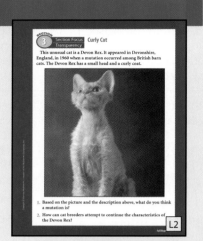

Section Focus Transparency 3 — Curly Cat

This unusual cat is a Devon Rex. It appeared in Devonshire, England, in 1960 when a mutation occurred among British barn cats. The Devon Rex has a small head and a curly coat.

1. Based on the picture and the description above, what do you think a mutation is?
2. How can cat breeders attempt to continue the characteristics of the Devon Rex?

L2

This is a representation of key blackline masters available in the Teacher Classroom Resources. See Resource Manager boxes within the chapter for additional information.

Key to Teaching Strategies

The following designations will help you decide which activities are appropriate for your students.

L1 Level 1 activities should be appropriate for students with learning difficulties.

L2 Level 2 activities should be within the ability range of all students.

L3 Level 3 activities are designed for above-average students.

ELL ELL activities should be within the ability range of English Language Learners.

COOP LEARN Cooperative Learning activities are designed for small group work.

LS Multiple Learning Styles logos are used throughout to indicate strategies that address different learning styles.

P These strategies represent student products that can be placed into a best-work portfolio.

Assessment

Assessment Transparency — Cell Reproduction

Directions: Carefully review the diagram and answer the following questions.

1. A cell produced by the fruit fly cell pictured above will most likely be ___.
   A identical to the fruit fly cell
   B a combination of its two parent fruit fly cells.
   C unable to reproduce
   D a genetic mutation
2. In which part of the cell are the chromosomes located?
   F Cell membrane
   G Cytoplasm
   H Nucleus
   J Mitochondrion
3. The fruit fly cell above contains eight chromosomes. How many chromosomes will cells produced by the above cell probably have?
   A sixteen   B eight   C four   D sixty-four

L2

Teaching

Teaching Transparency — Animal Cell Division

L2

Hands-on Activities

Activity Worksheets

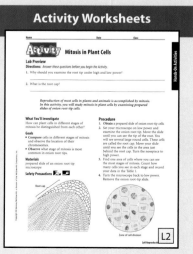

Activity — Mitosis in Plant Cells

Lab Preview
Directions: Answer these questions before you begin the Activity.
1. Why should you examine the root tip under high and low power?
2. What is the root cap?

Reproduction of most cells in plants and animals is accomplished by mitosis. In this activity, you will study mitosis in plant cells by examining prepared slides of onion root-tip cells.

What You'll Investigate
How can plant cells in different stages of mitosis be distinguished from each other?

Goals
• Compare cells in different stages of mitosis and observe the location of their chromosomes.
• Observe what stage of mitosis is most common in onion root tips.

Materials
prepared slide of an onion root tip
microscope

Safety Precautions

Procedure
1. Obtain a prepared slide of onion root-tip cells.
2. Set your microscope on low power and examine the onion root tip. Move the slide until you can see the tip of the root. You will see several large round cells. These cells are called the root cap. Move your slide until you see the cells in the area just behind the root cap. Turn the nosepiece to high power.
3. Find one area of cells where you can see the most stages of mitosis. Count how many cells you see in each stage and record your data in the Table 1.
4. Turn the microscope back to low power. Remove the onion root-tip slide.

L2

Laboratory Activities

Laboratory Activity — Observing Structures in Mitosis

Every cell comes from another cell. Cell division is the process by which a cell reproduces. Mitosis is the name given to the process.

Strategy
You will view cells in a prepared onion root-tip slide and identify a cell for each stage of mitosis. You will compare the four cells from the prepared onion root-tip slide with the diagrams below.

Materials
microscope
prepared slides of onion root tip

Procedure
1. Locate a cell that resembles Figure 1. Observe the cell. In Table 1, checkmark each structure you observe.
2. Locate a cell that resembles Figure 2. In the table, checkmark each structure you observe.
3. Locate a cell that is similar to Figure 3. In the table, checkmark each structure you observe.
4. Locate a cell that is similar to Figure 4. In the table, checkmark the structures you observe.

Figure 1 (Prophase) Figure 2 (Metaphase) Figure 3 (Anaphase) Figure 4 (Telophase)

L2

Meeting Different Ability Levels

Content Outline

Reinforcement

Directed Reading

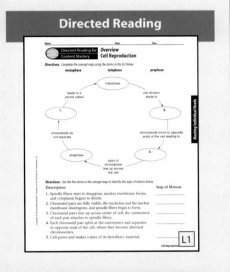

Assessment

Chapter Tests

Enrichment

Spanish Directed Reading

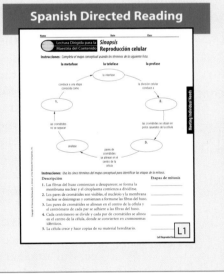

Test Practice Workbook

Chapter Review

Science Content Background

SECTION 1

Resources

Renewable Resources

Renewable resources include trees in forests; fish in lakes, rivers, and oceans; fertile agricultural soil; and fresh water in lakes and rivers. Nature replaces these resources, and they can be used forever as long as they are not overexploited in the short term. Some resources, like agricultural soil, can be considered renewable or nonrenewable. Soil is constantly replaced but at a very slow rate.

Fun Fact

Simple windmills may have been used in Persia as early as the seventh century A.D.

Nonrenewable Resources

Nonrenewable resources, which include minerals and fossil fuels, are present in limited supplies and are depleted by use. They are not replenished by natural processes within a reasonable amount of time. Fossil fuels, for example, take millions of years to form. Recycling nonrenewable resources can help sustain the supply of certain substances. In the future, most products will contain some recycled material.

Nuclear Power

In 1942 Enrico Fermi established the first successful nuclear chain reaction. Nuclear fission reactions release a great deal of energy, up to as much as 10 million times the energy of a typical chemical reaction. Nuclear reactors use uranium-235 for the production of power. Once started, the reactions are self-sustaining: the neutrons released by each splitting in turn split other atoms, causing a chain reaction. There is no danger of nuclear chain reactions starting in nature since uranium-235 makes up only 0.71% of the naturally occurring uranium. The rest is uranium-238, which is not fissible.

SECTION 2

Pollution

Acid Precipitation

Acid precipitation is a worldwide problem. Reports of highly acidic precipitation have come from Canada, England, Germany, France, Scandinavia, and the United States. Precipitation is normally slightly acidic, with a pH between 5.6 and 5.7 that is caused by atmospheric carbonic acid. But acid precipitation sometimes has a concentration of acid 1,000 times higher than normal. The average precipitation in much of the northeastern part of the United States and adjoining parts of Ontario has a pH between 4.0 and 4.5.

Greenhouse Effect

Carbon dioxide is one of the most abundant of the greenhouse gases. It occurs as a natural consequence of respiration. However, carbon dioxide is emitted into the atmosphere as a waste product of energy production. Coal, oil, natural gas, and biomass are all burned to provide heat and electricity for industrial processes, home heating, and cooking. These sources are increasing the amount of carbon dioxide in the atmosphere. Some evidence suggests that increased levels of carbon dioxide in the atmosphere may cause Earth's average temperature to increase.

Jeff Greenberg/Visuals Unlimited

Ozone Depletion

Ozone, a molecule made up of three oxygen atoms, traps excess ultraviolet radiation and prevents it from reaching Earth. In 1985, it was discovered that a significant thinning of the ozone layer over the Antarctic occurred during the southern hemisphere's spring. Some regions of the ozone layer showed 95 percent depletion. Ozone depletion is also occurring farther north. Measurements in arctic regions suggest a thinning of the ozone layer there. These findings have caused countries to stop producing ozone destroying chemicals.

Telegraph Colour Library/FPG International

Soil Loss

Erosion is a natural process that has occurred since Earth was formed. Humans have little control over the erosion caused by glaciers, rivers, and oceans. A number of human activities, mainly farming and logging, have increased erosion. Scientists estimate that between 2 and 3 billion metric tons of soil are lost from farmlands in the United States each year.

Soil Pollution—Solid Wastes

About 90 percent of our solid wastes are disposed of on land, mostly in landfills. Several methods of producing energy from solid waste are used on a small scale and further research is being done in this area. One example is a combustion chamber lined with water lines in which selected wastes are burned and the heat is used to produce steam to power a generator.

SECTION 3

The Three Rs of Conservation
Recycle

In 1994, the overall recycling rate in the U.S. was 23.6 percent, with the composting of yard waste accounting for 1/6 of this. The overall recycling rate of plastic was only 4.7 percent, whereas 33 percent of glass was recycled and 53 percent of steel. Paper and paper products are the most voluminous waste products, and they make up for about 40 percent of the solid waste produced in the United States.

Fun Fact

Recycling is an ancient practice. In prehistoric times, metal tools and weapons were melted down to make new ones.

SCIENCE Online

For additional content background on this topic, go to the Glencoe Science Web site at science.glencoe.com.

Conserving Resources

Chapter Vocabulary

natural resource
renewable resource
nonrenewable resource
petroleum
fossil fuel
hydroelectric power
nuclear energy
geothermal energy
pollutant
acid precipitation
greenhouse effect
ozone depletion
erosion
hazardous waste
recycling

What do you think?

Science Journal This photo is of compost. Compost, which consists mostly of rotting organic matter, can be used instead of fertilizer to enrich soil.

Conserving Resources

I t's sweltering and you haven't felt a breeze in hours. You lift the hose over your head and turn the faucet handle. Instead of clear, cool water, greenish-yellow sludge flows out. Yuck! Clean water isn't the only resource that is commonly taken for granted. In this chapter, you'll learn the difference between renewable and nonrenewable resources. You'll also read about the various energy sources available on Earth and how pollution can affect your life.

What do you think?

Science Journal Look at the picture below with a classmate. Discuss what this might be. Here's a hint: *It's enriching.* Write your answer or best guess in your Science Journal.

Theme Connection

Energy Even though the total amount of energy on Earth remains constant, the sources of usable energy are limited. Energy is often transformed from one form to another, such as fossil fuel energy into electricity and then into light energy.

L and, earth, dirt, soil—the ground beneath your feet is called by many names. You walk on it. People build roads and buildings on it. Plants grow in the top, nutrient-rich layer, called topsoil. Plants help keep topsoil in place by protecting it from wind and rain. What happens when topsoil is left unprotected?

Model topsoil loss

1. Use a mixture of moist sand and potting soil to create a miniature landscape in a plastic basin or aluminum-foil baking pan. Form hills and valleys in your landscape.

2. Use clumps of moss to cover areas of your landscape. Leave some sloping portions without plant cover.

3. Simulate a rainstorm over your landscape by spraying water on it from a spray bottle or by pouring a slow stream of water on it from a beaker.

Observe

In your Science Journal record your observations and describe what happened to the land that was not protected by plant cover.

Before You Read

FOLDABLES
Reading & Study Skills

Making a Concept Map Study Fold Make the following Foldable to help you organize information and by diagramming ideas about renewable and non-renewable resources.

1. Place a sheet of paper in front of you so the short side is at the top. Fold the bottom of the paper to the top, stopping about four centimeters from the top.

2. Draw an oval above the fold. Write *Natural Resources* inside the oval.

3. Fold the paper in half from the left side to the right side and then unfold. Through the top thickness of the paper, cut along the fold line to form two tabs.

4. Label the tabs *Renewable* and *Nonrenewable* and draw an oval around each word. Draw arrows from the large oval to the smaller ovals.

5. Before you read the chapter, list examples of each you already know on the front of the tabs. As you read the chapter add to your lists.

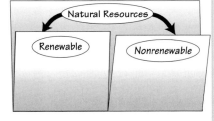

E ◆ 93

EXPLORE ACTIVITY

Purpose Use the Explore Activity to show students how plant cover protects topsoil. L2 ELL
LS Kinesthetic

Preparation Mix one part sand and two parts topsoil.

Materials sand and topsoil mixture, containers, clumps of moss or grass, spray bottles.

Teaching Strategies

- Have students vary the strength of the spray to simulate both light and heavy rainfall and compare the results.

- Point out that water flowing downhill is called "runoff." Have students note the formation of small streams and observe what happens to the land under and around these streams. Students should infer that this is how streams and rivers are formed.

Observe

Water washes the uncovered soil down slopes, forming gullies.

✔ *Assessment*

Performance Have students reuse the materials to demonstrate the effects of terracing. Remove the plants and form two hills, one with a steady incline and one with a series of ridges (terraces) cut into the incline. Observe what happens as rain falls. Soil does not wash away on the incline with ridges. Use **PASC**, p. 89.

Before You Read

FOLDABLES
Reading & Study Skills

Dinah Zike Study Fold

Purpose Students make a Foldable concept map to determine what they know about renewable and nonrenewable natural resources.

📁 For additional help, see Foldables Worksheet, p. 17 in **Chapter Resources Booklet,** or go to the Glencoe Science Web site at **science.glencoe.com.** See After You Read in the Study Guide at the end of this chapter.

SECTION

1

Resources

1 Motivate

Bellringer Transparency

Display the Section Focus Transparency for Section 1. Use the accompanying Transparency Activity Master. L2

ELL

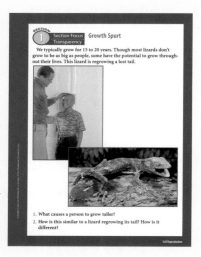

Tie to Prior Knowledge

Hold up a bottle of corn oil and a quart of motor oil. Ask students to explain how they are similar and different? Both are oil and come from living things. Corn is a renewable resource that grew in one summer. The motor oil is a nonrenewable resource that took millions of years to form from the remains of organisms.

✔ Reading Check

Answer resources that are constantly recycled or replaced by nature

---

As You Read

What **You'll Learn**

- **Compare** renewable and nonrenewable resources.
- **List** uses of fossil fuels.
- **Identify** alternatives to fossil fuel use.

Vocabulary

natural resource
renewable resource
nonrenewable resource
petroleum
fossil fuel
hydroelectric power
nuclear energy
geothermal energy

Why **It's Important**

Wise use of natural resources is important for the health of all life on Earth.

Figure 1

Cotton and wood are renewable resources. **A** Cotton cloth is used for rugs, curtains, and clothing. A new crop of cotton can be grown every year. **B** Wood is used for furniture, building materials, and paper. It will take 20 years for these young trees to grow large enough to harvest.

Natural Resources

An earthworm burrowing in moist soil eats decaying plant material. A robin catches the worm and flies to a tree. The leaves of the tree use sunlight during photosynthesis. Leaves fall to the ground, decay, and perhaps become an earthworm's meal. What do these living things have in common? They rely on Earth's **natural resources**—the parts of the environment that are useful or necessary for the survival of living organisms.

What kinds of natural resources do you use? Like other organisms, you need food, air, and water. You also use resources that are needed to make everything from clothes to cars. Natural resources supply energy for automobiles and power plants. Although some natural resources are plentiful, others are not.

Renewable Resources The Sun provides a constant supply of heat and light. Rain fills lakes and streams with water. When plants carry out photosynthesis, they add oxygen to the air. Sunlight, water, air, and the crops shown in **Figure 1** are examples of renewable resources. A **renewable resource** is any natural resource that is constantly recycled or replaced by nature.

✔ Reading Check *What are renewable resources?*

Section ✔ *Assessment* Planner

PORTFOLIO
Physics Integration, p. 97
PERFORMANCE ASSESSMENT
Try at Home MiniLAB, p. 96
Skill Builder Activities, p. 100
See page 122 for more options.

CONTENT ASSESSMENT
Section, p. 100
Challenge, p. 100
Chapter, pp. 122–123

Supply and Demand Even though renewable resources are recycled or replaced, they are sometimes in short supply, as shown in **Figure 2.** You know this is true if you've ever been asked to conserve water. Rain and melted snow replace the water in streams, lakes, and reservoirs. Sometimes, there may not be enough rain or snowmelt to meet all the needs of people, plants, and animals. In some parts of the world, especially desert regions, water usually is scarce.

Nonrenewable Resources Natural resources that are used up more quickly than they can be replaced by natural processes are **nonrenewable resources.** Earth's supply of nonrenewable resources is limited. You use nonrenewable resources when you take home groceries in a plastic bag, paint a wall, or travel by car. Plastics, paints, and gasoline are made from an important nonrenewable resource called petroleum, or oil. **Petroleum** is formed mostly from the remains of microscopic marine organisms buried in Earth's crust. It is nonrenewable because it takes hundreds of millions of years for it to form.

✔ Reading Check *What are nonrenewable resources?*

Minerals and metals found in Earth's crust are nonrenewable resources. Petroleum is a mineral. So are diamonds and the graphite in pencil lead. The aluminum used to make soft-drink cans is a metal. Iron, copper, tin, gold, silver, tungsten, and uranium also are metals. Many manufactured items, like the car shown in **Figure 3,** are made from nonrenewable resources.

Figure 2
In parts of Africa, firewood has become scarce. People in this village now use solar energy instead of wood for cooking.

Figure 3
Iron, a nonrenewable resource, is the main ingredient in steel. Steel is used to make cars, trucks, appliances, buildings, bridges, and even tires. *What other nonrenewable resources are used to build a car?*

SECTION 1 Resources **E ◆ 95**

② Teach

Natural Resources

Use an Analogy
Compare nonrenewable resources to a noninterest bearing savings account to which nothing is added. The depletion of the savings account depends on how fast withdrawals are made and how large they are.

Activity
Have pairs work together to make a list of the things they used or relied upon today. Have them circle the items as Food, Transportation, Clothing, or Household Items. Finally, have them make check marks by the items they think are renewable. Have groups compare and discuss their answers. L2 COOP LEARN
LS **Interpersonal**

✔ Reading Check

Answer resources that are used up more quickly than they can be replaced

IDENTIFYING
Misconceptions

Some students may not realize that fossil fuels and other mineral resources are nonrenewable. Point out that much of the coal used today was formed during the Carboniferous period. Have students research how long ago that was. about 345–280 million years ago

Resource Manager

Chapter Resources Booklet
  Transparency Activity, p. 44
  Directed Reading for Content Mastery, pp. 19, 20
Reading and Writing Skill Activities, p. 9

✔ Active Reading

News Summary Assign students the job of being television reporters. Allow different students to summarize the information on renewable and nonrenewable resources. Then have students present their summaries to the "television" audience.

Caption Answer

Figure 3 Most of the materials are nonrenewable and include chrome, plastic, and synthetic rubber.

Fossil Fuels

TRY AT HOME Mini LAB

Purpose to "mine" a model mineral deposit and attempt to restore the site to its original condition [L1] [IS] **Kinesthetic**

Materials chocolate-chip, or oatmeal-raisin cookie, or nut filled brownie; paper plate; toothpick

Teaching Strategy Suggest students use drops of water to soften the surface if they have trouble removing the "minerals."

Analysis

1. Students will experience difficulty in the restoration process.
2. The minerals closer to the surface are easier to remove than those found deeper within Earth's crust.
3. An ecosystem could be permanently damaged by mining.

✓ Assessment

Oral Which do you think is more expensive: mining at the surface or deep within Earth's crust? Explain. In general, surface mining is less expensive. It doesn't require as much machinery or time. Use **PASC,** p. 91.

TRY AT HOME Mini LAB

Observing Mineral Mining Effects

Procedure 🔲 🔩

1. Place a **chocolate chip cookie** on a **paper plate**. Pretend the chips are mineral deposits and the rest of the cookie is Earth's crust.
2. Use a **toothpick** to locate and dig up the mineral deposits. Try to disturb the land as little as possible.
3. When mining is completed, try to restore the land to its original condition.

Analysis

1. How well were you able to restore the land?
2. Compare the difficulty of digging for mineral deposits found close to the surface with digging for those found deep in Earth's crust.
3. Describe environmental changes that might result from a mining operation.

Figure 4
Coal is a fossil fuel. It often is obtained by strip mining, which removes all the soil above the coal deposit. The soil is replaced, but it takes many years for the ecosystem to recover. The graph shows that 84 percent of the energy used in the United States in 1999 came from fossil fuels.

Fossil Fuels

Coal, oil, and natural gas are nonrenewable resources that supply energy. Most of the energy you use comes from these fossil fuels, as the graph in **Figure 4** shows. **Fossil fuels** are fuels formed in Earth's crust over hundreds of millions of years. Cars, buses, trains, and airplanes are powered by gasoline, diesel fuel, and jet fuel, which are made from oil. Coal is used in many power plants to produce electricity. Natural gas is used in manufacturing, for heating and cooking, and sometimes as a vehicle fuel.

Fossil Fuel Conservation Billions of people all over the world use fossil fuels every day. Because fossil fuels are non-renewable, Earth's supply of them is limited. In the future, they may become more expensive and difficult to obtain. Also, the use of fossil fuels can lead to environmental problems. For example, mining coal can require stripping away thick layers of soil and rock, as shown in **Figure 4,** which destroys ecosystems. Another problem is that fossil fuels must be burned to release the energy stored in them. The burning of fossil fuels produces waste gases that cause air pollution, including smog and acid rain. For these reasons, many people suggest reducing the use of fossil fuels and finding other sources of energy.

You can use simple conservation measures to help reduce fossil fuel use. Switch off the light when you leave a room and turn off the television when you're not watching it. These actions reduce your use of electricity, which often is produced in power plants that burn fossil fuels. Hundreds of millions of automobiles are in use in the United States. Riding in a car pool or taking public transportation uses fewer liters of gasoline than driving alone in a car. Walking or riding a bicycle uses even less fossil fuel. Reducing fossil fuel use has an added benefit—the less you use, the more money you save.

Renewable energy 8%
Nuclear Power 8%
Natural gas 23%
Coal 22%
Oil 39%

Curriculum Connection

Social Studies Have students investigate ways petroleum was used in ancient cultures. Egyptians used petroleum to help preserve mummies. The Chinese used petroleum to heat and light their homes and to cook. Tar pits supplied crude oil that was used for fuel, cooking, and lighting in Latin America. At the same time, petroleum was used in Europe for lubricating wagon wheels and to make ointments. [L3] [IS] **Naturalist**

Resource Manager

Chapter Resources Booklet
  Note-taking Worksheets, pp. 33–35
  MiniLAB, p. 3
  Enrichment, p. 30
Cultural Diversity, p. 41

Figure 5
Most power plants use turbine generators to produce electricity. In fossil fuel plants, coal or oil is burned to boil water, producing steam that turns the turbine.

Fast-moving steam, water, or wind rushes across the turbine blades. This flow of energy causes the turbine blades to turn.

The turbine blades are attached to a shaft. When the blades turn, so does the shaft.

Electricity flows from the coil into electrical wires.

Magnet

Generator

The turning shaft is connected to an electric generator. A simple generator is a coil of wire that spins inside the field of a magnet. The turbine shaft spins the coil. The spinning coil generates electricity.

Turbine

Alternatives to Fossil Fuels

Another approach to reducing fossil fuel use is to develop other sources of energy. Much of the electricity used today comes from power plants that burn fossil fuels. As **Figure 5** shows, electricity is generated when a rotating turbine turns a coil of wires in the magnetic field of an electric generator. Fossil-fuel power plants boil water to produce steam that turns the turbine. Alternative energy sources, including water, wind, and atomic energy can be used instead of fossil fuels to turn turbines. Also, solar cells can produce electricity using only sunlight, with no turbines at all. Some of these alternative energy sources—particularly wind and solar energy—are so plentiful they could be considered inexhaustible resources.

Water Power Water is a renewable energy source that can be used to generate electricity. **Hydroelectric power** is electricity that is produced when the energy of falling water is used to turn the turbines of an electric generator. Hydroelectric power does not contribute to air pollution because no fuel is burned. However, it does present environmental concerns. Building a hydroelectric plant usually involves constructing a dam across a river. The dam raises the water level high enough to produce the energy required for electricity generation. Many acres behind the dam are flooded, destroying land habitats and changing part of the river into a lake.

Potential energy is stored energy. Kinetic energy is energy in motion, like a car moving along a street. In your Science Journal, explain why water stored behind a dam has potential energy. Describe how this potential energy becomes kinetic energy.

SECTION 1 Resources **E ◆ 97**

Alternatives to Fossil Fuels

Visual Learning

Figure 5 Have students trace the process of producing electricity using a turbine generator. Then have students identify at which point of the process different energy sources can be used to generate the energy. at the first stage of the process, where the turbine blades are turned

Fun Fact

The movement of coils of wire within a magnetic field is how electricity is produced. This electricity is called alternating current (AC) as opposed to electricity from batteries or photovoltaic cells, which is called direct current (DC).

Discussion

Hydroelectricity is a clean way to produce electricity, but should dams that flood thousands of acres be built? Have students discuss the advantages and disadvantages of this type of electricity production. Advantages: clean, doesn't use nonrenewable resources, provides inexpensive electricity; disadvantages: loss of natural habitats or human communities

The water will have potential energy because of its height. As the water falls, it loses height and therefore potential energy. At the same time, the water gains speed, or kinetic energy. Thus potential energy is converted into kinetic energy. P

Inclusion Strategies

Visually Impaired Natural waterfalls are not numerous enough or high enough, so dams are often built to raise the water level. Height is an important determinant of the amount of hydroelectric power produced. Have students feel the effects of water dropped from a cup held one, two, and four feet above their hands. L1
Kinesthetic

Teacher FYI

Students may wonder why they don't see the water actually turning turbines at waterfalls such as Niagara Falls. The reason is that water diverted before it actually gets to the falls is what goes through the turbines. During the night at Niagara Falls, more water is diverted than in the day in order to keep the daytime visitors happy.

Alternatives to Fossil Fuels, continued

Make a Model

Use a pinwheel and a fan to show how wind can be used to turn a turbine. Give some pinwheels to students and ask them to find the spot on the school grounds that would be best for generating electricity using the wind. L1 ELL
IS Naturalist

IDENTIFYING Misconceptions

Some students may think that nuclear radiation makes a person glow or turn green. Combat this misconception by asking students if they turn green when they receive dental X rays, which are a form of radiation. Explain that many forms of nuclear radiation are much more damaging than X rays. Large doses can be lethal, and smaller doses may cause cancer or premature aging.

Discussion

Ask students to compare modern windmills with old-style windmills found in Holland, Spain, or the United States. They both have blades that are turned by the force of the wind. Modern windmills are more streamlined and generate electricity. Older ones were used to grind grain or pump water from underground.

Extension

Have students explain why hydroelectric and wind energy can both be considered forms of solar energy. Solar energy drives the water cycle, which is necessary for hydroelectric energy. The Sun warms areas of Earth's surface, which results in the formation of wind. L2 Linguistic

Wind Power Wind power is another renewable energy source that can be used for electricity production. Wind turns the blades of a turbine, which powers an electric generator. When winds blow at least 32 km/h, energy is produced. Wind power does not cause air pollution, but electricity can be produced only when the wind is blowing. So far, wind power accounts for only a small percentage of the electricity used in the United States and Europe.

Nuclear Power Another alternative to fossil fuels makes use of the huge amounts of energy in the nuclei of atoms, as shown in **Figure 6. Nuclear energy** is released when billions of atomic nuclei from uranium, a radioactive element, are split apart in a nuclear fission reaction. This energy is used to produce steam that rotates the turbine blades of an electric generator.

Nuclear power does not contribute to air pollution. However, uranium is a nonrenewable resource, and mining it can disrupt ecosystems. Nuclear power plants also produce radioactive wastes that can seriously harm living organisms. Some of these wastes remain radioactive for thousands of years, and their safe disposal is a problem that has not yet been solved. Accidents are also a danger.

Figure 6
Nuclear power plants are designed to withstand the high energy produced by nuclear reactions.

The containment building is made of concrete lined with steel. The reactor vessel and steam generators are housed inside.

Control rods can be raised and lowered to control the reaction.

A fast-moving neutron from the nucleus of a uranium atom crashes into another atom.

The fuel rods are lowered to begin the nuclear reaction.

The steel reactor vessel contains uranium fuel rods, and control rods made of radiation-absorbing material. Water circulates through the vessel to prevent overheating.

The collision splits the atom, releasing more neutrons, which collide with other atoms or are absorbed by control rods. The heat produced by these collisions is used to produce steam.

Science Journal

Nuclear Power Plant Sometimes people think something is a good idea but they don't want it in their own backyards. Have students describe in their journals how they might feel and what they might do if they learned of plans to build a nuclear power plant near their neighborhood. L2 IS Intrapersonal

Geothermal Energy The hot, molten rock that lies deep beneath Earth's surface is also a source of energy. You see the effects of this energy when lava and hot gases escape from an erupting volcano or when hot water spews from a geyser. The heat energy contained in Earth's crust is called **geothermal energy.** Most geothermal power plants use this energy to produce steam to generate electricity.

Geothermal energy is available only where natural geysers or volcanoes are found. A geothermal power plant in California uses steam produced by geysers. The island nation of Iceland was formed by volcanoes, and geothermal energy is plentiful there. Geothermal power plants supply heat and electricity to about 90 percent of the homes in Iceland. Outdoor swimming areas also are heated with geothermal energy, as shown in **Figure 7.**

Solar Energy The most reliable source of energy for all life on Earth is the Sun. Solar energy is a leading alternative to fossil fuels. One use of solar energy is in solar-heated buildings, as shown in **Figure 8.** During winter in the northern hemisphere, the parts of a building that face south receive the most sunlight. Large windows placed on the south side of the building help heat it by allowing warm rays of sunshine into the building during the day. Floors and walls of most solar-heated buildings are made of concrete or stone that absorbs heat during the day. During the night, the stored heat is released slowly, keeping the building warm.

Figure 7
In Iceland, a geothermal power plant pumps hot water out of the ground to heat buildings and generate electricity. Leftover hot water goes into this lake, making it warm enough for swimming even when the ground is covered with snow.

Figure 8
The Zion National Park Visitor Center in Utah is a solar-heated building designed to save energy. The roof holds solar panels that are used to generate electricity. High windows can be opened to circulate air and help cool the building on hot days. The overhanging roof shades the windows during summer.

SECTION 1 Resources **E ◆ 99**

Reteach

Have students list reasons why renewable resources should be used wisely and nonrenewable resources should be conserved. L1

Challenge

Have students sort the following terms into renewable and nonrenewable resources: sisal, palladium, paprika, topaz, papaya, vinegar, diamond. Suggest they use a dictionary or the Internet to look up unfamiliar words. renewable: sisal, paprika, papaya, vinegar; nonrenewable: topaz, palladium, diamond

Assessment

Oral Have students explain which energy alternative to fossil fuels they think has the most promise to decrease fossil fuel use. Have them justify their answers. Use **Performance Assessment in the Science Classroom,** p. 89.

Free electrons

Layers of semiconductor atoms

Electric current flows through the calculator and back to the PV cell to form a complete circuit.

Light

Figure 9
Light energy from the Sun travels in tiny packets of energy called photons. Photons crash into the atoms of PV cells, knocking electrons loose. These electrons create an electric current.

Solar Cells Do you know how a solar-powered calculator works? How do spacecraft use sunlight to generate electricity? These devices use photovoltaic (foht oh vohl TAY ihk) cells to turn sunlight into electric current, as shown in **Figure 9.** Photovoltaic (PV) cells are small and easy to use. However, they produce electricity only in sunlight, so batteries are needed to store electricity for use at night or on cloudy days. Also, PV cells presently are too expensive to use for generating large amounts of electricity. Improvements in this technology continue to be made, and prices probably will go down in the future. As **Figure 10** shows, solar buildings and PV cells are just two of the many ways energy can be used to replace fossil fuels.

Section ① Assessment

1. What are natural resources?
2. Compare and contrast renewable and nonrenewable resources. Give five examples of each.
3. Name five energy sources that provide alternatives to fossil fuels.
4. Describe two ways solar energy can be used to reduce fossil fuel use.
5. **Think Critically** Explain why the water that is used to cool the reactor vessel of a nuclear power plant is kept separate from the water that is heated to produce steam for the turbine generators.

Skill Builder Activities

6. **Concept Mapping** Draw a concept map showing how the following terms are related: *renewable resources, nonrenewable resources, fossil fuels, natural gas, coal, oil, solar energy, PV cells, solar cookers, nuclear energy,* and *geothermal energy.* **For more help, refer to the** Science Skill Handbook.

7. **Solving One-Step Equations** Most cars in the U.S. are driven about 10,000 miles each year. If a car can travel 30 miles on one gallon of gasoline, how many gallons will it use in a year? **For more help, refer to the** Math Skill Handbook.

100 ◆ E CHAPTER 4 Conserving Resources

Answers to Section Assessment

1. the raw materials that organisms use for survival or to enhance life
2. Renewable: can be replaced quickly by nature, include water, plants, animals, sunlight, air; nonrenewable: cannot be replaced quickly by nature, include petroleum, diamonds, metals, phosphorous, topsoil.

3. nuclear, solar, geothermal, wind, and water power
4. Passively, to heat homes (and water) and thus reduce use of fuels for this purpose; directly, to make electricity directly so that fossil fuels don't have to be burned.
5. to prevent possible radioactive contamination

6. Fossil fuels and nuclear energy branch from nonrenewable; fossil fuels is divided into natural gas, coal, and oil. Solar and geothermal energy branch from renewable; solar is divided into PV cells and solar cookers.
7. 10,000/30 = 333.33 gallons per year

NATIONAL GEOGRAPHIC VISUALIZING SOLAR ENERGY

Figure 10

Sunlight is a renewable energy source that provides an alternative to fossil fuels. Solar technologies use the Sun's energy in many ways—from heating to electricity generation.

▼ ELECTRICITY Photovoltaic (PV) cells turn sunlight into electric current. They are commonly used to power small devices, such as calculators. Panels that combine many PV cells provide enough electricity for a home—or an orbiting satellite, such as the International Space Station, below.

▲ POWER PLANTS In California's Mojave Desert, a solar power plant uses hundreds of mirrors to focus sunlight on a water-filled tower. The steam produced by this system generates enough electricity to power 2,400 homes.

▼ COOKING In hot, sunny weather, a solar oven or panel cooker can be used to cook a pot of rice or heat water. The powerful solar cooker shown below reaches even higher temperatures. It is being used to fry food.

▼ INDOOR HEATING South-facing windows and heat-absorbing construction materials turn a room into a solar collector that can help heat an entire building, such as this Connecticut home.

▲ WATER HEATING Water is heated as it flows through small pipes in this roof-mounted solar heat collector. The hot water then flows into an insulated tank for storage.

E ◆ 101

NATIONAL GEOGRAPHIC

Visualizing Solar Energy

Have students examine the pictures and read the captions. Then ask the following questions.

How are photovoltic cells similar to chloroplasts? How are they different? Possible answer: Both chloroplasts and photovoltic cells capture sunlight and turn it into another form of energy. Chloroplasts convert solar energy to chemical energy, and photovoltic cells convert solar energy into electric energy.

What are some potential disadvantages of using solar energy as the only source of energy for your home? How could you overcome these disadvantages? Possible answer: Solar energy might not be consistent or reliable, a cloudy day could result in no heat or electricity. However, a method of storing solar energy for future use would overcome this problem.

Activity

Have students work in pairs to make posters that diagram an innovative way to capture or use the Sun's energy. Encourage creative and different thinking. Have students explain their diagrams to the class.

Extension

Have students research the percentage of energy used in the United States that was supplied by solar energy in the past year. Have the students compare this percentage to the percentage in 1950.

Resource Manager

Chapter Resources Booklet
Reinforcement, p. 27

Mathematics Skill Activities, p. 9

Life Science Critical Thinking/Problem Solving, p. 23

SECTION

Pollution

1 Motivate

Bellringer Transparency

Display the Section Focus Transparency for Section 2. Use the accompanying Transparency Activity Master. L2
ELL

Tie to Prior Knowledge

Most students will be familiar with some forms of pollution. Ask for examples. For each example, have students list what people can do to reduce that form of pollution.

SECTION

2 Pollution

What You'll Learn

- **Describe** types of air pollution.
- **Identify** causes of water pollution.
- **Explain** methods that can be used to prevent erosion.

Vocabulary
pollutant
acid precipitation
greenhouse effect
ozone depletion
erosion
hazardous waste

Why It's Important
By understanding the causes of pollution, you can help solve pollution problems.

Keeping the Environment Healthy

More than six billion people live on Earth. This large human population puts a strain on the environment, but each person can make a difference. You can help safeguard the environment by paying attention to how your use of natural resources affects air, land, and water.

Air Pollution

On a still, sunny day in almost any large city, you might see a dark haze in the air, like that in **Figure 11.** The haze comes from pollutants that form when wood or fuels are burned. A **pollutant** is a substance that contaminates the environment. Air pollutants include soot, smoke, ash, and gases such as carbon dioxide, carbon monoxide, nitrogen oxides, and sulfur oxides. Wherever cars, trucks, airplanes, factories, homes, or power plants are found, air pollution is likely. Air pollution also can be caused by volcanic eruptions, wind-blown dust and sand, forest fires, and the evaporation of paints and other chemicals.

Smog is a form of air pollution created when sunlight reacts with pollutants produced by burning fuels. It can irritate the eyes and make breathing difficult for people with asthma or other lung diseases. Smog can be reduced if people take buses or trains instead of driving or if they use vehicles, such as electric cars, that produce fewer pollutants than gasoline-powered vehicles.

Figure 11
The term *smog* was used for the first time in the early 1900s to describe the mixture of smoke and fog that often covers large cities in the industrial world.

Section ✓Assessment Planner

PORTFOLIO
Assessment, p. 110
PERFORMANCE ASSESSMENT
MiniLAB, p. 103
Skill Builder Activities, p. 110
See page 122 for more options.

CONTENT ASSESSMENT
Section, p. 110
Challenge, p. 110
Chapter, pp. 122–123

Figure 12

A Compare these two photographs of the same statue. The photo on the left was taken before acid rain became a problem. The photo on the right shows acid rain damage. **B** The pH scale indicates whether a solution is acidic or basic.

B

Acid rain | Pure water

0 1 2 3 4 5 6 7 8 9 10 11 12 13 14

◄── More acidic   Neutral   More basic ──►

Acid Precipitation

Chemistry INTEGRATION

Water vapor condenses on dust particles in the air to form droplets that combine to create clouds. Eventually, the droplets become large enough to fall to the ground as precipitation—mist, rain, snow, sleet, or hail. Air pollutants from the burning of fossil fuels can react with water in the atmosphere to form strong acids. Acidity is measured by a value called pH, as shown in **Figure 12. Acid precipitation** has a pH below 5.6.

Effects of Acid Rain Acid precipitation washes nutrients from the soil, which can lead to the death of trees and other plants. Runoff from acid rain that flows into a lake or pond can lower the pH of the water. If algae and microscopic organisms cannot survive in the acidic water, fish and other organisms that depend on them for food also die.

Preventing Acid Rain Sulfur from burning coal and nitrogen oxides from vehicle exhaust are the pollutants primarily responsible for acid rain. Using low-sulfur fuels, such as natural gas or low-sulfur coal, can help reduce acid precipitation. However, these fuels are less plentiful and more expensive than high-sulfur coal. Smokestacks that remove sulfur dioxide before it enters the atmosphere also help. Reducing automobile use and keeping car engines properly tuned can reduce acid rain caused by nitrogen oxide pollution. The use of electric cars, or hybrid-fuel cars that can run on electricity as well as gasoline, also could help.

Mini LAB

Measuring Acid Rain

Procedure 🔬 👓 🚱

1. Collect **rainwater** by placing a clean **cup** outdoors. Do not collect rainwater that has been in contact with any object or organism.
2. Dip a piece of **pH indicator paper** into the sample.
3. Compare the color of the paper to the pH chart provided. Record the pH of the rainwater.
4. Use separate pieces of pH paper to test the pH of **tap water** and **distilled water**. Record these results.

Analysis

1. Is the rainwater acidic, basic, or neutral?
2. How does the pH of the rainwater compare with the pH of tap water? With the pH of distilled water?

2 Teach

Acid Precipitation

Mini LAB

Purpose Students collect samples and determine the pH of rainwater. L2 COOP LEARN
Kinesthetic
Materials cups, pH paper, rain gauge (optional)

Teaching Strategies
- If your school has a rain gauge, this is a convenient place to obtain rainwater. Otherwise, cups can be placed outside to catch rain.
- Have students test the pH of rain on different days throughout the school year to detect variations.

Analysis
1. pH of most rainwater is acidic and averages 5.6. Student results may range from a pH of 4 to 7.
2. Tap water pH varies, but in most of the U.S. it is about 6; distilled water always has a pH of 7.

✓ Assessment

Performance Set up several liquids of unknown pH. Have students use pH paper to test each and determine whether it is an acid or base. Then have them make a chart showing the pH of each unknown liquid and comparing the liquids with substances of known pH. Use **PASC**, p. 109.

Curriculum Connection

Social Studies Vinegar is a mild acid that has been used for hundreds of years to preserve foods. Pickles and sauerkraut are examples of foods still eaten today that were developed to take advantage of vinegar's acidic properties, which kill many microorganisms. Have students research other foods that are prepared in pickling solution. Fish, fruits and vegetables, and pig's feet are pickled, to name a few. L2

Greenhouse Effect

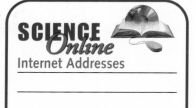

Carbon Dioxide Levels

CO_2* — values on y-axis: 320, 330, 340, 350, 360, 370

Year (x-axis): '75, '80, '85, '90, '95, '00

* parts per million

Figure 13
The moment you step inside a greenhouse, you feel the results of the greenhouse effect. Heat trapped by the glass walls warms the air inside. In a similar way, atmospheric greenhouse gases trap heat close to Earth's surface.

Greenhouse Effect

Sunlight travels through the atmosphere to Earth's surface. Some of this sunlight normally is reflected back into space. The rest is trapped by certain atmospheric gases, as shown in **Figure 13.** This heat-trapping feature of the atmosphere is the **greenhouse effect.** Without it, temperatures on Earth probably would be too cold to support life.

Atmospheric gases that trap heat are called greenhouse gases. One of the most important greenhouse gases is carbon dioxide (CO_2). CO_2 is a normal part of the atmosphere. It is also a waste product that forms when fossil fuels are burned. Over the past century, more fossil fuels have been burned than ever before, which is increasing the percentage of CO_2 in the atmosphere. The atmosphere might be trapping more of the Sun's heat, making Earth warmer. A rise in Earth's average temperature, possibly caused by an increase in greenhouse gases, is known as global warming.

Global Warming Temperature data collected from 1895 through 1995 indicate that Earth's temperature increased more than 1°C during that 100-year period. No one is certain whether this rise was caused by human activities or is a natural part of Earth's weather cycle. What kinds of changes might be caused by global warming? Changing rainfall patterns could alter ecosystems and affect the kinds of crops that can be grown in different parts of the world. The number of storms and hurricanes might increase. The polar ice caps might begin to melt, raising sea levels and flooding coastal areas. Warmer weather might allow tropical diseases, such as malaria, to become more widespread. Many people feel that the possibility of global warming is a good reason to reduce fossil fuel use.

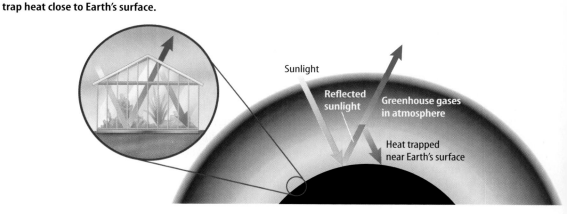

Sunlight

Reflected sunlight

Greenhouse gases in atmosphere

Heat trapped near Earth's surface

⬡ LAB DEMONSTRATION

Purpose to use changes in color due to determine relative pH

Materials purple cabbage, hot plate, pot, water, strainer, 4 test tubes, stand, goggles, test materials: club soda, vinegar, ammonia, baking soda water

Preparation Boil the cabbage, cool, and strain, retaining liquid.

Procedure Explain that purple cabbage juice can be used as a pH indicator. Add 1″ juice to each tube. Add a small amount of one test material to each tube. Observe.

Expected Outcome Acids turn cabbage juice purple, bases turn it blue. The darker the color, the stronger the acid or base.

✔Assessment

Have students sort the test materials into acids vinegar, club soda and bases ammonia, baking soda. Set up another tube. Add lemon juice until the color changes. Have students identify lemon juice as an acid or base. acid

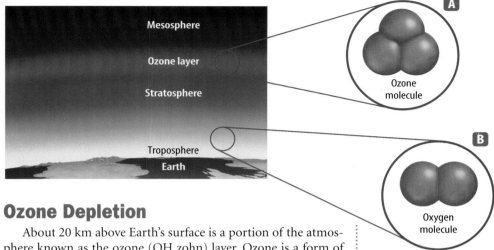

Ozone Depletion

About 20 km above Earth's surface is a portion of the atmosphere known as the ozone (OH zohn) layer. Ozone is a form of oxygen, as shown in **Figure 14.** The ozone layer absorbs some of the Sun's harmful ultraviolet (UV) radiation. UV radiation can damage living cells.

During the early autumn each year, the ozone layer temporarily becomes thinner over polar regions. The thinning of the ozone layer is called **ozone depletion.** This pollution problem is caused by gases called chlorofluorocarbons (klor oh FLOR oh kar bunz) (CFCs). CFCs are used in the cooling systems of refrigerators, freezers, and air conditioners. When CFCs leak into the air, they slowly rise into the atmosphere until they arrive at the ozone layer. CFCs react chemically with ozone, breaking apart the ozone molecules.

UV Radiation Because of ozone depletion, the amount of UV radiation that reaches Earth's surface could be increasing. UV radiation could be causing a rise in the number of skin cancer cases in humans. It also might be harming other organisms. The ozone layer is so important to the survival of life on Earth that world governments and industries have agreed to stop making and using CFCs.

Ozone that is high in the upper atmosphere protects life on Earth. Near Earth's surface though, it can be harmful. Ozone is produced when fossil fuels are burned. This ozone stays in the lower atmosphere, where it pollutes the air. Ozone damages the lungs and other sensitive tissues of animals and plants. For example, it can cause the needles of a Ponderosa pine to drop, harming growth.

✔ Reading Check *What is the difference between ozone in the upper atmosphere and ozone in the lower atmosphere?*

Figure 14
The atmosphere's ozone layer absorbs large amounts of UV radiation, preventing it from reaching Earth's surface.
Ⓐ Ozone molecules are made of three oxygen atoms. They are formed in a chemical reaction between sunlight and oxygen.
Ⓑ The oxygen you breathe has two oxygen atoms in each molecule.

Ozone Depletion

Teacher **FYI**
Although the production of CFC has halted, there is a reserve supply available for air conditioning and refrigeration units. In many cases, HFCs are being used as coolants to replace CFCs, as they do not lead to ozone completion.

Quick Demo
Have two students join hands to represent the normal state of oxygen (O_2) and three students join hands to represent ozone (O_3).

✔ Reading Check
Answer Ozone in the upper atmosphere is helpful to life; ozone in the lower atmosphere can be harmful to life as it pollutes the air.

IDENTIFYING Misconceptions
Students sometimes confuse common environmental problems. For example, they may think that not littering will help with the problem of acid rain. Make sure that for each problem, students understand the related causes and effects and what can be done to reduce the problem.

Resource Manager

Chapter Resources Booklet
  Enrichment, p. 31
Reading and Writing Skill Activities, p. 19
Performance Assessment in the Science Classroom, p. 48

 Cultural Diversity

Sun Exposure Australia leads the world in skin cancer because of the many fair-skinned people, the ozone hole over the country, and changes in culture. In the past, wealthy Australians avoided the Sun. After WWI, Australians embraced a tanned look. As a result, skin cancer rates rapidly increased. It has now become a culturally accepted practice to have children wear hats when they go outside.

Indoor Air Pollution

Discussion

Why might better-insulated buildings make indoor air pollution more of a problem? Less air enters and leaves a building. **Why do radon levels tend to be higher in wintertime?** People are more likely to keep windows tightly closed. Have students discuss the pros and cons of insulating buildings to this extent.

Health
INTEGRATION

Carbon monoxide has an affinity for hemoglobin in red blood cells, so when it attaches, it doesn't let go. This prevents red blood cells from functioning properly. Because of this, appliances designed for outdoor use should only be used outdoors, as they often are not equipped with ventilation devices for indoor use.

Teacher FYI

Radon is the second leading cause of lung cancer in the United States. Cigarette smoking is the leading cause.

IDENTIFYING
Misconceptions

Some students may think that people are responsible for all pollutants. Although many pollutants can be traced to people, radon is a naturally occurring substance. It is formed from the radioactive decay of uranium present in soil.

Health
INTEGRATION

Carbon monoxide enters the body through the lungs. It attaches to red blood cells, preventing the cells from absorbing oxygen. In your Science Journal, explain why heaters and barbecues designed for outdoor use never should be used indoors.

Figure 15

A The map shows the potential for radon exposure in different parts of the United States. Soils of the northern and northeastern portions of the country produce more radon gas than in most other areas. **B** A radon detection kit can tell the user if a dangerous level of radon is present.

Indoor Air Pollution

Air pollution can occur indoors. Today's buildings are better insulated to conserve energy. However, better insulation reduces the flow of air into and out of a building, so air pollutants can build up indoors. For example, burning cigarettes release hazardous particles and gases into the air. Even nonsmokers can suffer ill effects from secondhand cigarette smoke. As a result, smoking no longer is allowed in many public and private buildings. Paints, carpets, glues and adhesives, printers, and photocopy machines also give off dangerous gases, including formaldehyde. Like cigarette smoke, formaldehyde is a carcinogen, which means it can cause cancer.

Carbon Monoxide Carbon monoxide (CO) is a poisonous gas that is produced whenever charcoal, natural gas, kerosene, or other fuels are burned. CO poisoning can cause serious illness or death. Fuel-burning stoves and heaters must be designed to prevent CO from building up indoors. CO is colorless and odorless, so it is difficult to detect. Alarms that provide warning of a dangerous buildup of CO are being used in more and more homes.

Radon Radon is a naturally occurring, radioactive gas that is given off by some types of rock and soil, as shown in **Figure 15**. Radon has no color or odor. It can seep into basements and the lower floors of buildings. Radon exposure is the second leading cause of lung cancer in this country. A radon detector sounds an alarm when levels of the gas in indoor air become too high. If radon is present, increasing a building's ventilation can eliminate any damaging effects.

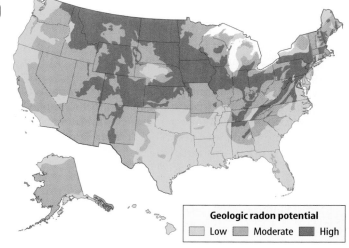

Geologic radon potential
Low   Moderate   High

Teacher FYI

If combustion were complete, only carbon dioxide and water would be produced. Complete combustion is hard to achieve, especially in a barbecue. This is why barbecues should not be used indoors.

Curriculum Connection

Health Have students research sources of indoor air pollution. Suggest different students study the effects of asbestos, formaldehyde, radon, cigarette smoke, and other substances found in homes. Have students combine their findings and present them as an informative bulletin board. L2 COOP LEARN

A When rain falls on roads and parking lots, it can wash oil and grease onto the soil and into nearby streams.

B Rain can wash agricultural pesticides and fertilizers into lakes, streams, or oceans.

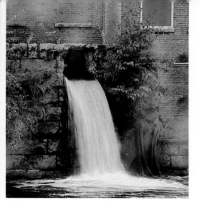

C Industrial wastes are sometimes released directly into surface waters.

Water Pollution

Pollutants enter water, too. Air pollutants can drift into water or be washed out of the sky by rain. Rain can wash land pollutants into waterways, as shown in **Figure 16.** Wastewater from factories and sewage-treatment plants often is released into waterways. In the United States and many other countries, laws require that wastewater be treated to remove pollutants before it is released. But, in many parts of the world, wastewater treatment is not always possible. Pollution also enters water when people dump litter or waste materials into rivers, lakes, and oceans.

Surface Water Some water pollutants poison fish and other wildlife, and can be harmful to people who swim in or drink the water. For example, chemical pesticides sprayed on farmland can wash into lakes and streams. These chemicals can harm the insects that fish, turtles, or frogs rely on for food. Shortages of food can lead to deaths among water-dwelling animals. Some pollutants, especially those containing mercury and other metals, can build up in the tissues of fish. Eating contaminated fish and shellfish can transfer these metals to people, birds, and other animals. In some areas, people are advised not to eat fish or shellfish taken from polluted waterways.

Algal blooms are another water pollution problem. Raw sewage and excess fertilizer contain large amounts of nitrogen. If they are washed into a lake or pond, they can cause the rapid growth of algae. When the algae die, they are decomposed by huge numbers of bacteria that use up much of the oxygen in the water. Fish and other organisms can die from a lack of oxygen in the water.

Figure 16
Pollution of surface waters can occur in several ways.

Water Pollution

Quick Demo

Drop food coloring into a glass jar or beaker full of water. Have students observe how the color spreads out and occupies the entire area. Explain that dumping a little waste into a lake might not be bad, but as more is added, the concentration increases. Add more drops of food coloring to illustrate this concept. **LS Visual-Spatial**

Activity

Obtain some aquarium water that has algae growing in it. Have students add varying amounts of commercial fertilizer to test tubes of the water. Place the tubes in sunlight, and add fresh water as the old water evaporates. In a few days, students should observe an algae bloom in one or more of the tubes. Continue the activity so that students can observe the effect of algal decay on the quality of the water. **L2**
LS Kinesthetic

Resource Manager

Chapter Resources Booklet
  Lab Activity, pp. 9–12
  Transparency Activity, pp. 47–48

Cultural Diversity

Significance of Water Water is so important for civilization that it has becomes part of human culture. Water and waterscapes have been described in words, drawings, songs, and other art forms by all cultures on Earth. Water also plays an important part in religion. From Japanese Shintoism to Christianity, water symbolizes cleansing in spiritual ceremonies.

Water Pollution, continued

Activity

Float some corn oil on the surface of water in a beaker. Ask students to try and clean up the oil with balls of cotton. They will observe that it is possible, but not very easy. L1 ELL

Visual Learning ___.

Figure 18 Have students study the illustration. Emphasize that groundwater is an important source of water for many people. Then prepare a beaker with sand or soil on top and gravel on the bottom. Pour a little water on the soil's surface and show students how the water percolates through the layers to the bottom of the beaker. Have students relate this to the movement of groundwater shown in the illustration. IS **Visual-Spatial**

Figure 17
In 1996, the oil tanker *Sea Empress* spilled more than 72 million kg of oil into the sea along the coast of Wales. More than $40 million was spent on the cleanup effort, but thousands of ocean organisms were destroyed, including birds, fish, and shellfish.

Figure 18
Water from rainfall slowly filters through sand or soil until it is trapped in underground aquifers. Pollutants picked up by the water as it filters through the soil can contaminate water wells.

Ocean Water Rivers and streams eventually flow into oceans, bringing their pollutants along. Also, polluted water can enter the ocean in coastal areas where factories, sewage-treatment plants, or shipping activities are located. Oil spills are a well-known ocean pollution problem. About 4 billion kg of oil are spilled into ocean waters every year. Much of that oil comes from ships that use ocean water to wash out their fuel tanks. Oil also can come from oil tanker wrecks, as shown in **Figure 17.**

Groundwater Pollution can affect water that seeps underground, as shown in **Figure 18.** Groundwater is water that collects between particles of soil and rock. This water can flow slowly through permeable layers of rock called aquifers. Groundwater comes from precipitation and runoff that soaks into the soil. If this water comes into contact with pollutants as it moves through the soil and into an aquifer, the aquifer could become polluted. Polluted groundwater is difficult—and sometimes impossible—to clean. In some parts of the country, chemicals leaking from underground storage tanks have created groundwater pollution problems.

Precipitation

Pond

Well

Stream

Water table

Aquifer

Impermeable rock

Science Journal

Well Water Have students imagine that they depend on a well as their source of water. They find out that pesticides that can injure their health have seeped into the groundwater the well draws from. Have students write in their Science Journals the changes they will make in their use of the well's water. L2 IS **Intrapersonal**

Inclusion Strategies

Hearing Impaired Fill a funnel with soil and place in a beaker. Add a teaspoon of food coloring to the top of the soil. Slowly pour water through the funnel. At first, water flowing out of the funnel is probably clear, but eventually colored water exits. Explain that soil may act as a filter for a time, but eventually pollutants will work their way through the soil. L1 ELL

A Contour plowing reduces the downhill flow of water.

Soil Loss

Fertile topsoil is important to plant growth. New topsoil takes hundreds or thousands of years to form. The Explore Activity at the beginning of this chapter shows that rain washes away loose topsoil. Wind also blows it away. The movement of soil from one place to another is called **erosion** (ih ROH zhun). Eroded soil that washes into a river or stream can block sunlight and slow photosynthesis. It also can harm fish, clams, and other organisms. Erosion is a natural process, but human activities increase it. When a farmer plows a field or a forest is cut down, soil is left bare. Bare soil is more easily carried away by rain and wind. **Figure 19** shows some methods farmers use to reduce soil erosion.

Soil Pollution

Soil can become polluted when air pollutants drift to the ground or when water leaves pollutants behind as it flows through the soil. Soil also can be polluted when people toss litter on the ground or dispose of trash in landfills.

Solid Wastes What happens to the trash you throw out every week? What do people do with old refrigerators, TVs, and toys? Most of this solid waste is dumped in landfills. Most landfills are designed to seal out air and water. This helps prevent pollutants from seeping into surrounding soil, but it slows normal decay processes. Even food scraps and paper, which usually break down quickly, can last for decades in a landfill. In populated areas, landfills fill up quickly. Reducing the amount of trash people generate can reduce the need for new landfills.

Figure 19
The farming methods shown here help prevent soil erosion. *Why is soil erosion a concern for farmers?*

B On steep hillsides, flat areas called terraces reduce downhill flow.

C In strip cropping, cover crops are planted between rows to reduce wind erosion.

D In no-till farming, soil is never left bare.

Soil Loss

Caption Answer
Figure 19 Erosion carries away soil that farmers need to grow crops.

Soil Pollution

Quick Demo
Bring a container of trash to class. Include a glass bottle, an aluminum can, plastic wrappers, a coffee filter with grounds, vegetable peelings, eggshells, and other household items. While wearing rubber gloves, remove each item and have students discuss whether the item is biodegradable. Explain that the biodegradable wastes may decay, but the nonbiodegradable wastes will not.
 Logical-Mathematical

Extension
Ask students to contact their town officials or trash collection agency to find out what happens to trash after it leaves their homes. Ask students to present their findings to the class. L2

Activity
Many household cleaners contain toxic chemicals. Numerous new products are available that are just as effective, but do not contain harmful chemicals. Have students obtain an adult's permission to investigate cleaning products in their homes to see what kinds of ingredients they contain. Caution students to take care when handling cleaning products or other chemicals. L2

Resource Manager

Earth Science Critical Thinking/Problem Solving, p. 7

Reading and Writing Skill Activities, p. 29

Teacher FYI

Pollution refers to the degradation of the environment. Erosion fits into this definition because as valuable topsoil is lost, land becomes less fertile. The erosion of land in arid areas may make these places resemble deserts, a process called desertification.

Soil Pollution,
continued

③ Assess

Reteach

Have students make a chart summarizing the causes and effects of air pollution, soil pollution, and water pollution. L1

Challenge

Challenge students calculate the following: **If your family produces an average of 1.8 kg of solid waste per person per day, how much waste will your entire family generate in the month of October?** Answers will vary depending on the number of family members (f). Students should use the following equation to solve this problem: $(f \times 1.8) \times 31 =$ amount of waste produced by the family.

✔Assessment

Content Have student pairs work together to write a song or poem about the dangers of environmental pollution. Use **PASC**, p. 151. P

Figure 20
Leftover paints, batteries, pesticides, drain cleaners, and medicines are hazardous wastes that should not be discarded in the trash. They should never be poured down a drain, onto the ground, or into a storm sewer. Most communities have collection facilities where people can dispose of hazardous materials like these.

Hazardous Wastes Waste materials that are harmful to human health or poisonous to living organisms are **hazardous wastes.** They include dangerous chemicals, such as pesticides, oil, and petroleum-based solvents used in industry. They also include radioactive wastes from nuclear power plants, from hospitals that use radioactive materials to treat disease, and from nuclear weapons production. Many household items also are considered hazardous like those shown in **Figure 20.** If these materials are dumped into landfills, they could seep into the soil, surface water, or groundwater over time. Hazardous wastes usually are handled separately from other types of trash. They are sealed in steel drums or treated in other ways to prevent them from polluting the environment.

✔ **Reading Check**　　*What are hazardous wastes?*

Section ② Assessment

1. List four ways in which air pollution affects the environment.
2. In what ways can an algal bloom affect pond life?
3. What methods can farmers use to prevent erosion?
4. Describe the possible causes and effects of ozone depletion.
5. **Think Critically** How could hazardous chemicals deposited in landfills eventually affect groundwater?

Skill Builder Activities

6. **Comparing and Contrasting** Compare and contrast the causes and effects of air and water pollution. **For more help, refer to the** Science Skill Handbook.
7. **Solving One-Step Equations** A pH of 4 is ten times more acidic than a pH of 5. A pH of 5 is ten times more acidic than a pH of 6. How many times more acidic is a solution with pH 4 than one with pH 6? **For more help, refer to the** Math Skill Handbook.

Answers to Section Assessment

1. smog, acid rain, enhanced greenhouse effect, ozone depletion
2. Algal blooms grow and eventually die. Their decay uses up oxygen, making it difficult for other organisms to survive.
3. contour farming, terracing, strip cropping, no-till farming
4. CFCs that escape into the air can cause ozone depletion; as ozone is depleted, more UV radiation reached Earth, resulting in more cases of skin cancer.
5. They can leach into the soil and be picked up by groundwater, making the water hazardous for people to drink.
6. The burning of fossil fuels causes most air pollution. Water pollution occurs when runoff carries pollutants from dumps and landfills into waterways. It also may occur from direct dumping of wastes into water. Air pollution causes smog, acid rain, enhanced greenhouse effect, and ozone depletion. Water pollution
   may cause algal blooms, the death of aquatic organisms, and contamination of drinking supplies.
7. A solution with a pH of 4 is 100 times more acidic than a solution with a pH of 6.

Activity

The Greenhouse Effect

You can create models of Earth with and without heat-reflecting greenhouse gases. Then, experiment with the models to observe the greenhouse effect.

What You'll Investigate
How does the greenhouse effect influence temperatures on Earth?

Materials
1-L clear, plastic, soft-drink bottle
   with top cut off and label removed (2)
thermometer (2)
*temperature probe
potting soil
masking tape
plastic wrap
rubber band
lamp with 100-W lightbulb
watch or clock with second hand
*Alternate materials

Goals
- **Observe** the greenhouse effect.
- **Describe** the effect that a heat source has on an environment.

Safety Precautions

Procedure
1. Copy the data table and use it to record your temperature measurements.
2. Put an equal volume of potting soil in the bottom of each container.
3. Use masking tape to attach a thermometer to the inside of each container. Place each thermometer at the same height above the soil.

Changes in Temperature		
Time (min)	Open Container Temperature (°C)	Closed Container Temperature (°C)
0		
2		
4		
6		

Shield each thermometer bulb by putting a double layer of masking tape over it.

4. Seal the top of one container with plastic wrap held in place with a rubber band.
5. Place the lamp with the exposed 100-W lightbulb between the two containers and exactly 1 cm away from each. Do not turn on the light.
6. Let the setup sit for 5 min, then record the temperature in each container.
7. Turn on the light. Record the temperature in each container every 2 min for 15 min to 20 min. Graph the results.

Conclude and Apply
1. **Compare and contrast** temperatures in each container at the end of the experiment.
2. What does the lightbulb represent in this experimental model? What does the plastic wrap represent?

Communicating Your Data

Average the data obtained in the experiments conducted by all the groups in your class. Prepare a line graph of these data. **For more help, refer to the** Science Skill Handbook.

Communicating Your Data
Have students write the final temperatures for the two conditions on the board. Students should compare data and see if the results were the same for everyone. Discuss how differences may have occurred.

Activity

BENCH TESTED

Purpose Students make models of the atmosphere and determine what happens when light shines on the model. L2 COOP LEARN
IS Interpersonal

Process Skills modeling, observing and inferring, interpreting data, communicating, comparing and contrasting, recognizing cause and effect, measuring in SI, making and using tables, making and using graphs

Time Required 50 minutes

Safety Precautions Caution students to use care in working with thermometers and 100-W light bulbs. Use only alcohol thermometers.

Teaching Strategies
- Drafts can affect results.
- Make sure the thermometers face outward to make it easier for students to read them.

Troubleshooting If the two thermometers did not read the same temperature when the experiment began, adjust readings so both data sets can be plotted on the same graph.

Answers to Questions
1. The temperatures of both containers has increased. The container covered with plastic wrap had a greater increase.
2. The light bulb represents the Sun; the plastic wrap represents carbon dioxide in the atmosphere.

✓ Assessment

Oral Have students summarize the information in their graphs in writing. Make sure summaries are clear and concise. Use **Performance Assessment in the Science Classroom,** p. 159.

SECTION
3
The Three R's of Conservation

1 Motivate

Bellringer Transparency

Display the Section Focus Transparency for Section 3. Use the accompanying Transparency Activity Master. L2

ELL

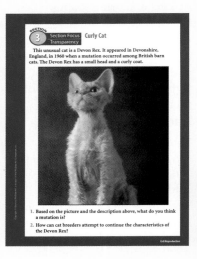

SECTION 3 Section Focus Transparency — **Curly Cat**

This unusual cat is a Devon Rex. It appeared in Devonshire, England, in 1960 when a mutation occurred among British barn cats. The Devon Rex has a small head and a curly coat.

1. Based on the picture and the description above, what do you think a mutation is?
2. How can cat breeders attempt to continue the characteristics of the Devon Rex?

Tie to Prior Knowledge

Most students will be familiar with the idea of recycling. Ask the class to describe some things that are commonly recycled. Ask for reasons why we recycle.

SECTION 3

The Three Rs of Conservation

As You Read

What You'll Learn
- **Recognize** ways you can reduce your use of natural resources.
- **Explain** how you can reuse resources to promote conservation.
- **Describe** how many materials can be recycled.

Vocabulary
recycling

Why It's Important
Conservation preserves resources and reduces pollution.

Figure 21
Automobile tires are almost indestructible. They usually are disposed of but can have other useful purposes.

Conservation

A teacher travels to school in a car pool. In the school cafeteria, students place glass bottles and cans in separate containers from the rest of the garbage. Conservation efforts like these can help prevent shortages of natural resources, slow growth of landfills, reduce pollution levels, and save people money. Every time a new landfill is created, an ecosystem is disturbed. Reducing the need for landfills is a major benefit of conservation. The three Rs of conservation are reduce, reuse, and recycle.

Reduce

You contribute to conservation whenever you reduce your use of natural resources. You use less fossil fuels when you walk or ride a bicycle instead of taking the bus or riding in a car. If you buy a carton of milk, reduce your use of petroleum by telling the clerk you don't need a plastic bag to carry it in.

You also can avoid buying things you don't need. For example, most of the paper, plastic, and cardboard used to package items for display on store shelves is thrown away as soon as the product is brought home. You can look for products with less packaging or with packaging made from recycled materials. What are some other ways you can reduce your use of natural resources?

Reuse

Another way to help conserve natural resources is to use items more than once. Reusing an item means using it again without changing it or reprocessing it, as shown in **Figure 21.** Bring reusable canvas bags to the grocery store to carry home your purchases. Donate clothes you've outgrown to charity so that others can reuse them. Take reusable plates and utensils on picnics instead of disposable paper items.

Section ✓*Assessment* Planner

PORTFOLIO
Challenge, p. 115
PERFORMANCE ASSESSMENT
Problem-Solving Activity, p. 114
Skill Builder Activities, p. 115
See page 122 for more options.

CONTENT ASSESSMENT
Section, p. 115
Challenge, p. 115
Chapter, pp. 122–123

Recycle

If you can't avoid using an item, and if you can't reuse it, the next best thing is to recycle it. **Recycling** is a form of reuse that requires changing or reprocessing an item or natural resource. If your city or town has a curbside recycling program, you already separate recyclables from the rest of your garbage. Materials that can be recycled include glass, metals, paper, plastics, and yard and kitchen waste.

✔ Reading Check *How is recycling different from reusing?*

Plastics Plastic is more difficult to recycle than other materials, mainly because several types of plastic are in use. A recycle code marked on every plastic container indicates the type of plastic it is made of. Clear plastic soft-drink bottles, like the one shown in **Figure 22,** are made of type 1 plastic and are the easiest to recycle. Most plastic bags are made of type 2 or type 4 plastic; they can be reused as well as recycled. Types 6 and 7 can't be recycled at all because they are made of a mixture of different plastics. Each type of plastic must be separated carefully before it is recycled because a single piece of a different type of plastic can ruin an entire batch.

Figure 22
Many soft-drink bottles are made of PET, which is the most common type of recyclable plastic. It can be melted down and spun into fibers to make carpets, yarn, paintbrushes, rope, and clothing.

Resource Manager

Chapter Resources Booklet
Transparency Activity, p. 46
Directed Reading for Content Mastery,
  pp. 21, 22
Activity Worksheet, pp. 7–8

Visual Learning

Figure 22 The objects in these photographs are made from the same type 1 plastic (PET). Ask students to bring in materials with this symbol on them. When the objects are collected, discuss why recycling is a good idea. Possible answer: It reduces the amount of nonbiodegradable materials going into landfills.

2 Teach

Reduce

Text Question Answer
Possible answer: Turn off lights in vacant rooms.

Discussion
Bring in a product that is clearly over-packaged. Have students suggest ways to reduce the amount of material used in the packaging of this item.

Reuse

Activity
Find an item that is commonly thrown out, such as a plastic soda bottle. Have students brainstorm a list of possible ways to reuse the bottle. L2
ELL IS **Interpersonal**

Recycle

✔ Reading Check

Answer Reusing does not require reprocessing; recycling does.

Extension
Reinforce the difference among reduce, reuse, and recycle. Give students the example of a soda bottle and ask them to come up with a plan to reduce, reuse, and recycle the bottle. Reduce: Buy one big bottle instead of many smaller bottles. Reuse: Wash bottle and use it to store drinking water. Recycle: Separate the bottles from trash so that they can be melted down and the plastic reused. L2

Recycle, continued

IDENTIFYING
Misconceptions

Many people think that recycled paper is paper that has been used by consumers. Most of it, however, comes from wood or paper scrap in logging or paper manufacturing. Some companies indicate how much recycled paper comes directly from consumers by labeling the percent that is post-consumer content.

Teacher FYI

Composting is considered recycling because the form of the materials is changed (through decay) so they can be used again.

Problem-Solving Activity

National Math Standards

Correlation to Mathematics Objectives
1, 2, 5, 6, 8–10

Answer

Students' lists should include some of each type of item. Possible exceptions would be yard wastes, depending on the season, and newspapers. The percentages will depend on student data. Tin cans are steel cans coated with tin. They should be included.

SCIENCE Online

Research Visit the Glencoe Science Web site at **science.glencoe.com** and find out how to make your own recycled paper. In your Science Journal, describe how you might use the paper you make.

Metals The manufacturing industry has been recycling all kinds of metals, especially steel, for decades. At least 25 percent of the steel in cans, appliances, and automobiles is recycled. Up to 100 percent of the steel in plates and beams used to build skyscrapers is made from reprocessed steel. One ton of recycled steel saves 2,500 pounds of iron ore and 1,000 pounds of coal. Using recycled steel to make new steel products reduces energy use by 75 percent. Other metals, including iron, copper, aluminum, and lead also can be recycled.

You can conserve metals by recycling food cans, which are mostly steel, and aluminum cans. It takes less energy to make a can from recycled aluminum than from raw materials. Also, remember that recycled cans do not take up space in landfills.

Glass Glass bottles and jars can be sterilized and reused. They also can be melted and re-formed into new bottles, especially those made of clear glass. Most glass bottles already contain at least 25 percent recycled glass. Glass can be recycled again and again. It never needs to be thrown away. Recycling a ton of glass saves more than a ton of mineral resources and cuts the energy used to make new glass by 25 percent or more.

Problem-Solving Activity

What items are you recycling at home?

Many people participate in community recycling programs. Recyclable items such as plastic, glass, newspapers, and metals may be picked up at the curbside or the resident may hire a licensed recycling handler to pick them up. What do you recycle in your home?

Identifying the Problem
The following bar graph shows the recycling rates in the U. S. of six types of household items for the years 1992, 1994, and 1995. How do you and your classmates recycling rates compare with the recycling rates shown on the chart?

Solving the Problem
1. For one week, list each glass, plastic, and aluminum item you use. Note which items you throw away and which ones you recycle.
Calculate the percentage of glass, plastic, and aluminum you recycled. How do your percentages compare with those on the graph?

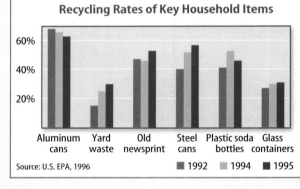

Recycling Rates of Key Household Items

Source: U.S. EPA, 1996

■ 1992   ■ 1994   ■ 1995

SCIENCE Online

Internet Addresses
_____
_____
_____
_____

Explore the Glencoe Science Web site at **science.glencoe.com** to find out more about topics in this section.

Resource Manager

Chapter Resources Booklet
Enrichment, p. 32
Lab Activity, pp. 13–16
Reinforcement, p. 29
Lab Management and Safety, p. 37

Paper Used paper is recycled into paper towels, insulation, newsprint, cardboard, and stationery. Ranchers and dairy farmers sometimes use shredded paper instead of straw for bedding in barns and stables. Used paper can even be made into compost. Recycling one ton of paper saves 17 trees, more than 26,000 L of water, close to 1,900 L of oil, and more than 4,000 kw of electric energy. You can do your part by recycling newspapers, notebook and printer paper, cardboard, and junk mail.

 Reading Check *What nonrenewable resource(s) do you conserve by recycling paper?*

Compost Grass clippings, leaves, and fruit and vegetable scraps that are discarded in a landfill can remain there for decades without breaking down. The same items can be turned into soil-enriching compost in just a few weeks, as shown in **Figure 23.** Many communities distribute compost bins to encourage residents to recycle fruit and vegetable scraps and yard waste.

Buy Recycled People have become so good at recycling that recyclable materials are piling up, just waiting to be put to use. You can help by reading labels when you shop and choosing products that contain recycled materials. What other ways of recycling natural resources can you think of?

Figure 23
Composting is a way of turning plant material you would otherwise throw away into rich garden soil. Dry leaves and weeds, grass clippings, vegetable trimmings, and nonmeat food scraps can be composted.

Section 3 Assessment

1. What is meant by the term *reuse*? How does it differ from recycling?
2. List three materials that can be recycled. Describe one product that can be made from each recycled material you listed.
3. Describe at least three actions you could take to reduce your use of natural resources.
4. Describe how you could reuse three items people usually throw away.
5. **Think Critically** Why is reusing something better than recycling it?

Skill Builder Activities

6. **Making and Using Tables** Make a table of data on the number of aluminum cans thrown away in the United States: *22.7 billion in 1982; 35.0 billion in 1986; 33.0 billion in 1990; 38.8 billion in 1994; 44.6 billion in 1998.* **For more help, refer to the** Science Skill Handbook.
7. **Communicating** Write a letter to a local newspaper suggesting ways to reuse or recycle an item or items that most people in your community currently throw away. **For more help, refer to the** Science Skill Handbook.

Reading Check

Answer oil

Text Question Answer
Answers will vary.

3 Assess

Reteach
Ask students to give their opinions about whether a soda company should reuse glass bottles by washing them out or recycle the bottles by melting them and making new. L1
IS Linguistic

Challenge
Have students investigate the trash generated by your school's cafeteria. Challenge them to devise a plan to reduce the amount of trash that is thrown away. Have them write a report on their investigation and plan. P

Assessment

Performance Hold up a newspaper and ask students to write specific examples of how a community can reduce its use of newspapers, reuse newspapers, and recycle newspapers. Use **Performance Assessment in the Science Classroom,** p. 91.

Answers to Section Assessment

1. Reuse means to use an object over again for its original task or to use it for another task. Unlike recycling, reuse does not involve making a big change to the object.
2. Possible answers: aluminum, iron, certain plastics, biodegradable materials into compost, paper
3. Possible answers: turn off lights in vacant rooms, buy materials with less packaging, carpool, buy items made from recycled materials
4. Possible answers: store water in plastic soda bottles, use plastic grocery bags as trash can liners, use margarine tubs to store left-over food.
5. There is less energy used in reusing than in recycling.
6. Check tables for accuracy.
7. Answers will vary. Look for creativity in the use of commonly discarded objects.

Activity

BENCH TESTED

Recognize the Problem

Purpose
Students will design and build a solar cooker.

Process Skills
designing and making a model, researching, comparing

Time Required
one class period

Thinking Critically

Discussion
Discuss with students the problems some people in the world face just trying to cook a meal. Explain to students that in some places where fuel is scarce, people use solar cookers to prepare food. **Why do people cook most food?** Possible answers: To improve taste; to kill harmful bacteria **Why does cooking food require energy?** Energy is needed to raise the temperature of the food.

Alternate Materials
Oven bags are available at most supermarkets. Kitchen timers are available at most hardware stores.

Safety Precautions
Remind students to use insulated gloves or tongs when handling hot objects.

Activity *Model and Invent*

Solar Cooking

The disappearance of forests in some places on Earth has made firewood extremely difficult and expensive to obtain. People living in these regions often have to travel long distances or sell some of their food to get firewood. This can be a serious problem for people who may not have much food to begin with. Is there a way they could cook food without using firewood?

Recognize the Problem

Can you design a solar cooker that cooks food without burning fuel?

Thinking Critically

How would you build a cooking device that uses the Sun's energy?

Possible Materials
poster board
cardboard boxes
aluminum foil
string
wire coat hangers
clear plastic sheets
*oven bags
black cookware
thermometer
stopwatch
*timer
glue
tape
scissors
*Alternate materials

Safety Precautions

Be careful when cutting your materials. Your solar cooker will get hot. When handling hot liquids or objects, use insulated gloves or tongs.

Goals
- **Research** designs for solar panel cookers or box cookers.
- **Design** a solar cooker that can be used to cook food.
- **Plan** an experiment to measure the effectiveness of your solar cooker.

Data Source
SCIENCE *Online* Visit the Glencoe Science Web site at **science.glencoe.com** for more information about solar cooker designs.

SCIENCE *Online*
Internet Addresses

_____
_____
_____
_____

Explore the Glencoe Science Web site at **science.glencoe.com** to find out more about topics in this activity.

Inclusion Strategies

Learning Disabled Assign these students the task of gathering the materials their group decides they want to use.

Planning the Model

1. **Design** a solar cooker. In your Science Journal, explain why you chose this design and draw a picture of it.

2. **Write** a summary explaining how you will measure the effectiveness of your solar cooker. What will you measure? How will you collect and organize your data? How will you present your results?

Check the Model Plans

1. **Compare** your solar cooker design to those of other students.

2. Share your experimental plan with students in your class. Discuss the reasoning behind your plan. Be specific about what you intend to test and how you are going to test it.

3. Make sure your teacher approves your plan before you start working on your model.

Making the Model

1. Using all of the information you have gathered, construct a solar cooker that follows your design.

2. **Test** your design to determine how well it works. Try out a classmate's design. How do the two compare?

Analyzing and Applying Results

1. Combine the results for your entire class and decide which type of solar cooker was most effective. How could you design a more effective solar cooker, based on what you learned from this activity?

2. Do you think your results might have been different if you tested your solar cooker on a different day? Explain. Why might a solar cooker be more useful in some regions of the world than in others?

3. Based on what you've read and the results obtained by you and your classmates, do you think that your solar cooker could boil water? Explain.

4. **Compare** the amount of time needed to cook food with a solar cooker and with more traditional cooking methods. Assuming plenty of sunlight is available, would you prefer to use a solar cooker or a traditional oven? Explain.

Communicating
Your Data

Prepare a demonstration showing how to use a solar cooker. **Present** your demonstration to another class of students or to a group of friends or relatives. **For more help, refer to the** Science Skill Handbook.

Planning the Model

Teaching Strategies

- Comparisons of solar cookers will be difficult if students do not use the same method of testing them.

- You might want to have a cook-off with the two best solar ovens to see which one could cook a small red potato in the shortest time. Be sure both potatoes are the same size.

Trouble Shooting Students can move the cookers during the testing to keep them in the sun.

Making the Model

Expected Outcome

Solar cookers should be able to raise the temperature of a cup of water to at least 75°C. A well-designed cooker might reach temperatures approaching 150°C.

Analyzing and Applying Results

1. Answers will depend on the designs of the solar cookers that are compared.

2. Results would vary in different weather conditions. Solar cookers function best on clear, sunny days. Solar cookers are more useful in areas that have many clear, sunny days.

3. Answers will depend on the success of the design. Some well-designed cookers could boil water.

4. Solar cookers generally take two to three times as long to cook a meal as a traditional oven. However, the energy for a solar cooker is free and the energy for a traditional oven is not.

✓Assessment

Process Have students use a foam cup of water with a thermometer in it to test whether their solar ovens can boil water. Be sure that each group uses the same amount of water for the test and that students record the time it takes to boil the water. Based on the results, have students rank the solar cooker designs from best to worst. Use **PASC,** p. 89.

Communicating
Your Data

Students should prepare a poster that shows the construction of their solar cooker and an explanation of how it works.

Science **and** Language Arts

Pre-Reading Activity

Have students think about the renewable and nonrenewable resources they use daily. Have students list in their Science Journals all the renewable and nonrenewable resources they can see on the school grounds and in the classroom.

Respond to the Reading

Active Reading Strategies

Visualize Try to visualize the scenes described by the poet as you read. **Do the settings remind you of places you know? Do the descriptions of the seasons differ from the seasons you experience in your community? How?**

Respond Be aware of the mood of the poem as you read. Although the poem does not talk about conserving resources, there is an implied understanding about the importance of conserving resources and reducing pollution. **Do you think the beauty of your neighborhood has been plagiarized? What things can you do to preserve the beauty of nature?**

Answers to Questions

1. The four verses correspond to the four seasons.
2. pollution from the use of nonrenewable resources such as fossil fuels; clear-cutting trees for buildings
3. Civilization has plagiarized beauty.

Beauty Plagiarized
by Amitabha Mukerjee

Respond to the Reading

1. What do the four verses in the poem correspond to?
2. What has destroyed nature's beauty?
3. To plagiarize is to copy without giving credit to the source. In this poem, who or what has plagiarized beauty?

I wandered lonely as a cloud –
Except for a motorboat,
Nary a soul in sight.
Beside the lake beneath the trees,
Next to the barbed wire fence,
There was a picnic table
And beer bottle caps from many years.
A boat ramp to the left,
And the chimney from a power station on the other side,
A summer haze hung in the air,
And the lazy drone of traffic far away.

Crimson autumn of mists and mellow fruitfulness
Blue plastic covers the swimming pools
The leaves fall so I can see
Dark glass reflections in the building
That came up
where the pine cones crunched underfoot . . .

And then it is snow
White lining on trees and rooftops . . .
And through my windshield wipers
The snow is piled dark and grey . . .
Next to my driveway where I check my mail
Little footprints on fresh snow —
A visiting rabbit.

I knew a bank where the wild thyme blew
Over-canopied with luscious woodbine
It is now a landfill —
Fermentation of civilization
Flowers on TV
Hyacinth rose tulip chrysanthemum
Acres of colour
Wind up wrapped in decorous plastic,
In this landfill where oxlips grew. . .

Reading Further

A Walk in the Woods: Rediscovering America on the Appalachian Trail, by Bill Bryson, Broadway Books, 1999.

The Best American Science & Nature Writing 2000, ed. Burkhard Bilger, Houghton Mifflin Co., 2000.

Lost Woods: The Discovered Writing of Rachel Carson, by Rachel Carson, ed. Linda Lear, Beacon Press, 1999.

Understanding Literature

Cause and Effect Recognizing cause and effect relationships can help you make sense out of what you read. One event causes another event. The second event is the effect of the first event. In the poem, the author describes the causes and effects of pollution and waste. For example, the summer haze is the effect of the "chimney from a power station" as well as the "traffic far away." What other effects do pollution and the use of nonrenewable resources have on nature in the poem?

The poet also makes a connection between the four seasons of the year and the pollution and waste products created by civilization. For example, in the spring, a landfill for dumping garbage replaces a field of wildflowers. Describing four seasons instead of one reinforces the poet's message that the beauty of nature has been stolen, or plagiarized.

Science Connection The poet describes renewable and nonrenewable resources. For example, the lake and tree described in the first verse are renewable resources. The beer bottle caps in the same verse are nonrenewable. Can you identify all the nonrenewable resources in the poem? How does the narrator contribute to the use of fossil fuels and nonrenewable resources?

Linking Science and Writing

Write a Poem Copy the poem you just read in pencil. Change the poem by erasing the lines that describe nonrenewable resources. Add lines to the poem that show how recycling, reusing, and other conservation measures could restore the beauty of the four seasons.

Career Connection

Ecologist

Vandana Shiva is the director of the Research Foundation for Science, Technology, and Natural Resource Policy in Dehradun, India. Shiva had an early appreciation for global natural resources as a daughter of a forester growing up in The Himalayan forest. As an adult she has become involved in the efforts of the Chipko Indian women's movement to save trees in The Himalaya. Her involvement in this movement led to the banning of logging in The Himalayan area above 1,000 meters.

SCIENCE*Online* To learn more about careers in ecology, visit the Glencoe Science Web site at **science.glencoe.com.**

Career Connection

The field of ecology encompasses many different careers and areas of expertise, from air quality management and hazardous waste management to forestry and conservation, agricultural sciences and biological sciences. Students interested in pursuing such careers should focus on mathematics, biology, chemistry, physics, and computer science.

SCIENCE Online
Internet Addresses

_____
_____
_____

Explore the Glencoe Science Web site at **science.glencoe.com** to find out more about topics in this feature.

Understanding Literature

Answer to Question

Answers will vary but might include that bottle caps litter the picnic area and that exhaust fumes from cars make the snow banks dark and gray.

Science Connection

Review what nonrenewable and renewable resources are. It should be stressed that even renewable resources can be rendered nonrenewable. This happens when renewable resources are "mined," that is, if they are removed at a rate that prevents their renewal, or if the environment that supports them deteriorates faster than renewal can take place. For example, although forests are considered a renewable resource, if they are not carefully managed they can disappear as a result of excessive logging or clear-cutting. Also, although Earth's supply of air is inexhaustible, the quality of Earth's air can be affected by human activity, and air quality directly affects other renewable resources.

Linking Science and Writing

Teaching Strategies

Use a quickwrite exercise to help students prepare for rewriting lines in the poem. Working in groups, have students list ways of recycling, reusing, and reducing solid waste. Also, have students brainstorm on ways to reduce the use of fossil fuels. Encourage students to be creative. They can then use these ideas to help them complete the lines in the poem.

Reviewing Main Ideas

Preview

Students can answer the questions in their Science Journals. Discuss the answers as you go through the chapter. **LS** **Linguistic**

Review

Students can write their answers, then compare them with those of other students. **LS** **Interpersonal**

Reteach

Students can look at the illustrations and describe details that support the main ideas of the chapter. **LS** **Visual-Spatial**

Answers to Chapter Review

SECTION 1

3. Renewable: the cotton clothes and air; nonrenewable: the gasoline and metals in the car

SECTION 2

3. leaching of fertilizer into the water

SECTION 3

3. Recycling reduces the need to alter environments to gather raw materials and it decreases energy use.

Reviewing Main Ideas

Section 1 Resources

1. Natural resources are the parts of the environment that supply materials needed for the survival of living organisms.

2. Renewable resources are being replaced continually by natural processes.

3. Nonrenewable resources cannot be replaced or are replaced very slowly. *What renewable and nonrenewable resources appear in this photograph?*

4. Energy sources include fossil fuels, solar energy, geothermal energy, and nuclear power.

Section 2 Pollution

1. Most air pollution is made up of waste products from the burning of fossil fuels.

2. The greenhouse effect is the warming of Earth by a blanket of heat-reflecting gases in the atmosphere.

3. Water can be polluted by acid rain and by the spilling of oil or other wastes into waterways. *What could have caused this algal bloom?*

4. Solid wastes and hazardous wastes dumped on land or disposed of in landfills can pollute the soil. Erosion can cause the loss of fertile topsoil.

Section 3 The Three Rs of Conservation

1. You can reduce your use of natural resources in many ways.

2. Reusing items is an excellent way to practice conservation.

3. Recycling is a form of reuse in which materials are changed so they can be used again. *How does recycling benefit the environment?*

4. Materials that can be recycled include paper, metals, glass, plastics, yard waste, and nonmeat kitchen scraps.

 FOLDABLES Reading & Study Skills

After You Read

Use the Foldable you made at the beginning of the chapter to list ways your community conserves resources under the tabs.

FOLDABLES Reading & Study Skills

After You Read

After students have read the chapter and completed the Foldable described in Before You Read, have them do the activity on the student page.

Dinah Zike

Visualizing Main Ideas

Complete the following concept map on air pollution.
Use the terms smog, acid precipitation, *and* ozone depletion.

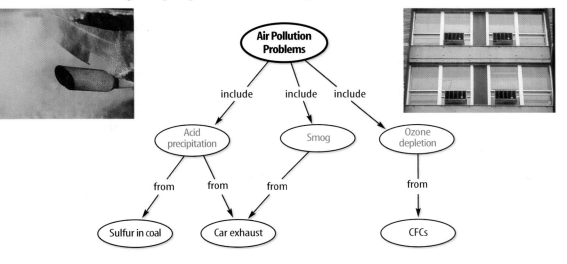

Air Pollution Problems
include — include — include

Acid precipitation — Smog — Ozone depletion

from — from — from — from

Sulfur in coal — Car exhaust — CFCs

Vocabulary Review

Vocabulary Words

a. acid precipitation
b. erosion
c. fossil fuel
d. geothermal energy
e. greenhouse effect
f. hazardous waste
g. hydroelectric power
h. natural resource
i. nonrenewable resource
j. nuclear energy
k. ozone depletion
l. petroleum
m. pollutant
n. recycling
o. renewable resource

THE PRINCETON REVIEW **Study Tip**

When you read a chapter, make a list of things you find confusing or do not completely understand. Then ask your teacher to explain them.

Using Vocabulary

Explain the differences in the vocabulary words given below. Then explain how the words are related. Use complete sentences in your answers.

1. fossil fuel, petroleum
2. erosion, pollutant
3. ozone depletion, acid precipitation
4. greenhouse effect, fossil fuels
5. hazardous wastes, nuclear energy
6. hydroelectric power, fossil fuels
7. acid precipitation, fossil fuels
8. ozone depletion, pollutant
9. recycle, nonrenewable resources
10. geothermal energy, fossil fuels

CHAPTER STUDY GUIDE   E ◆ 121

Visualizing Main Ideas

See student page.

Vocabulary Review

Using Vocabulary

1. Petroleum is a type of fossil fuel.
2. Erosion is a pollutant because it degrades the environment.
3. These are both types of air pollution, but one does not cause the other.
4. The burning of fossil fuels and the release of excess carbon dioxide may enhance the greenhouse effect.
5. The use of nuclear energy generates radioactive materials, which are hazardous wastes.
6. The use of hydroelectric power can decrease the use of fossil fuels.
7. Coal is a fossil fuel. The burning of coal that contains sulfur causes acid precipitation.
8. The pollutant called CFC causes ozone depletion.
9. Recycling is a good way of conserving nonrenewable resources.
10. The use of geothermal energy can decrease the use of fossil fuels.

Checking Concepts

1. B
2. C
3. B
4. B
5. C
6. C
7. B
8. B
9. A
10. C

Thinking Critically

11. Fossil fuels were formed from plants and animals. Wood is from a plant.
12. Desert region; sunshine is more constant there than at the poles.
13. to prevent erosion of topsoil
14. Yes; it is constantly replaced and has many uses.
15. Solar, wind, geothermal, and water energy are renewable resources. Nuclear energy is not a renewable resource, but no severe shortages are expected.

Checking Concepts

Choose the word or phrase that best answers the question.

1. Which of the following is a fossil fuel?
   A) wood
   B) oil
   C) nuclear power
   D) photovoltaic cell

2. Of the following, which is considered a renewable resource?
   A) coal
   B) oil
   C) sunlight
   D) aluminum

3. Which energy resource uses heat from below Earth's crust?
   A) solar energy
   B) geothermal energy
   C) hydroelectric energy
   D) photovoltaic energy

4. An architect wants to design a solar house in the northern hemisphere. For maximum warmth, which side of the house should have the most windows?
   A) north
   B) south
   C) east
   D) west

5. Which of the following contributes to ozone depletion?
   A) carbon dioxide
   B) radon
   C) CFCs
   D) carbon monoxide

6. What is a substance that contaminates the environment called?
   A) acid rain
   B) pollution
   C) pollutant
   D) ozone

7. If there were no greenhouse effect in Earth's atmosphere, which of the following statements would be true?
   A) Earth would be much hotter.
   B) Earth would be much colder.
   C) The temperature of Earth would be the same.
   D) The polar ice caps would melt.

8. What is the process in which glass bottles are crushed, melted, and shaped into new bottles?
   A) reuse
   B) recycling
   C) reduction
   D) coal

9. Which of the following can change solar energy into electricity?
   A) photovoltaic cells
   B) smog
   C) nuclear power plants
   D) geothermal power plants

10. What is a radioactive gas that can cause indoor air pollution?
    A) ozone
    B) carbon dioxide
    C) radon
    D) chlorofluorocarbons (CFCs)

Thinking Critically

11. Why do burning wood and burning fossil fuels produce similar pollutants?

12. Which would make a better location for a solar power plant—a polar region or a desert region? Why?

13. Why is it beneficial to grow another crop on soil after the major crop has been harvested?

14. Is garbage a renewable resource? Why or why not?

15. Solar, nuclear, wind, water, and geothermal energy are alternatives to fossil fuels. Are they all renewable? Why or why not?

Chapter ✔Assessment Planner

Portfolio Encourage students to place in their portfolios one or two items of what they consider to be their best work. Examples include:
• Physics Integration, p. 97
• Assessment, p. 110
• Challenge, p. 115

Performance Additional performance assessments, Performance Task Assessment Lists, and rubrics for evaluating these activities can be found in Glencoe's **Performance Assessment in the Science Classroom.**

Developing Skills

16. Drawing Conclusions Would you save more energy by recycling or reusing a plastic bag?

17. Recognizing Cause and Effect Forests use large amounts of carbon dioxide during photosynthesis. How might cutting down a large percentage of Earth's forests affect the greenhouse effect?

18. Making and Using Graphs Make a bar graph of the following data.

Estimated Recycling Rates	
Item	**Percent Recycled**
Aluminum cans	60
Glass beverage bottles	31
Plastic soft-drink containers	37
Newsprint	56
Magazines	23

19. Forming Hypotheses Form a hypothesis about why Americans throw away more aluminum cans each year.

20. Comparing and Contrasting Compare and contrast contour farming, terracing, strip cropping, and no-till farming.

Performance Assessment

21. Poster Create a poster to illustrate and describe three things students at your school can do to conserve natural resources.

TECHNOLOGY

Go to the Glencoe Science Web site at **science.glencoe.com** or use the **Glencoe Science CD-ROM** for additional chapter assessment.

Test Practice

Some of Earth's important natural resources are pictured in the two boxes below.

Sun
Water
Wind

Coal
Iron ore
GAS
Petroleum

Review the pictures and answer the following questions.

1. Which of the following is a major characteristic of all of the natural resources shown in Box B?
   A) They are made and used by humans on a regular basis.
   B) They are substances made out of metal.
   C) They are materials that occur naturally in a solid form not a liquid form.
   D) They are used up by humans faster than nature can replace them.

2. The resources in Box A are different from the resources in Box B because only the resources in Box A are _____
   F) easily and quickly replaced by nature.
   G) easily and quickly created by humans.
   H) never made by nature.
   J) never used by humans.

Test Practice

The Test-Taking Tip was written by The Princeton Review, the nation's leader in test preparation.
1. D
2. F

Developing Skills

16. Reusing the bag would save energy because it wouldn't need to be changed back into its raw form and then a new bag made.

17. Cutting large forests could result in more carbon dioxide in the atmosphere, possibly resulting in an enhanced greenhouse effect and accelerated global warming.

18. Bars (highest to lowest): aluminum cans, newsprint, plastic soft drink containers, glass beverage bottles, magazines

19. Answers will vary. Students should support their answers.

20. Contour farming and terracing are similar in that they are farming methods for hillsides that reduce soil erosion. Strip cropping compares to no-till farming in that they are both methods of reducing soil erosion by leaving soil covered by vegetation. The first two methods contrast to the last two in that they are used on hillsides, while the last two are used on level ground.

Performance Assessment

21. Posters should involve reducing, reusing, or recycling. Use **PASC**, p. 145.

✔Assessment Resources

📁 **Reproducible Masters**

Chapter Resources Booklet
   Chapter Review, pp. 37–38
   Chapter Tests, pp. 39–42
   Assessment Transparency Activity, p. 49

Glencoe Science Web site
   Interactive Tutor
   Chapter Quizzes

Glencoe Technology
   🖥 Assessment Transparency
   💿 Interactive CD-ROM Chapter Quizzes
   💿 ExamView Pro Test Bank
   💿 Vocabulary PuzzleMaker Software
   📼 MindJogger Videoquiz DVD/VHS

Section/Objectives	Standards		Activities/Features
Chapter Opener	**National**	**State/Local**	**Explore Activity:** Recognize environmental differences, p. 125 **Before You Read,** p. 125
	See p. 6T for a Key to Standards.		
Section 1 Biodiversity 🕐 3 sessions 📦 1.5 blocks 1. **Define** biodiversity. 2. **Explain** why biodiversity is important in an ecosystem. 3. **Identify** factors that limit biodiversity in an ecosystem.	National Content Standards: UCP1, UCP4, A1, C1, C4, C5, F2, F5		**Math Skills Activity:** Analyzing Data for Biodiversity, p. 129 **Visualizing Threatened and Endangered Species,** p. 132 **MiniLAB:** Demonstrating Divided Habitats, p.133 **MiniLAB:** Testing the Effects of Acid Rain, p. 135 **Health Integration,** p. 136 **Activity:** Oily Birds, p. 137
Section 2 Conservation Biology 🕐 3 sessions 📦 1.5 blocks 1. **Identify** several goals of conservation biology. 2. **Recommend** strategies to prevent the extinction of species. 3. **Explain** how an endangered species can be reintroduced into its original habitat.	National Content Standards: UCP1, UCP4, A1, C1, C4, C5, F2, F5		**Science Online,** p. 139 **Earth Science Integration,** p. 140 **Science Online,** p. 142 **Activity:** Biodiversity and the Health of a Plant Community, pp. 144–145 **Science and Society:** Rain Forest Troubles, pp. 146–147

Activity Materials	Reproducible Resources	Section Assessment	Technology
Explore Activity: meterstick, hand lens, string or tape, field guides	**Chapter Resources Booklet** Foldables Worksheet, p. 17 Directed Reading Overview, p. 19 Note-taking Worksheets, pp. 31–32	GLENCOE'S **ASSESSMENT** ADVANTAGE	
MiniLAB: banana, jar, pieces of cloth or stocking, rubber band **MiniLAB:** 100 mustard seeds, water, 2 plastic cups, vinegar, paper towel, 2 self-sealing plastic bags **Activity:** 2 beakers; bird feathers; vegetable oil; red, blue, and green food coloring; paper towels, water, cotton balls, cotton swabs, sponge, toothbrush, dish soap	**Chapter Resources Booklet** Transparency Activity, p. 42 MiniLABs, pp. 3, 4 Enrichment, p. 29 Reinforcement, p. 27 Directed Reading, p. 20 Transparency Activity, pp. 45–47 Lab Activity, pp. 9–12 Activity Worksheet, pp. 5–6 **Cultural Diversity,** p. 19 **Reading and Writing Skill Activities,** pp. 1, 37 **Mathematics Skill Activities,** p. 45	Portfolio Extension, p. 128 Science Journal, p. 130 Performance Math Skills Activity, p. 129 MiniLAB, p. 133 MiniLAB, p. 135 Skill Builder Activities, p. 136 Content Section Assessment, p. 136	🔊 Section Focus Transparency 🔊 Teaching Transparency 💿 Interactive CD-ROM/DVD 🎧 Guided Reading Audio Program
Activity: plain white paper, colored paper, ruler, scissors, pens, die *Need materials?* Contact Science Kit at 1-800-828-7777 or www.sciencekit.com on the Internet.	**Chapter Resources Booklet** Transparency Activity, p. 43 Enrichment, p. 30 Reinforcement, p. 28 Directed Reading, pp. 21, 22 Lab Activity, pp. 13–16 Activity Worksheet, pp. 7–8 **Lab Management and Safety,** p. 73 **Home and Community Involvement,** p. 33 **Science Inquiry Labs,** pp. 37, 39	Portfolio Curriculum Connection, p. 141 Performance Skill Builder Activities, p. 143 Content Section Assessment, p. 143	🔊 Section Focus Transparency 💿 Interactive CD-ROM/DVD 🎧 Guided Reading Audio Program

End of Chapter Assessment

GLENCOE'S **ASSESSMENT** ADVANTAGE

Blackline Masters	Technology	Professional Series
Chapter Resources Booklet Chapter Review, pp. 35–36 Chapter Tests, pp. 37–40 **Standardized Test Practice by The Princeton Review,** pp. 27–30	📼 MindJogger Videoquiz 💿 CD-ROM Explorations and Quizzes 💿 Vocabulary Puzzle Makers 💿 ExamView Pro Test Bank 💿 Interactive Lesson Planner 💿 Interactive Teacher's Edition	Performance Assessment in the Science Classroom (PASC)

Transparencies

Section Focus

SECTION 1 Section Focus Transparency — Pass It On

You may have noticed that tall parents often have tall children and dark-haired parents often have dark-haired children. Even though offspring are similar to their parents, they do not look exactly alike.

1. Do children ever look exactly the same?
2. How are the members of this family different? How are they the same?
3. What helps us predict how the descendants of living things will look?

L2

SECTION 2 Section Focus Transparency — Dog Days

Humans have kept dogs for 12,000 to 14,000 years. At first, all dogs had jobs, such as herding or guarding. Today, some dogs have jobs, but many others are kept as pets.

1. What determines how big a dog can get?
2. How can a gray puppy and a brown puppy be littermates?
3. What environmental conditions could make one dog look different than its identical twin?

L2

SECTION 3 Section Focus Transparency — Two Quarts of Oil and a Side Salad, Please

Ever since plants and animals were domesticated, people have tried to enhance desirable traits and eliminate undesirable ones. Recently, scientists have learned how to insert new segments of DNA directly into cells. An early example of this technology is the oil-eating bacteria seen below.

1. Are there any advantages to changing an organism's DNA?
2. Are there any dangers in making these sorts of changes?

L2

This is a representation of key blackline masters available in the Teacher Classroom Resources. See Resource Manager boxes within the chapter for additional information.

Key to Teaching Strategies

The following designations will help you decide which activities are appropriate for your students.

L1 Level 1 activities should be appropriate for students with learning difficulties.

L2 Level 2 activities should be within the ability range of all students.

L3 Level 3 activities are designed for above-average students.

ELL ELL activities should be within the ability range of English Language Learners.

COOP LEARN Cooperative Learning activities are designed for small group work.

LS Multiple Learning Styles logos are used throughout to indicate strategies that address different learning styles.

P These strategies represent student products that can be placed into a best-work portfolio.

Assessment

Assessment Transparency — Heredity

Directions: Carefully review the Punnett Square and answer the following questions.

An AaBb Plant is to be Bred with Itself

A: Tall
a: Short
B: Fast-growing
b: Slow-growing

1. Using the table above, you can hypothesize that the reason short, slow growing trees are rare is that ____.
   A tall, fast-growing trees will help them grow
   B water and sunlight will help them grow
   C only a few of the offspring will have the aabb genotype
   D most of the offspring are fast growing Aa and AA trees
2. According to the information above, which genotype is required for a tall, fast-growing tree?
   F AaBB   H Aabb
   G AABb   J AABB
3. The genotype of both parents is AaBb. According to the information above, what characteristics will the parents have?
   A Tall, fast-growing
   B Tall, slow-growing
   C Short, fast-growing
   D Short, slow-growing

L2

Teaching

SECTION 2 Teaching Transparency — Pedigree

L2

Hands-on Activities

Activity Worksheets

Activity — Predicting Results

L2

Laboratory Activities

LAB 1 Laboratory Activity — Genetic Traits

L2

Meeting Different Ability Levels

Content Outline

L2

Reinforcement

L2

Directed Reading

L1

Assessment

Chapter Tests

L2

Enrichment

L3

Spanish Directed Reading

L1

Test Practice Workbook

L2

Chapter Review

L2

Science Content Background

Gloria H. Chomica/Masterfile

SECTION 1
Biodiversity
Definitions and Understandings

Biodiversity refers to the variety of life forms, the genetic information they carry, and the ecosystems in which the life forms exist. Humans are dependent upon and interact with biotic and abiotic systems for sustenance of life, health, well being, and recreation. Many biologists think that rich biodiversity results in ecosystems having greater resilience and more efficient recovery from natural and human induced stresses.

Fun Fact

On a typical day, Earth loses 116 square miles of rain forests and adds 72 square miles of desert as the human population increases by 25,000.

Factors Affecting Biodiversity—Erosion

Erosion is a natural process that has occurred since Earth was formed. Humans have little control over the erosion caused by glaciers, rivers, and oceans. A number of human activities, mainly farming and logging, have increased erosion. Scientists estimate that erosion removes about 2 billion metric tons of soil from farmlands in the United States each year.

Factors Affecting Biodiversity— Ozone Depletion

Ozone, a molecule made up of three oxygen atoms, traps excess ultraviolet radiation and prevents it from reaching Earth. In 1985, it was discovered that a significant thinning of the ozone layer over the Antarctic occurred during the Southern Hemisphere's spring. Some regions of the ozone layer showed 95 percent depletion. Ozone depletion is also occurring farther north. Measurements in arctic regions suggest a thinning of the ozone layer there as well. These findings have caused several countries to become involved in efforts to protect the ozone layer.

Factors Affecting Biodiversity— Global Warming

Carbon dioxide is the most abundant of the greenhouse gases. It occurs as a natural consequence of respiration. However, much larger quantities of this gas are added to the atmosphere as a waste product of energy consumption. Coal, oil, natural gas, and biomass are all burned to provide heat and electricity for industrial processes, home heating, and cooking. A major step toward slowing global warming is to increase the efficiency of energy utilization.

Factors Affecting Biodiversity—Acid Rain

Acid rain is a worldwide problem. Reports of highly acidic rain have come from Canada, England, Germany, France, Scandinavia, and the United States. Rain is normally slightly acidic, with a pH between 5.6 and 5.7 due to atmospheric carbon dioxide that dissolves to produce carbonic acid. But acid rains sometimes have a concentration of acid 1,000 times higher than normal. The average pH of rain in much of northeastern United States and adjoining parts of Ontario is between 4.0 and 4.5

SECTION 2 Conservation Biology
Endangered Species Act

The Endangered Species Act of 1973 resulted in a uniform listing of both foreign and U.S. species and defined "endangered" and "threatened." Plants as well as animals were included in these lists. The Fish and Wildlife Service of the Department of Interior and the Natural Marine Fisheries Service of the Department of Commerce share responsibility for the administration of the Endangered Species Act.

The Endangered Species Act promotes stewardship of a rich biodiversity through measures of conservation of natural habitats and biological processes, eradication and prevention of invasive exotic pest plants and animals, reintroduction of natural plant and animal species, and enhancement of degraded habitats or creation of new aquatic, wetland, and terrestrial habitats. Wildlife management strategies are directed toward preservation, restoration, and enhancement of natural ecosystems. Practical wildlife management strategies result in maintenance of natural processes that benefit all species.

SCIENCE Online

For additional content background on this topic, go to the Glencoe Science Web site at science.glencoe.com.

Stanley Breeden/DRK Photo

Conserving Life

Chapter Vocabulary

biodiversity
extinct species
endangered species
threatened species
introduced species
native species
acid rain
ozone depletion
conservation biology
habitat restoration
captive populations
reintroduction programs

What do you think?

Science Journal The tracking band on the duck's leg allows ecologists and conservation biologists to estimate the size of a population or study migration patterns. Information like this can help determine if populations are healthy and can help us know more about the species in case we need a plan to protect it.

Conserving Life

Every year since you can remember, your family has driven to this remote area to spend a week camping. The fresh air, the lack of city noise, and the views remind you that your modern lifestyle comes at a cost. Even in the few years that you have been coming here, you notice that there are fewer birds and other animal species than there used to be. In this chapter, you'll learn about biodiversity, endangered and threatened species, and pollution. You'll see that enjoyment of nature is only one of many important reasons for conserving life.

What do you think?

Science Journal Look at the picture below with a classmate. Discuss what is happening. Here's a hint: *This is one method that biologists use to help preserve habitat for wildlife.* Write your answer in your Science Journal.

124 ◆ E

ThemeConnection

Systems and Interactions Biodiversity is threatened because human actions alter systems in the biosphere and change interactions. Interventions to help alleviate these threats may help preserve biodiversity.

Do human actions affect the number of species present in an ecosystem? What happens to organisms that are pushed out of an area when the environment changes?

Recognize environmental differences

1. Using string or tape, mark off 1-m × 1-m area of lawn, sports field, or sidewalk.

2. Count and record the different species of plants and animals present in the sample area. Don't forget to include insects or birds that fly over the area, or organisms found by gently probing into the soil.

3. Repeat steps 1 and 2 in a partially wooded area, in a weedy area, or at the edge of a pond or stream.

Observe

Make notes about your observations in your Science Journal. What kinds of human actions could have affected the environment of each sample area?

Before You Read

FOLDABLES
Reading & Study Skills

Making a Know-Want-Learn Study Fold Make the following Foldable to help identify what you already know and what you want to know about biodiversity.

1. Place a sheet of paper in front of you so the long side is at the top. Fold the paper in half from top to bottom.

2. Fold both sides in. Unfold the paper.

3. Through the top thickness of paper, cut along each of the fold lines to the top fold, forming three tabs. Label each tab *Know, Want,* and *Learned* as shown and then, *Biodiversity* across the front of the paper.

4. Before you read the chapter, write what you know and what you want to know about biodiversity under their tabs.

5. As you read the chapter, add to or correct what you have written under the tabs.

E ◆ 125

Purpose Use the Explore Activity to allow students to compare biodiversity in two areas, showing the effect of human activities on ecosystems.

Preparation Before going outside, decide on convenient areas to compare. Collect guidebooks on area wildlife.

Materials metersticks, hand lens, string or tape, field guides

Teaching Strategies

- Be sure students are well-supervised, especially if they are investigating near water.
- Alert students to the appearance of any poisonous plants they might encounter.
- Have students compare their findings. Discuss differences and similarities.

Observe

In general, the area that has been converted to use by humans, such as a lawn or sidewalk, will have fewer species than the natural area. Many human actions can affect environment, including cutting down trees, putting down concrete, and so on.

✓ Assessment

Performance Give students the following list of places and ask them to sequence them from least to most biodiversity: school lawn, school parking lot, nearby forest, classroom floor. classroom floor, school parking lot, school lawn, nearby forest Use **Performance Assessment in the Science Classroom,** p. 89.

Before You Read

FOLDABLES
Reading & Study Skills

Dinah Zike Study Fold

Purpose This activity provides students with an opportunity to review what they know about conserving life and to make them think about what they would like to know. The resulting Foldable can be used as an assessment tool at the end of the chapter to determine what the students have learned.

📁 For additional help, see Foldables Worksheet, p. 17 in **Chapter Resources Booklet,** or go to the Glencoe Science Web site at **science.glencoe.com.** See After You Read in the Study Guide at the end of this chapter.

SECTION

1

Biodiversity

As You Read

What You'll Learn
- **Define** biodiversity.
- **Explain** why biodiversity is important in an ecosystem.
- **Identify** factors that limit biodiversity in an ecosystem.

Vocabulary
biodiversity
extinct species
endangered species
threatened species
introduced species
native species
acid rain
ozone depletion

Why It's Important
Knowledge of biological diversity can lead to strategies for preventing the loss of species.

Figure 1
The forest has more species and is richer in biodiversity than a wheat field.

The Variety of Life

Imagine walking through a forest ecosystem like the one shown in **Figure 1.** Trees, shrubs, and small plants are everywhere. You see and hear squirrels, birds, and insects. You might notice a snake or mushrooms. Hundreds of species live in this forest. Now, imagine walking through a wheat field. You see only a few species—wheat plants, insects, and weeds. The forest contains more species than the wheat field does. The forest has a higher biological diversity, or biodiversity. **Biodiversity** refers to the variety of life in an ecosystem.

Measuring Biodiversity The most common measure of biodiversity is the number of species that live in an area. Ecosystems with more species have greater biodiversity. For example, coral reefs contain thousands of species, including corals, fish, algae, crabs, shrimp, worms, and sponges. The cold, dark, ocean floor might be home to only a few hundred species of fish, crabs, worms, and other organisms. Algae cannot grow there because sunlight does not reach deep into the water. Coral reefs have a higher biodiversity than the deep ocean floor.

126 ◆ E

Section ✓Assessment Planner

Figure 2
This map shows the number of mammal species found in each of the North American countries. In general, biodiversity increases as you get closer to the equator.

CANADA
163

UNITED STATES
367

MEXICO
439

Differences in Biodiversity Biodiversity tends to increase as you move toward the equator because temperatures tend to be warmer. For example, Costa Rica is a small Central American country about the size of West Virginia. Yet it is home to more bird species than the United States and Canada combined. **Figure 2** compares mammal biodiversity in North American countries. Ecosystems with the highest biodiversity usually have warm, moist climates. In fact, tropical regions contain two-thirds of all of Earth's land species.

✓ Reading Check *What kind of climate usually has a high biodiversity?*

Why is biodiversity important?

Would you rather have a summer picnic on a paved parking lot or on cool grass under a shade tree near a stream? Many people find pleasure in nature's biodiversity. Perhaps you like to visit scenic areas to hike, swim, relax, or enjoy the views. Many painters, writers, and musicians find inspiration for their work by spending time outdoors. However, beauty and pleasure are not the only reasons why biodiversity is important.

SECTION 1 Biodiversity **E ◆ 127**

Section 1 Biodiversity **E ◆ 127**

Why is biodiversity important?

Activity

To establish the importance of biodiversity, have students list 20 things they use regularly that come from living organisms. Possible answers: sponges, cotton clothing, glue, paper L2

✔ Reading Check

Answer Biodiversity provides people with food, clothing, building materials, medicines, and natural beauty to enjoy.

Extension

Have students make an alphabet of biodiversity. Use a dictionary and, for each letter of the alphabet, find a species used by people. For "x," it is acceptable if the species name contains an x. Write how the species is used. L2 ELL IS **Linguistic** P

Humans Need Biodiversity What foods do you like to eat? If you eat meat or fish, your meals probably include beef, chicken, pork, tuna, shrimp, or clams. Rice, peanuts, green beans, strawberries, or carrots are plant foods you might enjoy. Eating a variety of foods is a good way to stay healthy. Hundreds of species help feed the human population all around the world.

Biodiversity can help improve food crops. During the 1970s, plant diseases wiped out much of the corn crop in the United States. Plant breeders discovered a small population of wild corn, called maize, growing in Mexico. By crossbreeding the wild maize with domestic corn, they developed strains of corn that are resistant to many diseases. Crossbreeding with wild plants also has been used to produce disease-resistant wheat and strains of rice that grow well under drought conditions.

Biodiversity provides people with many useful materials. Furniture and buildings are made from wood and bamboo. Fibers from cotton, flax, and wool are woven into clothing. Most of the medicines that are used today originally came from wild plants, including those shown in **Figure 3.**

✔ Reading Check
Why is biodiversity important to people?

Figure 3
Although most medicines are now made in factories, many originally came from wild plants.

A The velvet bean plant is the original source of L-dopa, a drug used to treat Parkinson's disease.

B An extract from the bark of the Pacific yew was traditionally used to treat arthritis and rheumatism. It is now known that the bark contains taxol, which is a treatment for some types of cancer.

C The bark of the cinchona tree contains quinine, which has been used to cure malaria in millions of people.

D Ephedra contains a decongestant used in the treatment of asthma and other respiratory ailments.

128 ◆ **E** **CHAPTER 5** Conserving Life

🔷 LAB DEMONSTRATION

Purpose to determine the biodiversity of a fish tank
Materials fish tank that includes several species of fish, snails, and plants
Preparation Bring in a community fish tank.
Procedure As a class, count the number of organisms and list the different species

contained in the tank. Ask which is the better measure of biodiversity. species count
Expected Outcome The number of organisms will usually be larger than the number of species.

✔ Assessment

Have students look at a paragraph in their textbook. Have them imagine that each different word is a separate species. Have them count the number of species and the number of individuals per species. Answers will vary.

Maintaining Stability Forests usually contain many different kinds of plants. If one type of plant disappears, the forest still exists. Biodiversity allows for stability in an ecosystem.

A loss of biodiversity can weaken an ecosystem. Consider what might happen if a disease infects one grapevine in a vineyard, as shown in **Figure 4.** The vines grow close together, and a disease could move easily from one plant to the next. Soon, the entire vineyard could be infected. Many farmers and gardeners have found that planting alternate rows of different crops can help prevent disease and reduce or eliminate the need for pesticides.

Figure 4
Disease has spread from one grapevine to another in this vineyard.

Math Skills Activity

Analyzing Data for Biodiversity

Example Problem
Temperate rain forest ecosystems in Alaska and California are similar. Which one has the higher mammal and bird biodiversity?

Biodiversity in Temperate Rain Forest Ecosystems		
Number of Species	**California**	**Alaska**
Mammals	49	38
Birds	94	79
Totals	143	117

Solution

1 *This is what you know:*
The coastal temperate rain forest of Alaska has 38 mammal species and 79 permanent bird species. The coastal temperate rain forest of California has 49 mammal species and 94 permanent bird species.

2 *This is what you need to find:*
Which of these ecosystems has the higher bird and mammal biodiversity?

3 *This is the data table you need to create:*
Calculate the total number of bird and mammal species in each ecosystem.

4 *Compare the totals to determine which ecosystem has the larger number of bird and mammal species:*
The ecosystem with the larger number of species has a higher bird and mammal biodiversity.

Practice Problem

Compare the biodiversity of the temperate rain forest ecosystems of Oregon and British Columbia. The Oregon ecosystem has 55 mammal species and 99 permanent bird species. The British Columbia ecosystem has 68 mammal species and 116 permanent bird species.

For more help, refer to the Math Skills Handbook.

SECTION 1 Biodiversity **E ◆ 129**

Resource Manager

Chapter Resources Booklet
Lab Activity, pp. 9–12
Note-taking Worksheets, pp. 31–32
Mathematics Skill Activities, p. 45

Cultural Diversity

George Washington Carver Carver (1865–1943) is best known for helping southern farmers diversify their crops. He helped them understand that growing only one crop could deplete nutrients in the soil, and encouraged growing crops that would add nitrogen to the soil (i.e. peanuts, peas, soybeans). Have students research the uses Carver identified for the peanut, including peanut butter. L2

Discussion
In ecosystems, many species are often dependent on a few key species. Biologists call these keystone species. For example, many tropical rain forest organisms depend on the fig tree for food, so the fig tree is a keystone species. Have students look up the word keystone and explain why it is an appropriate term. A keystone is the central supporting element of a whole. L2
IS Linguistic

Math Skills Activity

National Math Standards
Correlation to Mathematics Objectives
1, 5, 8, 9, 10

Teaching Strategies
- Use a map to show students the location of this ecosystem, which extends along the Pacific Coast from Alaska to Northern California. Then explain the meaning of coastal temperate rain forest. (coastal = coast, temperate = moderate temperatures, rain forest = amount of annual rainfall from 40 to 300 inches).
- Have students hypothesize why Oregon's boidiversity is so much lower than that of British Columbia. Possible answer: There is a greater presence of human actions along Oregon's coast, such as logging, farming, and other development.
- Have students make a table like the one shown, using the data for Oregon and British Columbia.

Answer to Practice Problem
British Columbia has 184 species compared to 154 for Oregon. British Columbia shows the highest biodiversity.

Why is biodiversity important?, continued

Use an Analogy

Some scientists use an airplane rivet analogy to explain how living things depend on each other. If a few rivets (metal bolts or pins) off an airplane are lost, the airplane might not be affected. But as more rivets are lost, the chances increase that the plane will eventually fall apart. Rivets are analogous to species and the airplane to the biosphere. **IS** **Logical-Mathematical**

What reduces biodiversity?

✔ Reading Check

Answer changes in the environment and competition from other species

Figure 5
The passenger pigeon is an extinct species. These North American birds were over-hunted by frontier settlers in the 1800s, who used them as a source of food and feathers.

Figure 6
This graph shows the five mass extinctions in Earth's history. The mass extinctions appear as peaks on the graph.

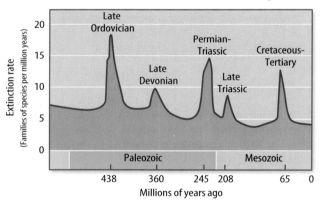

Mass Extinctions in Earth's History

Extinction rate (Families of species per million years)

- Late Ordovician
- Late Devonian
- Permian-Triassic
- Late Triassic
- Cretaceous-Tertiary

Paleozoic — Mesozoic

438   360   245   208   65   0
Millions of years ago

What reduces biodiversity?

Earth Science INTEGRATION

Flocks of thousands of passenger pigeons used to fly across the skies of North America. Few people today have ever seen one of these birds. The passenger pigeon, shown in **Figure 5,** has been extinct for almost 100 years. An **extinct species** is a species that was once present on Earth but has died out.

Extinction is a normal part of nature. The fossil record shows that many species have become extinct since life appeared on Earth. Extinctions can be caused by competition from other species or by changes in the environment. A mass extinction that occurred about 65 million years ago wiped out almost two-thirds of all species living on Earth, including the dinosaurs. This extinction, shown on the graph in **Figure 6,** might have been caused by a huge meteorite that crashed into Earth's surface. Perhaps the impact filled the atmosphere with dust and ash that blocked sunlight from reaching Earth's surface. This event might have caused climate changes that many species could not survive. Mass extinctions eventually are followed by the appearance of new species that take advantage of the suddenly empty environment. After the dinosaurs disappeared, many new species of mammals appeared on Earth.

✔ Reading Check   *What are some causes of extinction?*

Loss of Species Not everyone agrees about the reason for the extinction of the dinosaurs. One thing is clear—human actions had nothing to do with it. Dinosaurs were extinct millions of years before humans were on Earth. Today is different. The rate of extinctions appears to be rising. From 1980 to 2000, close to 40 species of plants and animals in the United States became extinct. It is estimated that hundreds, if not thousands, of tropical species became extinct during the same 20-year period. Human activities probably contributed to most of these extinctions. As the human population grows, many more species could be lost.

Figure 7
The African black rhinoceros is an endangered species, partly because people continue to kill these animals for their horns. As the map shows, this species once lived throughout southern, eastern, and central Africa.

AFRICA

Past range
Present range

Endangered Species To help prevent extinctions, it is important to identify species that could soon disappear. A species in danger of becoming extinct is classified as an **endangered species.** The African black rhinoceros shown in **Figure 7** is endangered. Rhinoceroses are plant eaters. They use their horns to battle each other for territory and to protect themselves against lions and other predators. For centuries, humans have considered rhinoceros horn to be a rare treasure. It is so valuable that poachers continue to hunt and kill these animals, even though selling rhinoceros horn is against international law. In 1970, about 100,000 black rhinoceroses lived in Africa. In the year 2000, fewer than 3,000 lived there.

Threatened Species If a species is likely to become endangered in the near future, it is classified as a **threatened species.** The Australian koala, shown in **Figure 8,** is threatened. People once hunted koalas for their fur. In the 1930s, people realized the koala was in danger. Laws were passed that prohibited the killing of koalas, and the koala populations began to recover. Koalas rely on certain species of Australian eucalyptus trees for food and shelter. Since the 1930 laws were passed, Australia's human population grew and the koala's habitat began to disappear. By the year 2000, nearly two thirds of the koala's habitat had been lost to logging, agriculture, cities, and roads.

Figure 8
Koalas are related to kangaroos and opossums. The loss of their habitat threatens the future of wild koala populations.

SECTION 1 Biodiversity **E** ◆ **131**

Discussion

Elephants are threatened because people use their tusks to make ivory objects, including art and jewelry. Most world governments have banned the trade of ivory. Ask students if they feel it was right to ban the trade of ivory or if they feel people should have the right to decide for themselves whether they should buy it or not.

Quick Demo

Show students a chessboard and have them imagine that each square is a habitat that can support two pawns. Put two pawns in one square to visually present this idea. **How many pawns can the entire chessboard support?** $64 \times 2 = 128$ **If one whole row of land were removed to create a shopping center, what pawn population could the area support?** (Put play buildings on these spaces to visually present this idea.) $56 \times 2 = 112$ Explain that as natural areas are cleared, there is less habitat to support the species that inhabit that area.

Resource Manager

Chapter Resources Booklet
Transparency Activity, pp. 45–47
Enrichment, p. 29

Life Science Critical Thinking/Problem Solving, pp. 5, 13, 21

Science Journal

Going, Going, Gone Have students research and describe in their Science Journals one threatened species, one endangered species, and one extinct species. Make sure they explain the reason why the species is in peril or extinct.

 L2 ELL **Linguistic**

Visualizing Threatened and Endangered Species

Have students examine the pictures and read the captions. Then ask the following questions.

Based on these examples, what seems to be the primary cause of a species becoming threatened or endangered in the United States? Possible answer: habitat destruction and human development.

The vernal pool tadpole shrimp is endangered and the desert tortoise is threatened. What is the difference between being endangered and being threatened? Possible answer: a threatened species is in danger of becoming extinct but there still is time to help the species recover on its own. An endangered species is in immediate danger of becoming extinct and probably will require human intervention to survive.

Activity

Have students research some other endangered or threatened species and make a poster based on their findings.

Extension

Have students choose an endangered species and write a plan to help the species recover. They should include possible plans to restore the species' habitat, help it reproduce (in a controlled environment), and for it to be reintroduced into the wild. Encourage students to choose plants as well as animals.

Figure 9

The United States Fish and Wildlife Service lists more than 1,200 species of animals and plants as being at risk in the U.S. Of these, about 20 percent are classified as threatened and 80 percent as endangered.

VERNAL POOL TADPOLE SHRIMP This endangered species lives in the seasonal freshwater ponds of California's Central Valley. Pollution, urban sprawl, and other forces have destroyed some 90 percent of the vernal pools in the valley. Loss of habitat makes the survival of these tiny creatures highly uncertain.

CALIFORNIA CONDOR The endangered condor came close to extinction at the end of the 20th century. Some condors have been raised in captivity and successfully released into the wild.

HALEAKALA SILVERSWORD One of the world's most spectacular plants, this threatened species is making a recovery. The plant shown here is blooming in Hawaii's Haleakala (ha lee ah kuh LAH) crater.

DESERT TORTOISE The future of the threatened desert tortoise is uncertain. Human development is eroding tortoise habitat in the southwestern United States.

SOUTHERN SEA OTTER The threatened sea otter lives in shallow waters along the Pacific coast of the United States. For centuries, sea otters were hunted for their fur.

Teacher FYI

Deforestation is a problem occurring worldwide. It is becoming a serious problem in South America. In the rain forest, many animals live in trees and do not move down to the ground. Discuss with students what happens to plants and animals as the forests are cleared for farms and ranches or harvested and not replanted.

Habitat Loss In the Explore Activity at the beginning of this chapter, you probably observed that lawns and sidewalks have a lower biodiversity than sunny woods or weed-covered lots. When people alter an ecosystem, perhaps by replacing a forest or meadow with pavement or a lawn, the habitats of some species may become smaller or disappear completely. If the habitats of many species are lost, biodiversity might be reduced.

Habitat loss is a major reason why species become threatened or endangered as shown in **Figure 9,** or extinct. The Lake Erie water snake, shown in **Figure 10,** is classified as a threatened species because of habitat loss. These snakes live along the rocky shores of islands in Lake Erie. The islands are popular recreation spots. The development of these areas for boat docks and buildings has seriously reduced the amount of habitat available to the snakes. Also, these snakes are often killed by people who mistakenly think they are poisonous. Adult snakes range from 0.5 m to 1.0 m long, and they feed on fish, frogs, and salamanders. Because they have sharp teeth for capturing prey, they can bite. However, they are not dangerous to humans, especially if left undisturbed.

Conservation strategies for protecting the Lake Erie water snake include preserving its habitat by limiting development in some areas. Also, a public education program has been developed to inform people about this predator species and its importance in the Lake Erie ecosystem.

Figure 10
The Lake Erie water snake has become a threatened species.

 A The building of boat docks, roads, and shopping centers is reducing the snake's habitat.

B These snakes are not dangerous to humans, but many are killed by people who fear snakes.

SECTION 1 Biodiversity **E ◆ 133**

TRY AT HOME
Mini LAB

Demonstrating Divided Habitats

Procedure 🛠 🧤
1. Put a small piece of **banana** in an **open jar.** Set the jar indoors near a place where food is prepared or fruit is thrown away. Wash your hands when you are finished.
2. Check the jar every few hours. When at least five fruit flies are in it, place a **piece of cloth or stocking** over the top of the jar and secure it with a **rubber band.**
3. Count and record the number of fruit flies in the jar every two days for three weeks.

Analysis
1. Explain why all the flies in the jar eventually die.
2. Use your results to hypothesize why habitat loss can reduce biodiversity.

What reduces biodiversity?, continued

TRY AT HOME
Mini LAB

Purpose to observe what happens when a fruit fly habitat is divided **IS Visual-Spatial**

Materials banana, jar, cloth or stocking, rubber band

Teaching Strategy
• Fruit flies are easy to catch if it is warm outside. Some produce sections of supermarkets may also have fruit flies.
• Explain that putting cloth on the jar prevents the migration of the fruit flies; this is similar to habitat division.
• Each week, have students report how many flies they have.

Troubleshooting Catch fruit flies to give to students who have trouble finding them. If it is winter, you can order nonflying fruit flies from a biological supply company.

Analysis
1. The flies could not migrate to new areas, so when their food supply was used up, they died.
2. It can prevent organisms from migrating. In a small area, they may run out of food and perish.

✓ Assessment

Content Have students consider the following scenario: a fruit fly colony begins in a jar with a piece of banana. There are two males and two females. Have students draw a line graph to show possible population growth over an eight-week period. Use **Performance Assessment in the Science Classroom,** p. 111.

Resource Manager

Chapter Resources Booklet
    MiniLAB, p. 3
    Reinforcement, p. 27
Earth Science Critical Thinking/Problem Solving, p. 12

What reduces biodiversity?, continued

Activity

Have students make a list on the board of ways they can conserve resources by reducing, reusing, or recycling; thereby slowing the loss of habitat. L2
COOP LEARN IS **Interpersonal**

Make a Model

Use graph paper to show the problem of divided habitats. Have students draw a line to create a square measuring twenty cells by twenty cells. This represents the habitat of a musk ox. One ox needs 200 cells for sufficient habitat to survive. **How many musk oxen would this land support?** 2 Now divide the land with two roads, one cutting the land vertically and one horizontally. The roads are major highways that the musk oxen cannot cross. Ask if the musk oxen will be able to survive. No, their habitats are now too small.

Extension

Have students investigate and write a report on problems with introduced species. Possible topics: the brown tree snake, kudzu, sea lamprey, starling, zebra mussel L2
IS **Linguistic**

Figure 11
Introduced species can reduce or eliminate populations of native species in an ecosystem.

A The ruffe was introduced into the Great Lakes by ships from other parts of the world. It quickly takes over habitat and food sources used by native fish.

B Purple loosestrife was brought to North America from Europe and Asia in the 1800s. Dense patches of loosestrife grow and crowd out the native plants that some animals need for food and shelter.

Divided Habitats Biodiversity can be reduced when a habitat is divided by roads, cities, or farms. Small patches of habitat usually have less biodiversity than large areas. One reason for this is that large animals like mountain lions and grizzly bears require hunting territories that cover hundreds of square kilometers. If their habitat becomes divided, they are forced to move elsewhere.

Small habitat areas also make it difficult for species to recover from a disaster. Suppose a fire destroys part of a forest, and all the salamanders living there are destroyed. Later, after new trees have grown, salamanders from the undamaged part of the forest move in to replace those that were lost. But, what if fire destroys a grove of trees surrounded by parking lots and buildings? Trees and salamanders perish. Trees might grow back but the salamanders might never return, because none are nearby to move into the area.

Introduced Species When species from another part of the world are introduced into an ecosystem, they can have a dramatic effect on biodiversity. An **introduced species** is a species that moves into an ecosystem as a result of human actions. Introduced species often have no competitors or predators in the new area, so their populations grow rapidly. Introduced species can crowd out or consume native species. **Native species** are the original organisms in an ecosystem.

In the early 1800s, European settlers brought goats with them to Santa Catalina Island off the coast of California. The goats overgrazed the land, completely eliminating 48 of the native plant species and exposing patches of bare soil. The bare soil provided a place for hardy, introduced weeds to take root. The weeds crowded out native species. Late in the twentieth century, after goats were removed from the island, some native plant species began to recover. **Figure 11** shows introduced species that have reduced biodiversity in other ecosystems.

Science Journal

Managing Resources The prickly pear cactus is a fast-growing cactus that was brought to Australia because it made a good living fence. However, it quickly spread out of control. Have students investigate and report on how Australians solved this problem. L2 IS **Linguistic**

Inclusion Strategies

Gifted Have students research the recent observations of mutated frogs, such as frogs with three rear legs. Explore possible reasons for these mutations and have students choose the explanation that seems most plausible. L3

Pollution

Biodiversity also is affected by pollution of land, water, or air. Soil that is contaminated with oil, chemicals, or other pollutants can harm plants or limit plant growth. Because plants provide valuable habitat for many species, any reduction in plant growth can limit biodiversity.

Figure 12
Acid rain can damage the leaves and other tissues of trees.

Water Pollution Water-dwelling organisms are easily harmed by pesticides, chemicals, oil, and other pollutants that contaminate the water. Water pollutants often come from factories, ships, or runoff from roads, lawns, and farms. Waterways also can be polluted when people dispose of wastes improperly. For example, excess water from streets and roads runs into storm drains during rainstorms. This water usually flows untreated into nearby waterways. Storm drains should never be used to dispose of used motor oil, paints, solvents, or other liquid wastes. These pollutants can kill aquatic plants, fish, frogs, insects, and the organisms they depend on for food.

Air Pollution A form of water pollution known as acid rain is caused by air pollution. **Acid rain** forms when sulfur dioxide and nitrogen oxide released by industries and automobiles combine with water vapor in the air. As **Figure 12** shows, acid rain can have serious effects on trees. It washes calcium and other nutrients from the soil, making the soil less fertile. One tree species that is particularly vulnerable to acid rain is the sugar maple. Many sugar maple trees in New England and New York have suffered major damage from acid rain. Acid rain also harms fish and other organisms that live in lakes and streams. Some lakes in Canada have become so acidic that they have lost almost all of their fish species. In the United States, 14 eastern states have acid rain levels high enough to harm aquatic life.

Just as cigarette smoke can harm the lungs of people, air pollution from factories, power plants, and automobiles can harm sensitive tissues of many organisms. For example, air pollution can damage the leaves or needles of trees, weakening the trees and making it harder for them to survive attacks by insects, disease, pests, or environmental stresses such as drought.

Mini LAB

Testing the Effects of Acid Rain

Procedure
1. Soak **50 mustard seeds** in water and another **50 mustard seeds** in **vinegar** (an acid) for 24 hours.
2. Wrap each group of seeds in put a **moist paper towel** and put them into separate, **self-sealing plastic bags**.
3. Seal and label each bag.
4. After 3 days, open each bag and record the number of seeds that show evidence of growth.

Analysis
1. Describe the effect of an acid on mustard seed growth.
2. Explain how acid rain could affect plant biodiversity.

SECTION 1 Biodiversity **E ◆ 135**

Pollution

Pollution, continued

Health
INTEGRATION

Students may suggest limiting the amount of time spent in the Sun or wearing protective hats, sunglasses, and sunblock.

3 Assess

Reteach

Have students explain what biodiversity is, why it is important, and how it is threatened. Have students use construction paper to put together a mini-book containing their answers.
L2

Challenge

Have students make a plan to slow the loss of an endangered or threatened species that lives nearby.

✓Assessment

Performance Have each student make a poster showing an endangered or threatened organism and the problems it is encountering. Use **Performance Assessment in the School Classroom,** p. 145.

Health
INTEGRATION

Overexposure to the Sun's radiation can cause health problems such as cataracts, which cloud the lens of the eye, and skin cancer. In your Science Journal, describe ways to limit your exposure to damaging rays.

Global Warming The term "global warming" means that average global temperatures are increasing. Carbon dioxide gas (CO_2) is released into the atmosphere whenever wood, coal, gas, or any other fuel burns. In recent times, the percentage of CO_2 in the atomsphere is increasing because of the large amounts of fuels being burned. This might increase Earth's average temperature and lead to climate changes that might affect biodiversity. For example, if the polar ice caps begin to melt, flooding in coastal ecosystems worldwide might occur.

Ozone Depletion The atmosphere includes a sort of sunscreen, called the ozone layer, which protects life on Earth from the Sun's harmful radiation. The ozone layer consists of ozone gas and is about 15 km to 30 km above Earth's surface. Ozone absorbs ultraviolet (UV) radiation from the Sun. The ozone layer prevents damaging amounts of UV radiation from reaching Earth's surface. Scientists have discovered that the ozone layer is becoming thinner. The thinning of the ozone layer is called **ozone depletion.** It allows increased amounts of UV radiation to reach Earth's surface. This increase can harm living organisms. For humans, it could mean more cases of skin cancer. Ozone depletion occurs over much of Earth. Data taken in the late 1990s indicates that ozone levels over the United States, for example, had decreased by five to ten percent.

Section ① Assessment

1. What is biodiversity? Give two reasons why it is important.
2. How are endangered species different from extinct species?
3. Why are habitat loss and habitat division threats to biodiversity?
4. In what ways do introduced species threaten biodiversity?
5. **Think Critically** Aluminum, which is commonly found in soil, is toxic to fish. It damages their ability to absorb oxygen through their gills. Acid rain can wash aluminum out of the soil and into nearby waterways. Explain how acid rain could affect biodiversity in a pond.

Skill Builder Activities

6. **Identifying and Manipulating Variables and Controls** Lack of calcium in the soil can damage trees. Design an experiment to test the hypothesis that acid rain is removing calcium from forest soil. **For more help,** refer to the Science Skill Handbook.

7. **Using a Database** Create an endangered species database that includes the following for each species: *common and scientific names, continent(s) on which it is found, habitat description,* and *why it is endangered*. Sort the database to obtain a list of endangered species from each continent. **For more help,** refer to the Technology Skill Handbook.

Answers to Section Assessment

1. The variety of life in an area; it provides people with food, materials, medicine, stability, beauty.
2. Extinct species are gone forever; endangered species may soon become extinct.
3. Habitat loss means there is less area in which an organism can obtain what it needs. Habitat division restricts the movement of organisms and may block access to what they need.
4. They can compete with or prey on native organisms, and often have no natural predators in the area.
5. It could result in one or more species dying, reducing biodiversity.
6. Answers will vary, but should involve a control group that receives normal water or rain and a variable group that receives acid water or rain. The levels of calcium in both soils then would be measured.
7. Database setups will vary, but should include all the categories listed.

Activity

Oily Birds

You probably have seen videos of waterbirds covered with oil after an oil spill. Nearly 4 billion kg of oil are spilled from ships or dumped into the ocean each year. Oil floats on water. It can coat the feathers of waterbirds. These birds depend on their feathers for insulation from the cold. Oiled feathers lose their insulating qualities, so oiled birds are exposed to the cold. Oil-coated feathers also prevent the birds from flying and can cause them to drown. Rescue teams try to clean off the oil, but as you'll find out in this activity, this is a difficult task.

What You'll Investigate
How difficult is it to clean oil from bird feathers?

Goal
- **Experiment** with different methods for cleaning oil from bird feathers.

Materials
beakers (2)	water
bird feathers	cotton balls
(white or light colored)	cotton swabs
vegetable oil or olive oil	sponge
red, blue, and	toothbrush
green food coloring	dish soap
paper towels	

Safety Precautions

Procedure

1. Fill your beaker with vegetable oil and add several drops of red, blue, and green food coloring. Submerge your feathers in the oil for several minutes.

2. Lay paper towels on the table. Remove the feathers from the oil after allowing the excess oil to drip back into the beaker. Lay the feathers on the paper towels.

3. Using a paper towel, blot the oil from one feather. Run your fingers over the feather to determine if the oil is gone.

4. Using the cotton swaps and cotton balls, wipe the oil from a second feather. Check the feather for oil when finished.

5. Using a toothbrush, brush the oil from a third feather. Check it for oil when you are finished.

6. Use a sponge to clean the fourth feather. Check it for oil when you are finished.

7. Put several drops of dish soap into a beaker and fill the beaker with water. Soak the fifth feather in the solution. Check the feather for oil after it has soaked for several minutes.

Conclude and Apply

1. **Identify** the method or methods that best removed the oil from the feathers.

2. **Describe** the condition of the feathers after you finished cleaning them. How would the condition of these feathers affect birds?

3. **Infer** why rescuers would be hesitant to use soap when cleaning live birds.

4. **Infer** how oil pollution affects water mammals such as otters and seals.

Communicating Your Data

Share your results with your classmates. Decide which methods you would use to try to clean a live bird.

Resource Manager

Chapter Resources Booklet
Activity Worksheet, pp. 5–6

Communicating Your Data

Create a data table on the board listing all the methods students could use for cleaning live birds. Record the students choices on the table.

Activity

BENCH TESTED

Purpose Students will experience the difficulty of cleaning oil pollution from bird feathers.

Process Skills observing and inferring, describing

Time Requirement 30 minutes

Safety Precautions Instruct students to wash their hands thoroughly after completing the activity.

Teaching Strategy
- In their Science Journals, ask students to write a brief description of the feathers after each cleaning attempt.
- Introduce or conclude the activity with photos or video footage of birds trapped in petroleum and rescue efforts to save them.

Troubleshooting Make certain each pair of students have all their supplies at the table before starting the activity so that messes can be contained in one location.

Answers to Questions
1. The dish soap will work best, but it will not remove all the oil.
2. Answers will vary, but often feathers will become ruffled, torn, or broken during the activity.
3. Soap will also make feathers less waterproof, and the soap could prove to be toxic for birds already in a weakened state.
4. Oil also causes the fur of water mammals to lose its waterproofing ability, exposing the animals to the cold.

✓ Assessment

Content Ask each group to write an international treaty of rules and regulations that would prevent the majority of oil spills around the world from occurring. Use **PASC,** p. 169.

SECTION
2
Conservation Biology

1 Motivate

Bellringer Transparency

Display the Section Focus Transparency for Section 2. Use the accompanying Transparency Activity Master. L2

ELL

SECTION 2 Section Focus Transparency — Dog Days

Humans have kept dogs for 12,000 to 14,000 years. At first, all dogs had jobs, such as herding or guarding. Today, some dogs have jobs, but many others are kept as pets.

1. What determines how big a dog can get?
2. How can a gray puppy and a brown puppy be littermates?
3. What environmental conditions could make one dog look different than its identical twin?

Tie to Prior Knowledge

Most students will have visited some local, state, or national park. Ask about rules or laws enforced by the park rangers to protect these habitats. Answers may include the prohibition of littering, harming or feeding the animals, or taking natural objects from the park.

SECTION
2 Conservation Biology

Protecting Biodiversity

The study of methods for protecting biodiversity is called **conservation biology.** Conservation biologists develop strategies to prevent the continuing loss of members of a species. Conservation strategies must be based on a thorough understanding of the principles of ecology. Because human activities are often the reason why a species is at risk, conservation plans also must take into account the needs of the human population. Humans needs and those of other species often conflict. It can be difficult to develop conservation plans that satisfy both. Conservation biologists must consider law, politics, society, and economics, as well as ecology, when they look for ways to conserve Earth's biodiversity.

The Florida manatee, shown in **Figure 13,** is an endangered species. Manatees are plant-eating mammals that live in shallow water along the coasts of Florida and the Carolinas. These animals move slowly, occasionally rising to the surface to breathe. They swim below the surface, but not deep enough to avoid the propellers of powerboats. Many manatees have been injured or killed by powerboat propellers. Boaters cannot always tell when manatees are nearby, and it is difficult to enforce speed limits to protect the manatees. Also, the manatee's habitat is being affected by Florida's growing human population. More boat docks are being built, which can add to the number of boats in the water. Water pollution from boats, roads, and coastal cities is also a problem.

Reading Check *How do humans affect manatee habitats?*

Figure 13
Conservation biologists are working to protect the endangered Florida manatee by limiting habitat loss, reducing pollution, and encouraging boaters to obey speed limits. These rescued manatees are being rehabilitated at the Columbus Zoo in Ohio.

Section ✔Assessment Planner

PORTFOLIO
Curriculum Connection, p. 141
PERFORMANCE ASSESSMENT
Skill Builder Activities, p. 143
See page 150 for more options.

CONTENT ASSESSMENT
Section, p. 143
Challenge, p. 143
Chapter, pp. 150–151

Figure 14
In the 1970s, the American bald eagle and American alligator were listed as endangered, so conservation plans were put in place. By the 1990s, their numbers had increased, so they were moved to the threatened species list.

Conservation Biology at Work

Almost every conservation plan has two goals. The first goal is to protect a species from harm. The second goal is to protect the species' habitat. Several conservation strategies can be used to meet these goals.

Legal Protections Laws can be passed to help protect a species and its habitat. In the early 1970s, people became concerned about the number of species extinctions occurring in the United States. In response to this concern, the U.S. Endangered Species Act of 1973 became a law. This act makes it illegal to harm, collect, harass, or disturb the habitat of any species on the endangered or threatened species lists. The act also prevents the U.S. government from spending money on projects that would harm these species or their habitats. The Endangered Species Act has helped several species, including those shown in **Figure 14,** recover from near extinction.

The United States and other countries worldwide have agreed to work together to protect endangered or threatened species. In 1975, The Convention on International Trade in Endangered Species of Wild Fauna and Flora, known as CITIES, came into existence. One of its goals is to protect certain species by controlling or preventing international trade in these species or any part of them, such as elephant ivory. About 5,000 animal species and 25,000 plant species are protected by this agreement.

SCIENCE Online

Data Update For an online update of species currently listed as endangered or threatened, visit the Glencoe Science Web site at **science.glencoe.com**. In your Science Journal, write a description of one of these species and explain why it is believed to be in danger.

2 Teach

Protecting Biodiversity

✔ Reading Check

Answer Humans pollute the water. They also drive power boats, which can injure manatees, through the water.

Conservation Biology at Work

IDENTIFYING Misconceptions

Students may think a conservation biologist is the same thing as an animal rights activist. Conservation biologists are concerned with the protection of species. Animal rights activists are concerned with the protection of individual animals. Sometimes their interests conflict, such as when conservation biologists advocate killing some animals to protect another species.

Resource Manager

Chapter Resources Booklet
  Transparency Activity, p. 43
Directed Reading for Content Mastery,
  pp. 21, 22

SCIENCE Online
Internet Addresses

_____
_____
_____

Explore the Glencoe Science Web site at **science.glencoe.com** to find out more about topics in this section.

Conservation Biology at Work, continued

Earth Science
INTEGRATION

Fences surround many of these features. Others have walkways built above them for visitors to travel on, and have signs posted which warn visitors not to stray from the path.

Extension

Ask students to research a national or state park in your local area. Have them find when and why it was created, and any unique features. [L2]

Visual Learning

Figure 15 Ask students to use the illustration to explain how wildlife corridors reduce the problem of divided habitats. Organisms pass under highways through the corridors, allowing them the range of habitat they need to survive.

Fun Fact

Adult male grizzly bears usually need at least 250 square miles of habitat to survive. Female grizzlies require less.

Earth Science
INTEGRATION

Yellowstone National Park contains many volcanic features such as geysers, hot springs, and mud volcanoes. The land surrounding these features is fragile. Research what the National Park Service has done to protect this fragile environment. Communicate to your class what you learn.

Figure 15
A Wildlife corridors allow animals to pass safely under roads and highways. **B** This map shows the types of habitat where most populations of Florida panthers are found. Notice the major highways that cross these areas.

Habitat Preservation

Even if a species is protected by law, it cannot survive unless its habitat also is protected. Conservation biology often focuses on protecting habitats, or even whole ecosystems. One way to do this is to create nature preserves, such as national parks and protected wildlife areas.

The United States established its first national park—Yellowstone National Park—in 1872. At that time, large animals like grizzly bears, elk, and moose ranged over much of North America. These animals roam across large areas of land in search of food. If their habitat becomes too small, they cannot survive. The grizzly bear, for example, requires large quantities of food each day. To feed itself, a grizzly needs a territory of several hundred square kilometers. Without national parks and wildlife areas, some animals would be far fewer in number than they are today.

Wildlife Corridors

The successful conservation of a species like the grizzly bear requires enormous amounts of land. However, it is not always possible to create large nature preserves. One alternative is to link smaller parks together with wildlife corridors. Wildlife corridors allow animals to move from one preserve to another without having to cross roads, farms, or other areas inhabited by humans. As **Figure 15** shows, wildlife corridors are part of the strategy for saving the endangered Florida panther. A male panther needs a territory of 1,300 km² or more, which is larger than many of the protected panther habitats.

Panthers
Florida Habitats
Pinelands
Freshwater marsh
Cypress swamp
Prairies
Hardwood swamp
Swamp & Coastal

Teacher FYI

Yellowstone National Park was established because of the area's unique geology. In 1872, the wildlife of the park could be found in many places in the U.S. As the human population grew and took over more land, wildlife in many unprotected places perished.

Inclusion Strategies

Gifted Have students research and discuss whether it is best to create a few large protected areas or several smaller protected areas. A large area will have more biodiversity, but is not always a feasible option. [L3]

Habitat Restoration Habitats that have been changed or harmed by human activities often can be restored. **Habitat restoration** is the process of taking action to bring a damaged habitat back to a healthy condition.

Rhode Island's Narragansett Bay was once an important fishing area. It supported populations of flounder, bay scallops, blue crabs, and other important food species. Eelgrass, which is an underwater plant that grows in shallow parts of the bay, provides habitat for the young of many of these species. As the human population of Rhode Island grew, most of the bay's eelgrass beds disappeared. Fish and shellfish populations declined. People who lived in the area knew that something needed to be done. Students in Rhode Island schools have helped restore eelgrass habitat by growing thousands of eelgrass seedlings, like those shown in **Figure 16,** for transplanting into the bay.

Figure 16
By restoring eelgrass habitat, conservation biologists hope to preserve populations of shellfish and fish in Narragansett Bay.

 When is habitat restoration used?

Wildlife Management Preserving or restoring a habitat does not mean that all the species living there are automatically protected from harm. Park rangers, guards, and volunteers often are needed to manage the area. In South Africa, guards patrol wildlife parks to prevent poachers from killing elephants for their tusks. Officials protect the mountain gorillas of Rwanda by limiting the number of visitors allowed to see them. Some wildlife preserves allow no visitors other than biologists who are studying the area.

Hunters and wildlife managers often work together to maintain healthy ecosystems in parks and preserves. People usually are not allowed to hunt or fish in a park unless they purchase a hunting or fishing license. The sale of licenses provides funds for maintaining the wildlife area. It also helps protect populations from overhunting. For example, licenses may limit the number of animals a hunter is allowed to take, or permit hunting only during seasons when a species is not reproducing. Hunting regulations also can help prevent a population from becoming too large for the area.

SECTION 2   Conservation Biology   **E ◆ 141**

Conservation Biology at Work, continued

Figure 17
The Arabian oryx was saved from extinction because a captive population was created before the wild population disappeared.

Research Visit the Glencoe Science Web site at **science.glencoe.com** to learn more about the Arabian oryx reintroduction program. In your Science Journal, write a summary of this program's progress.

Captive Populations The Arabian oryx, shown in **Figure 17,** is native to desert lands of the Arabian Peninsula. People hunt the oryx for its horns and hide. Hunting increased during the twentieth century, when four-wheel-drive vehicles became available to hunters. In 1962, to prevent the species from becoming extinct, several oryx were taken to the Phoenix Zoo in Arizona. By 1972, no more wild oryx lived in the desert. A **captive population** is a population of organisms that is cared for by humans. The captive population of oryx in Arizona did well. Their numbers increased, and hundreds of Arabian oryx now live in zoos all over the world.

Keeping endangered or threatened animals in captivity can help preserve biodiversity. It is not ideal, however. It can be expensive to provide proper food, adequate space, and the right kind of care. Also, captive animals sometimes lose their wild behaviors. If that happens, they might not survive if they're returned to their native habitats. The best approach is to preserve the natural habitats of these organisms so they can survive on their own.

Reintroduction Programs In some cases, members of captive populations can be released into the wild to help restore biodiversity. In the 1980s, wildlife managers began reintroducing captive oryx into their desert habitat. **Reintroduction programs** return captive organisms to an area where the species once lived. Programs like this can succeed only if the factors that caused the species to become endangered are removed. In this case, the reintroduced oryx must be protected from illegal hunting.

Plants also can be reintroduced into their original habitats. The island of St. Helena in the South Atlantic was home to the rare St. Helena ebony tree. In the 1500s, European settlers introduced goats to the island. Settlers also cut trees for firewood and timber. Goats overgrazed the land, and native trees were replaced by introduced species. By 1850, the St. Helena ebony was thought to be extinct. In 1980, two small ebony trees were found on the island, high on a cliff. Small branches were cut from these trees and rooted in soil. These cuttings have been used to grow thousands of new ebony trees. The new trees are being replanted all over the island.

Resource Manager

Chapter Resources Booklet
   Activity Worksheet, pp. 7–8
   Lab Activity, pp. 13–16
Lab Management and Safety, p. 73

Internet Addresses
_____
_____
_____

Explore the Glencoe Science Web site at **science.glencoe.com** to find out more about topics in this section.

Seed Banks Throughout the world, seed banks have been created to store the seeds of many endangered plant species. If any of these species become extinct in the wild, the stored seeds can be used to reintroduce them to their original habitats.

Relocation Reintroduction programs do not always involve captive populations. In fact, reintroductions are most successful when wild organisms are transported to a new area of suitable habitat. The brown pelican, shown in **Figure 18,** was once common along the shores of the Gulf of Mexico. Pelicans eat fish that eat aquatic plants. In the mid-twentieth century, DDT—a pesticide—was used widely to control insect pests. It eventually ended up in the food that pelicans ate. Because of DDT, the pelican's eggshells were so thin that they would break before the chick inside was ready to hatch. Brown pelicans completely disappeared from Louisiana and Texas. After DDT was banned, 50 of these birds were taken from Florida to Louisiana. Since then, the population has grown. In the year 2000, more than 7,000 brown pelicans lived in Louisiana and Texas.

Figure 18
Brown pelicans from Florida were relocated successfully to Louisiana.

 Reading Check *What two things led to the recovery of the brown pelican?*

Section ② Assessment

1. What are the differences between ecology and conservation biology?

2. How does the U.S. Endangered Species Act protect species?

3. Why do most conservation plans include habitat preservation strategies?

4. What factors can sometimes make it difficult to reintroduce captive animals into their natural habitats?

5. **Think Critically** As a conservation biologist, you are helping to restore eelgrass beds in Narragansett Bay. What information will you need to prepare an effective conservation plan?

Skill Builder Activities

6. **Recognizing Cause and Effect** Imagine creating a new wildlife preserve in your part of the country. Identify uses of the area that would allow people to enjoy it without harming the ecosystem. What kinds of uses might damage the habitat of species that live there? **For more help, refer to the** Science Skill Handbook.

7. **Communicating** Find information on an endangered or threatened species and a conservation plan that is being used to preserve it. In your Science Journal, write a summary of the conservation plan. **For more help, refer to the** Science Skill Handbook.

SECTION 2 Conservation Biology **E** ◆ **143**

Answers to Section Assessment

1. Ecology—studies interactions within ecosystems; conservation biology—studies ways to protect biodiversity, must take many factors (i.e. economics, politics) into consideration.

2. It makes it illegal to kill endangered or threatened species, to harm their habitats, or use federal funds to build in places that might harm these species.

3. Providing or protecting habitats is the best way to make sure species get what they need.

4. wild behaviors may have been lost; the original problems may not have been solved

5. Information on the cause of eelgrass decline. Which species depend on the grass? How do local people feel about restoring the ecosystem?

6. Answers will vary, but uses may include hiking, camping, hunting, and fishing. Destructive uses may include logging, farming, and strip-mining.

7. Answers will vary, but should include an endangered or threatened species and plans to protect it.

Activity

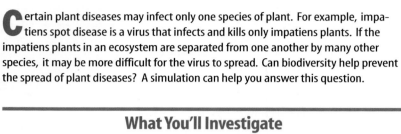

BENCH TESTED

What You'll Investigate

Purpose

Students will investigate the relationship between plant biodiversity and the spread of plant diseases. **IS Logical-Mathematical**

Process Skills

observing and inferring, using numbers, recording data, interpreting data, using data tables, comparing, predicting

Time Required

45 minutes

Procedure

Teaching Strategy

Once all students have constructed their playing boards, follow the first few steps of round 1 together as a class to make certain everyone understands how the game is played.

Troubleshooting

Draw a sample of the field grid for the class to see. Save time by cutting out the colored squares before the activity, or have a paper cutter available for students to use to quickly cut their squares. **CAUTION:** Advise students to use care when using paper cutter.

Expected Outcome

Students should realize that fields with high plant biodiversity will resist the spread of infectious diseases much better than fields with a low biodiversity. They will also discover that mixing up plant species within an ecosystem will decrease the spread of disease.

Activity

Biodiversity and the Health of a Plant Community

Certain plant diseases may infect only one species of plant. For example, impatiens spot disease is a virus that infects and kills only impatiens plants. If the impatiens plants in an ecosystem are separated from one another by many other species, it may be more difficult for the virus to spread. Can biodiversity help prevent the spread of plant diseases? A simulation can help you answer this question.

What You'll Investigate

How does biodiversity affect the spread of a plant disease?

Materials

plain white paper
colored paper (red, orange, yellow, green, blue, black)
ruler
scissors
pens
die

Safety Precautions

Use care when cutting with scissors.

Goals

- **Record data** on the spread of a plant disease.
- **Compare** the spread of disease in communities with different levels of biodiversity.
- **Predict** a way to increase a crop harvest.

Procedure

1	2	3	4	5
16				6
15				7
14				8
13	12	11	10	9

1. On a piece of white paper, draw a square that measures 10 cm on each side. This represents a field. In the square, make a grid with five equal rows and five equal columns, as shown. Number the outer cells from 1 through 16, as shown. The inner cells are not numbered.

2. Cut 1.5-cm × 1.5-cm tiles from colored paper. Cut out 25 black tiles, 25 red tiles, 10 orange tiles, 10 yellow tiles, 5 green tiles, and 5 blue tiles. The black tiles represent a plant that has died from a disease. The other colors represent different plant species.

For example, all the red tiles represent one plant species, all the blue tiles are another species, and the remaining colors are different species.

3. There are four rounds in this simulation. For each round, distribute one plant per square as instructed. Roll the die once for each square, proceeding from square 1 to square 2, and so on through square 16.

Round 1—High Biodiversity
Distribute five red, five orange, five yellow, five green, and five blue plants in the field.

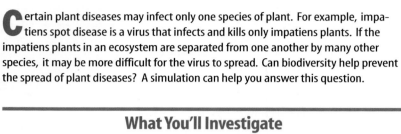

144 ◆ E **CHAPTER 5** Conserving Life

Extension

Have students research how top predators and a high biodiversity of herbivores help maintain a higher biodiversity of plants and other organisms for an entire ecosystem. Top predators prey on herbivores preventing them from overgrazing plant species. When there is a large variety of herbivores in an ecosystem, they will eat a wider variety of plants preventing any one type of plant from dominating.

Inclusion Strategies

Visually Impaired Ask some of your students to prepare activity squares to be used by those who are color blind and cannot distinguish between red and green or other color pairs. Instead of using different colored tiles, the tiles can be made to have different shapes. For example, tiles can have one, two, three, or all four corners snipped off.

Procedures

Round 2—Moderate Biodiversity

Distribute ten orange, ten yellow, and five green plants in the field.

Round 3—Low Biodiversity

Distribute all 25 of the red tiles in the field.

Round 4—Challenge

You want a harvest of as many red plants as possible. Decide how many red plants you will start with and whether you will plant any other species. Strategically place your tiles on the board. Follow steps 3 through 5 of the procedure.

4. To begin, place a black tile over half of square 1. Roll the die and use the Disease Key to see if the plant in square 1 is infected. If it is, cover it with the black tile. If not, remove the black tile. For example, suppose square 1 has an orange plant on it. Place a black tile over half of the square and roll the die. If you roll a 1, 3, 4, or 5, the plant does not get the disease, so remove the black tile. Proceed through all the squares, until you have rolled the die 16 times.

5. If two plants of the same species are next to each other, the disease will spread from one to the other. Suppose squares 2 and 3 contain red plants. If you roll a 1 for square 2, the red plant on squares 2 and 3 die. In this case, the die does not need to be rolled for square 3. Similarly, if the inner square next to square 2 also contains a red plant, it dies and should be covered with a black tile.

6. For each round, record in a data table the number of tiles of each species you started with and the number of each species left alive at the end of the round.

Disease Key	
Roll of Die	**Infected Color**
1	Red
2	Orange
3	Yellow
4	Blue
5	Green
6	All colors

Round _____		
Color of Species	**Number at Start**	**Number at End**
Red		
Orange		
Yellow	Answers will vary	
Blue		
Green		
TOTAL		

Conclude and Apply

Error Analysis

Inspect the grids made by students before they begin the activity. Make certain they arrange the tiles properly before beginning each round.

Answers to Questions

1. Answers may vary depending on the roll of the die, but round 3 should have the fewest survivors.

2. One disease is not likely to infect more than one species of plant. A high biodiversity of plants isolates a disease to one or a few individual plants preventing it from spreading throughout the population.

3. Varying crop species in a field creates a higher biodiversity and reduces the risk of disease wiping out an entire crop.

Conclude and Apply

1. Which round had the lowest number of survivors?

2. Why does a high biodiversity help a community survive?

3. Why do organic farmers often grow crops of different species in the same field?

*C*ommunicating Your Data

Share your results from Round Four with your classmates. Decide which arrangement and number of red tiles yields the best harvest.

ACTIVITY   E ◆ 145

Assessment

Process Ask students to infer why exotic species of plants introduced into an ecosystem often choke out native species, lowering the plant biodiversity. Exotic species are often immune to the diseases of the new ecosystem, or there are no predators in the ecosystem to reduce their populations. As a result, they crowd out native species reducing the plant biodiversity. Use **PASC,** p. 89.

*C*ommunicating Your Data

Have students test their set ups several times to determine the best possible arrangements of plant species. Make a display of these arrangements in the classroom.

Content Background

As rain forests are lost, yet undiscovered compounds in plants that may be of use in the treatment of many diseases also are lost. Several treatments for cardiovascular disease and cancer have been developed from rain forest sources. The most commonly used drug in the world, aspirin, is based on the chemistry of a compound taken from tropical willow trees.

The source of these treatments is the diversity of plant life in the rain forest. The heavy rainfall, high humidity and warm temperatures are responsible for the diversity of trees, which themselves support diverse species of vines, mosses, lichens, and orchids. In turn, these plants support communities of insects, spiders, and amphibians. Many of these organisms are host-specific, and thus are limited to living in one tree species.

This diversity of life depends entirely on a rapid recycling of nutrients; so rapid that soil formation in the tropics is very poor. Much of the tropical rain forest is being cleared to allow the expansion of agriculture. In a common technique called *slash-and-burn* agriculture, land is cleared and trees burned to produce nutrient rich ash that can be put into the poor soil. Heavy rains quickly wash away these nutrients, resulting in rapid depletion of an area's productivity and requiring further agricultural expansion.

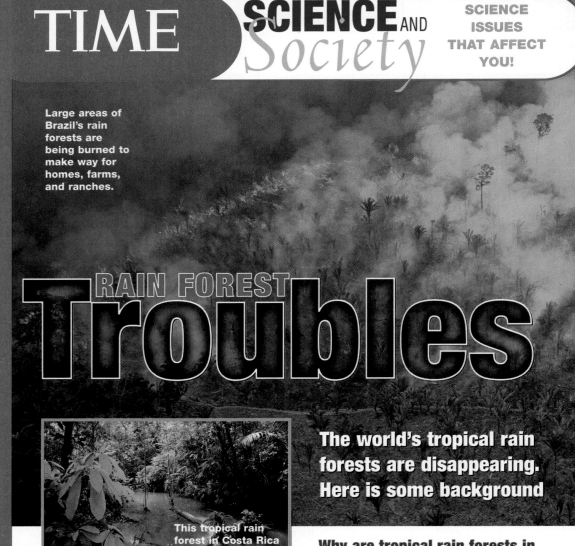

TIME SCIENCE AND Society

SCIENCE ISSUES THAT AFFECT YOU!

Large areas of Brazil's rain forests are being burned to make way for homes, farms, and ranches.

RAIN FOREST Troubles

The world's tropical rain forests are disappearing. Here is some background

This tropical rain forest in Costa Rica is untouched by human development.

Where are Earth's tropical rain forests?

Tropical rain forests are located on both sides of the equator. The average temperature in a rain forest is about 25 °C and doesn't vary much between day and night. Rain forests receive between 200 cm and 400 cm of rain each year.

Why are tropical rain forests in trouble?

Humans destroy as many as 20 million hectares of tropical rain forests each year. Farmers who live in tropical areas cut the trees to sell the wood and farm the land. After a few years, the crops use up the nutrients in the soil and more land must be cleared for farming. The logging and mining industries also contribute to the loss of valuable rain forest resources.

146 ◆ E

Resources for Teachers and Students

The Complete National Geographic, 109 years of National Geographic Magazine on CD-Rom, The National Geographic Society, 1998.

Life on Earth: a Natural History, by David Attenborough, Little, Brown, 1979.

Life on Earth: a Natural History Written and Hosted by David Attenborough, 1996, British Broadcasting Corporation and BBC Enterprises, Ltd. Available through Warner Home Video.

Why are rain forests so special?

Scientists estimate that there are about 30 million plant and animal species on this planet—and at least half of them live in rain forests! Tropical rain forests contain the highest diversity of life on Earth. In one hectare of Brazil's rain forest, you can find 425 different kinds of trees. That's at least ten times the number of trees from comparable areas of Europe and North America. And in one corner of Peru's rain forest, there are 1,300 different types of butterflies.

Even though tropical rain forests are located thousands of miles from the United States, they impact our lives every day. Plants in the forest remove carbon dioxide from the atmosphere and give off oxygen. Some of these plants are already used in medicines, and many more are being studied to determine their usefulness. But if the plants disappear, so might the cures waiting to be discovered.

What can be done to conserve the rain forests?

Conservationists suggest a number of solutions.

- Have governments protect rain forest land by establishing parks and conservation areas.
- Reduce the demand for industrial timber and paper. If people in nontropical areas find ways to cut back on their use of rain forest wood to build homes and make paper, trees will be saved.
- Require industries to use different tree-removal methods that cause less damage. Encourage loggers to plant new trees to replace the ones they cut down.
- Teach farmers alternative farming methods to decrease the damage to rain forest land.

- Offer money or lower taxes to farmers and logging companies for not cutting down trees on rain forest land.

How practical are these solutions?

Carrying out these plans would be difficult. Farmers who clear land to plant crops are concerned about their daily survival. "I have ten children and we must eat," said a farmer from the African nation of the Ivory Coast.

Most scientists believe that, at this rate, most of the rain forests will be gone by 2050. The problem extends much farther than the local farmers—the whole world strips rain forest resources in its demand for products such as food ingredients and lumber for building homes. But giving up is not a solution either. "It's going to take a lot to slow down the current rate of destruction," said one conservationist. "We don't have any choice, so we just have to keep churning forward."

Helping to save rain forests is Pedro Sanchez, a leading soil scientist. He specializes in research to find ecologically beneficial ways to farm tropical soils. He says, "Science can be a lot of fun, and I've always liked big challenges. Soil management provides an exciting challenge to find ways to feed the hungry world." And it helps to save the rain forests, too.

The delicate Alexandra butterfly lives in the rain forests of Papua New Guinea.

CONNECTIONS Present Prepare a multimedia presentation for an elementary class. Teach the class what the rain forest is, where rain forests are located, and how people benefit from rain forests.

SCIENCE
Online
For more information, visit
science.glencoe.com

CONNECTIONS Suggest that students prepare their presentations to illustrate how the survival of species is interrelated. Suggest they begin with illustrations of the various trees of the forest and the different habitat layers they form. They can follow these with illustrations of plants that depend on the trees. Subsequent illustrations may focus on insects that in turn serve as food for birds and mammals.

SCIENCE
Online
Internet Addresses

Explore the Glencoe Science Web site at **science.glencoe.com** to find out more about topics in this feature.

Discussion

Why is biodiversity so high in the tropical rain forest? Possible answers: Environmental conditions are favorable for growth of many species of plants; high humidity and rainfall promote rapid recycling of leaves and other natural litter; the forest is arranged in layers from the ground to tree trunks to the canopy, and each layer supports many differently adapted organisms.

How much diversity is found in the tropical rain forest? Estimates range from 5 to 30 million different species of plants and animals found in the rain forest alone.

Activity

Have students search discarded nature magazines to obtain pictures of different kinds of rain forest organisms. Organize these pictures according to where the organisms are found in the forest. For example, many butterfly species are found in the upper layers of the canopy, while many orchids are found growing on the limbs of trees. **Ⓝ Visual-Spatial**

Investigate the Issue

Organize the class into small groups. Have each group research the diversity of a different type of organism. Suggest students look for pictures of elaborately colored birds, butterflies, orchids, primates, and so on. When students are finished with their research, have them discuss the following questions. **Should the diversity of life in the rain forest be preserved for its own sake? Should we be concerned with conservation only because of potential medical benefits to humanity?**

Reviewing Main Ideas

Preview

Students can answer the questions in their Science Journals. Discuss the answers as you go through the chapter. **LS Linguistic**

Review

Students can write their answers, then compare them with those of other students. **LS Interpersonal**

Reteach

Students can look at the illustrations and describe details that support the main ideas of the chapter. **LS Visual-Spatial**

Answers to Chapter Review

SECTION 1

3. Humans caused the passenger pigeon extinction; dinosaur extinction occurred naturally.
4. It can divide habitats, which decreases biodiversity.

SECTION 2

3. Species need sufficient habitat to survive and maintain biodiversity.
4. by preventing the extinction of a species, and being reintroduced into the wild

Reviewing Main Ideas

Section 1 Biodiversity

1. A measure of biodiversity is the number of species present in an ecosystem.

2. In general, biodiversity is greater in warm, moist climates than in cold, dry climates.

3. Extinction occurs when the last member of a species dies. *How was the ancient extinction of the dinosaurs different from the recent extinction of the passenger pigeon?*

4. Habitat loss, pollution, overhunting, and introduced species can cause a species to become threatened or endangered. *In what ways can a road or highway affect biodiversity in an ecosystem?*

Section 2 Conservation Biology

1. Conservation biology is the study of methods for protecting Earth's biodiversity.

2. The Endangered Species Act preserves biodiversity by making it illegal to harm threatened or endangered species.

3. Habitat preservation, habitat restoration, and wildlife management strategies can be used to preserve species. *How does habitat preservation affect the amount of biodiversity?*

4. Reintroduction programs can be used to restore a species to an area where it once lived. *How can captive populations contribute to biodiversity?*

FOLDABLES
Reading & Study Skills

After You Read

Write what you learned about biodiversity under the right tab of your Know-What-Learn Study Fold. Explain the importance of biodiversity.

FOLDABLES
Reading & Study Skills

After You Read

After students have read the chapter and completed the Foldable described in Before You Read, have them do the activity on the student page.

Dinah Zike

Visualizing Main Ideas

Complete the following concept map using the following terms: habitat restoration, captive populations, relocation, and endangered species.

Vocabulary Review

Vocabulary Words

a. acid rain
b. biodiversity
c. captive population
d. conservation biology
e. endangered species
f. extinct species
g. habitat restoration
h. introduced species
i. native species
j. ozone depletion
k. reintroduction program
l. threatened species

Using Vocabulary

Explain the differences in the vocabulary words given below. Then explain how the words are related.

1. habitat restoration, threatened species
2. endangered species, extinct species
3. biodiversity, conservation biology
4. biodiversity, captive population
5. acid rain, ozone depletion
6. introduced species, endangered species
7. native species, introduced species
8. biodiversity, extinct species
9. reintroduction program, native species

Visualizing Main Ideas

See student page.

Vocabulary Review

Using Vocabulary

1. Habitat restoration can help threatened species survive.
2. An endangered species is in jeopardy of becoming an extinct species.
3. Conservation biology studies methods of protecting biodiversity.
4. Captive populations can slow the decline in biodiversity.
5. Acid rain and destruction of the ozone layer are environmental problems that can harm organisms. They are not directly related.
6. Introduced species can create or jeopardize endangered species.
7. Introduced species have no natural predators in the area, therefore they may threaten native species.
8. When the number of extinct species increases, biodiversity declines.
9. Reintroduction programs bring native species back to an area where their population has declined.

Checking Concepts

1. A
2. B
3. A
4. B
5. A
6. C
7. A
8. B
9. A
10. C

Thinking Critically

11. reducing use of fossil fuels, cutting fewer trees, planting more trees
12. fixing the problem or problems that led to the species' decline in nature and then reintroducing the organism into its natural habitat; captive breeding to maintain population
13. B
14. Answers will vary, but may include that residents want the species removed but conservation biologists want them to stay, or that biologists want residents to change how they do things, such as fertilizer application or waste treatment.
15. Without sufficient habitat, organisms cannot obtain what they need from the environment.

Chapter 5 Assessment

Checking Concepts

Choose the word or phrase that best answers the question.

1. Which state probably has the greatest biodiversity?
   A) Florida
   B) Maine
   C) New Hampshire
   D) West Virginia

2. Jen has a tank with 20 guppies. June has a tank with 5 guppies, 5 mollies, 5 swordtails, and 5 platys. Which of the following is true?
   A) June has more fish than Jen.
   B) June's tank has more biodiversity than Jen's tank.
   C) Jen has more fish than June.
   D) Jen's tank has more biodiversity than June's tank.

3. Which of the following is not considered an endangered species?
   A) Florida panther
   B) Florida manatee
   C) California condor
   D) American alligator

4. Which of these is the greatest threat to the Lake Erie water snake?
   A) air pollution
   B) habitat loss
   C) ozone
   D) introduced species

5. What damages the ozone layer?
   A) air pollution
   B) global warming
   C) acid precipitation
   D) biodegradable materials

6. Which of the following gases contributes to global warming?
   A) oxygen
   B) nitrogen
   C) carbon dioxide
   D) acidic water vapor

7. What would you call a species that never lived on an island until it was brought there by people?
   A) introduced
   B) endangered
   C) native
   D) threatened

8. Which of the following conservation strategies involves passing laws to protect species?
   A) habitat restoration
   B) legal protections
   C) reintroduction programs
   D) captive populations

9. Which of these organisms is extinct?
   A) passenger pigeon
   B) African elephant
   C) wheat
   D) black rhinoceros

10. The water hyacinth is native to South America. People brought it to the waterways of Florida, where it grows out of control, killing native plants and blocking water flow. Which of the following best describes the water hyacinth?
    A) threatened
    B) extinct
    C) introduced
    D) endangered

Thinking Critically

11. What action(s) could people take to help reduce the types of air pollution that might contribute to global warming?

12. What conservation strategies would most likely help preserve a species whose members are found only in zoos?

13. Four ways to design a road system for a national park are shown below. Which arrangement would best avoid dividing this habitat into pieces?

    a. b. c. d.

14. Why might the protection of an endangered species create conflict between local residents and conservation biologists?

15. Why is habitat loss the most serious threat to biodiversity?

Chapter ✓Assessment Planner

Portfolio Encourage students to place in their portfolios one or two items of what they consider to be their best work. Examples include:
- Extension, p. 128
- Science Journal, p. 130
- Curriculum Connection, p. 141

Performance Additional performance assessments, Performance Task Assessment Lists, and rubrics for evaluating these activities can be found in Glencoe's **Performance Assessment in the Science Classroom.**

Developing Skills

16. Concept Mapping Draw an events-chain concept map using the following terms: *species, extinct species, endangered species,* and *threatened species.*

17. Recognizing Cause and Effect Design a wildlife management plan to allow deer hunting in a state park without damaging the ecosystem.

18. Making and Using Graphs Use the data in the table to make a bar graph.

Wildlife Habitat Lost		
Country	Area Lost (km²)	Area Remaining (km²)
Ethiopia	770,700	330,300
Vietnam	265,680	66,420
Indonesia	708,751	746,860

19. Forming Hypotheses In divided wildlife areas, large animals have a greater chance of becoming extinct than other organisms do. Suggest a hypothesis to explain why this is true.

20. Comparing and Contrasting Explain how legal protections and wildlife management are similar and different.

Performance Assessment

21. Poster Use images from magazines to create a display about how humans threaten Earth's biodiversity.

TECHNOLOGY

Go to the Glencoe Science Web site at **science.glencoe.com** or use the **Glencoe Science CD-ROM** for additional chapter assessment.

Test Practice

A construction team is building a road that runs through an area near two lakes. The team must choose between road plan A and plan B.

Plan A

Plan B

1. A conservation biologist is asked to evaluate how each plan would affect the biodiversity of the ecosystem that includes the two lakes. The biologist urges the road construction team to follow plan A. Why?
  A) It introduces new species.
  B) It does not divide the habitat into small areas.
  C) It makes the road easier to drive along and view animals.
  D) It helps keep more water in both of the lakes.

2. Which species is least likely to be affected if the road construction team follows plan B?
  F) water snakes   **H)** algae
  G) frogs   **J)** birds

Test Practice

The Test-Taking Tip was written by The Princeton Review, the nation's leader in test preparation.
1. B
2. J

Developing Skills

16. map should show progression from: species → threatened → endangered → extinct

17. Answers will vary, but should allow deer hunting when the population rises and prohibit it when populations decline or when species are reproducing.

18. Graphs should show: Area lost (most to least)—Ethiopia, Indonesia, Vietnam; Area remaining (most to least)—Indonesia, Ethiopia, Vietnam

19. Large animals need more habitat to meet their needs. In a divided habitat, organisms may be confined to areas that are too small to ensure their survival.

20. Legal protections stop the killing of endangered or threatened organisms. Wildlife management usually affects a specific locale—national or state park—and allows hunting or collection of organisms, but tries to prevent their excessive loss.

Performance Assessment

21. Possible threats to include: pollution, habitat loss, divided habits, introduced species. Use **PASC,** p. 145.

✓Assessment Resources

 Reproducible Masters

Chapter Resources Booklet
  Chapter Review, pp. 35–36
  Chapter Tests, pp. 37–40
  Assessment Transparency Activity, p. 47

Glencoe Science Web site
  Interactive Tutor
  Chapter Quizzes

Glencoe Technology
  🔋 Assessment Transparency
  🖫 Interactive CD-ROM Chapter Quizzes
  🖫 ExamView Pro Test Bank
  🖫 Vocabulary PuzzleMaker Software
  📼 MindJogger Videoquiz DVD/VHS

Standardized Test Practice

QUESTION 1: B

Students must use information from the passage to identify the best supported answer choice.

- **Choice A** No; this is the reverse order of the food chain described in the passage.
- **Choice B** Yes; this is the food chain described in the passage.
- **Choice C** No; this is not the food chain described in the passage.
- **Choice D** No; this is not the food chain described in the passage.

QUESTION 2: J

Students must use information from the passage to identify the best-supported answer choice.

- **Choice F** No; this is a producer.
- **Choice G** No; this is an herbivore.
- **Choice H** No; this is a source of energy.
- **Choice J** Yes; this is a predator.

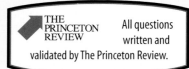
Read the passage. Then read each question that follows the passage. Decide which is the best answer to each question.

Interactions in Ecosystems

Fearing for their safety and the safety of their livestock, early settlers of northern Wisconsin killed the native timberwolves. Timberwolves are a natural predator of white-tailed deer. Over time the deer population increased in size. The available vegetation could not support the deer population. Even though emergency feeding stations were set up, thousands of deer died of starvation. The deer population now is kept down by controlled hunting seasons. In some areas wolves have been reintroduced.

An ecosystem consists of organisms, from many different species, living together and connected by the flow of energy, nutrients and matter. Organisms in an ecosystem can be classified as either producers or consumers. Most producers use the Sun's radiant energy and convert it into chemical energy through photo-synthesis. Consumers take in and use this chemical energy. Herbivores eat producers, carnivores eat other consumers, and omnivores eat both producers and consumers. As organisms die, decomposers take in and use the energy in the dead organisms. In doing so, they release nutrients into the soil and carbon dioxide into the air that are used by producers again.

The loss of one species from an ecosystem may lead to the overpopulation or extinction of other species. This loss degrades the ecosystem upon which humans and other organisms depend for clean air, water, and food.

Test-Taking Tip Use the figure to help you visualize the ecosystem that is being described in the passage.

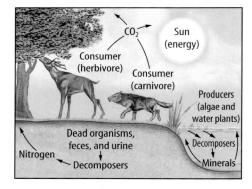

The major components of an ecosystem

1. Food chains are a way of showing how energy, nutrients and matter flow through an ecosystem. Which of the following is a food chain of the ecosystem described in the passage?
   A) carnivore, producer, herbivore
   B) producer, herbivore, carnivore
   C) carnivore, producer, decomposer
   D) decomposer, carnivore, herbivore

2. Predators are consumers that capture and eat other consumers. The presence of a predator limits the size of the prey population. This means that food and other resources are less likely to become scarce. What is the predator in this passage?
   F) vegetation
   G) deer
   H) Sun
   J) timberwolf

Read each question and choose the best answer.

1. Within an ecosystem there are many populations as well as abiotic factors. Groups of populations that interact within a specific area of an ecosystem are referred to as which of the following?
   A) a habitat
   B) a community
   C) a food web
   D) an atmosphere

Test-Taking Tip Think about the levels of an ecosystem and how they relate to each other.

World Population

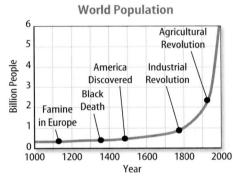

2. Refer to the World Population graph. In which of the following years were the birth rate and the death rate nearly equal?
   F) 1,800
   G) 2,000
   H) 1,200
   J) 1,600

Test-Taking Tip Consider what you know about the effects of birth and death rates on population size.

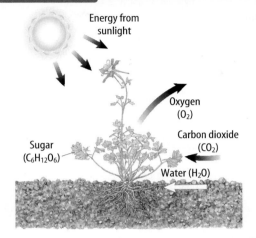

Energy from sunlight

Oxygen (O_2)

Carbon dioxide (CO_2)

Sugar ($C_6H_{12}O_6$)

Water (H_2O)

3. The conversion of energy is important to all life on Earth. Some producers use sunlight as an energy source, converting it into chemical energy through photosynthesis. Other producers that live where sunlight does not reach them, can use which of the following as an energy source?
   A) water   C) soil
   B) air   D) chemicals

Test-Taking Tip Read about converting energy before answering the question.

Consider this question carefully before writing your answer on a separate sheet of paper.

4. Ecologists are encouraging people to take buses and trains rather than drive their own cars. They say this will help reduce air pollution. How will having more people take public transportation reduce air pollution?

Test-Taking Tip Imagine how 100 people on a train instead of 100 cars on the highway would affect air pollution.

QUESTION 1: B
Students must understand populations and ecosystems. Only B, *a community*, is correct.

QUESTION 2: H
Students must understand that if the birth rate and the death rate are equal, then there is no growth in the population. Only H, *1,200*, notes a year on the graph in which the growth rate does not change.

QUESTION 3: D
Students must understand producers and energy conversion in order to identify D, *chemicals*, as the correct answer choice. Choices A, B, and C are used whether or not the producer receives sunlight.

QUESTION 4: Answers will vary.
Students should understand that transporting many people in one large vehicle or other mode of transportation consumes less energy and produces less pollution than transporting each person individually.

Teaching Tip

Suggest that students brainstorm a list of ideas and then organize these ideas before writing a response.

Student Resources

CONTENTS

About the Field Guide

- This field guide contains a key that enables the user to classify or identify some biomes.
- This field guide applies globally; local and regional resources are available for more specific local use. Several sources of information are listed below.
- In using a field guide, students will apply steps of a scientific method as they observe, investigate, and draw conclusions.
- Encourage students to use this field guide outside the classroom.

Tie to Prior Knowledge

Students will probably be familiar with your local biome. However, they may not be aware of the diversity of organisms present. Have students list as many plants and animals as they can think of that they have seen in your local biome.

Field Activity

Student answers should be based on information obtained from a local weather station or newspaper. Student graphs will not be identical to the graphs in the field guide but should resemble one closely enough to draw conclusions. The types of organisms found will vary depending on the biome in which you live.

Why don't you find polar bears in Florida or palm trees in Alaska? Organisms are limited to certain areas where they can live and survive due to factors such as temperature, amount of rainfall, and type of soil that is found in a region. A biome's boundaries are determined by climate more than anything else. Climate is a way of categorizing temperature extremes and yearly precipitation patterns. Use this field guide to identify some of the world's biomes and to determine which biome you live in.

Interpreting Land Biome Climates

The following graphs represent typical climates in seven different biomes. To read each biome graph, use the following information. Axis A shows the months of the year. Axis B shows the average amount of precipitation for each month. Axis C shows the average high and low temperature for each month.

Key	
☐	Temperature range (°C)
☐	Precipitation (cm)

Biomes

Tundra

Winters in the tundra are long and harsh, and summers are short. There is little precipitation. In the tundra, you can find mosses, lichens, grasses, and sedges. Weasels, arctic foxes, snowshoe hares, snowy owls, and hawks can live there.

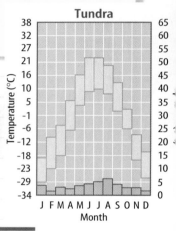

Tundra

Field Activity

Research to find last year's monthly averages for rainfall, high temperature, and low temperature for your area or a nearby city. For further help on last year's averages, visit the Glencoe Science Web site at **science.glencoe.com.** Prepare a graph of data using the example above. Based on your findings, which biome graph most closely matches your data? What biome do you live in? What type of plant and animal life do you expect to find in your biome?

Resources for Teachers and Students

Biomes of the World, Volumes 1–9, by Michael Allaby, Grolier Educational, 1999.

The Natural History of North America, by Edward Ricciuti, Random House, Cresent, 1995.

SCIENCE Online
Internet Addresses

Explore the Glencoe Science Web site at **science.glencoe.com** to find out more about topics in this field guide.

Taiga

Winters in the taiga are cold and severe with much snow. Growing seasons are short. Conifers such as spruces, firs, and larches are common. In the taiga, you find caribou, wolves, moose, bear, ducks, loons, and owls.

Taiga
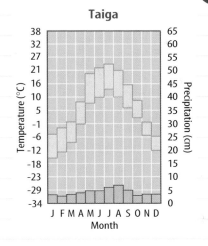

Temperate Deciduous Forest

The temperate deciduous forest has cold winters, hot summers, and moderate precipitation. In a temperate deciduous forest, you can see trees such as oak, hickory, and beech, which lose their leaves every autumn. Wolves, deer, bears, small mammals, and birds are common in a temperate deciduous forest.

Temperate Deciduous Forest

FIELD GUIDE E ◆ 157

Discussion

Lead students in a discussion about plants and animals of the biome in which you live. **Why might you not be able to observe the expected types of plants and animals in your biome?** Many plants and animals live only in certain areas of a given biome. For example, pink ladies slipper orchids are found in temperate forests, but only in certain soils. Therefore, you could live in a temperate region and never see a pink ladies slipper.

Teacher FYI

The taiga is forest that lies south of the tundra. Most trees that grow in the taiga are conifers. Usually these areas are too cold and have soil that is too poor to support the growth of tall trees. The taiga is home to many species of birds, including several species of woodpeckers and owls. Mammals that live in the taiga biome include elk, lynx and snowshoe hares.

Using Science Words

Word Meaning Have students investigate the meaning of the word *deciduous*, which is derived from Latin. The word *deciduous* means "to fall off" and describes the seasonal shedding of leaves by trees. Trees that shed their leaves each year are called deciduous trees.

Curriculum Connection

Geography The Grand Canyon has starkly different climate zones that are arranged vertically instead of horizontally. The floor of the canyon has a hot, dry climate and vegetation similar to that of the Sonoran Desert. The rim of the canyon has piñon pines, which are typical of mid-altitude mountain slopes. Explain to students that the rim of the canyon is far above its floor, accounting for its major climatic differences. Have students locate the Grand Canyon on a map of the United States and determine in which biome it is located. **LS Visual-Spatial**

Field Guide

Quick Demo

Obtain a map of the United States. Use the information in the field guide to show students how the United States is divided into biomes.
IS Visual-Spatial

Extension

Explain to students that biomes are not static, permanent divisions. The biome of a particular area can change over time. Have students research an area that has been classified into different biomes in different time periods throughout history. Have them report their findings to the class.
IS Logical-Mathematical

Discussion

What are some adaptations that grasslands organisms might have? Explain. Possible answers: These organisms must be adapted to living without much water in the summer and winter. The organisms must also be able to withstand hot summers and cold winters, or be able to migrate.

Temperate Rain Forest

Temperate Rainforest

The summers and the winters in the temperate rain forest are mild. Temperatures rarely fall below freezing. The temperate rain forest has heavy precipitation and high humidity. Trees with needlelike leaves, mosses, and ferns are common. Many organisms including salamanders, frogs, black bears, cougars, pileated woodpeckers, and owls live in the temperate rain forest.

Grassland

There is little precipitation during the grassland's cold winters and hot summers. The plants in the grassland are predominantly grasses although there are also a few trees. The grassland supports grazing animals, wolves, prairies dogs, foxes, ferrets, snakes, lizards, and insects.

Grassland

SCIENCE Online
Internet Addresses

_____

_____

_____

Explore the Glencoe Science Web site at **science.glencoe.com** to find out more about topics in this field guide.

Science Journal

Transitional Biome The grasslands are a transitional biome. This means that if amounts of average precipitation change, the area will become a different biome. Have students write a paragraph in their Science Journals that describes what they think would happen if a grassland biome received either more or less precipitation. **IS Linguistic**

Desert

Deserts are warm to hot in the daytime and cool in the evening. They receive sparse precipitation throughout the year. Cacti, yuccas, Joshua trees, and bunchgrasses grow in the desert. Small rodents, jackrabbits, birds of prey, and snakes are common in the desert.

Desert

Temperature (°C): 38, 32, 27, 21, 16, 10, 5, -1, -6, -12, -18, -23, -29, -34

Precipitation (cm): 65, 60, 55, 50, 45, 40, 35, 30, 25, 20, 15, 10, 5, 0

Month: J F M A M J J A S O N D

Content Background

Deserts are known for venomous species of spiders and scorpions. However, only a few of the many species of spiders and scorpions are venomous enough to endanger humans. For example, the tarantula and giant hairy scorpion look fierce, but they are not deadly to humans.

Fun Fact

Many students think deserts are large expanses of sand that have little or no life. In fact, most deserts contain a large variety of plants and animals that are specially adapted to living in desert environments.

Tropical Rain Forest

Temperature (°C): 38, 32, 27, 21, 16, 10, 5, -1, -6, -12, -18, -23, -29, -34

Precipitation (cm): 65, 60, 55, 50, 45, 40, 35, 30, 25, 20, 15, 10, 5, 0

Month: J F M A M J J A S O N D

Tropical Rain Forest

The tropical rain forest is hot all year with precipitation almost every day. A great diversity of plants grow in the tropical rain forest. It is where many birds, reptiles, insects, monkeys, and sloths live.

Visual Learning

Tropical Rain Forest As students study the illustration, have them note the canopy, or heavy layer of growth at the top level of the forest. In many parts of the rain forest, this canopy allows little light to penetrate to the forest floor. Many plants have adaptations that allow them to grow close to the top of the canopy in order to receive light. **What can you infer light levels are like in the understory, which is below the canopy?** Light levels are low here, and plants grow in the shade.

Inclusion Strategies

Learning Disabled Have students make "biome boxes" using shoe boxes. Direct them to label their boxes with a particular biome name. They should then cut out or draw pictures that represent the plant and animal life found in that biome and arrange them in the biome box.

Field Guides

About the Field Guide

- A field guide enables the user to classify or identify an item or concept.
- In using a field guide, students apply steps of a scientific method as they observe, investigate, and draw conclusions.
- This Waste Management field guide applies nationally; local and regional fields guides are usually available for more specific local use.
- Encourage students to use the field guide outside.

Tie to Prior Knowledge

Have students recall items they have used so far today that are made of recyclable plastics. Have them bring in empty, plastic soft-drink bottles, milk jugs and other plastic items and show the recycling code that is imprinted on each item.

Field Activity

Numbers are placed on plastic products by recyclers to indicate the type of plastic resin used in their manufacture. The Plastics Code System is presented in **Table 1**. It is the basis for sorting plastics sent for recycling, but does not necessarily mean they are recyclable. The largest percentage should be Code 4; the smallest, Code 7. Have students research to find out what, if any, uses there are for each code of reclaimed plastic.

Managing waste properly can reduce the use of resources and prevent pollution. To cut down on waste production and reduce harm to the environment, people can follow the three Rs of waste management: reduce, reuse, and recycle. For example, a 450-g, family-sized box of cereal uses a lot less cardboard than 18 25-g single-serving boxes use. Finding other functions for used items could include donating magazines that you already have read to local hospitals, nursing homes, or even your doctor's office. You can use many products every day that are recyclable. Also, you can help complete the cycle by purchasing items that are made from recycled materials.

Types of Recyclables

Recycled items are either pre- or post-consumer. Pre-consumer items are made of pieces that were left over during manufacturing. Pre-consumer items have never been used by a consumer. Post-consumer items are made of products that have been used, recycled, and made into something new. Cereal boxes, plastic bottles, writing paper, paper towels, and tissues often include post-consumer recycled materials.

Waste Management

Paper

White paper, newspaper, magazines, and telephone books are common paper goods that can be recycled. New products made from these items include newsprint, cardboard, egg cartons, and building materials. Not all glossy and colored papers are recyclable at all recycling centers. As with any recycled material, you should check with your local recycling center for specific instructions about properly sorting your paper goods.

Field Activity

Collect recyclable plastics in your school for one week. Using the Plastics Code System Table, organize the plastic products by code number so that they can be recycled. In your Science Journal, make a bar graph showing the amount and types of plastic you collected.

Resources for Teachers and Students

Use Less Stuff: Environmental Solutions for Who We Really Are, by Robert M. Lilienfeld and William L. Rathje, Fawcett Rook Group, 1998.

The McGraw-Hill Recycling Handbook, by Herbert F. Lund, McGraw-Hill Professional Book Group, 2000.

The Toilet Papers: Recycling Waste and Conserving Water, by Sim Van der Ryn, Chelsea Green Publishing, 2000.

Plastics

Plastics are difficult products to recycle. Most plastics are composed of complex molecules that tend not to break down easily. Many types of plastics exist, and they often cannot be recycled together. **Table 1** lists the codes that are used to sort plastic items for recycling. Plastic is recycled into lumber, containers, carpet, and other products.

Table 1	The Plastics Code System	
Code	Material	
1	PETE	Polyethylene terephthalate
2	HDPE	High-density polyethylene
3	PVC	Polyvinyl chloride
4	LDPE	Low-density polyethylene
5	PP	Polypropylene
6	PS	Polystyrene
7	Other	All others and mixed

Glass

Glass often is separated by color before recycling. Most glass bottles are recyclable, but some glassware such as lightbulbs is too thin to be recycled. New products made from recycled glass include food and beverage containers.

Activity

Have students work in groups to hunt for classroom items that could be recycled. Eventually, call a halt to the search and ask a member from each group to write the results on the board. Have the class compare and discuss the results. Additionally, discuss with them the fate of any hazardous wastes that might be generated in their science classroom.

Extension

Challenge students to find out what recycling programs are actually in place in their school. Of the items the class found that could be recycled, which ones will be recycled? Have students present their findings to the class.

Content Background

Code 2 plastic, also known as HDPE (high density polyethylene) is the most useful kind for recycling. Among other things, it is used to make translucent, milk jugs. Because of its neutral color, it can be changed into various colors during recycling. During recycling, bales of HDPE are broken and ground into small flakes about 1 cm in diameter. The small flakes are washed and floated in a solution to remove heavy impurities. The clean, plastic pieces are then dried by hot air and packaged to be used for the production of plastic pipes, traffic cones, plastic lumbers, combs, trash cans, and bottles for holding materials other than food.

Use Science Words

Word Meaning The first six code numbers of plastic are also referred to by what type of plastic they contain. Some terms used to describe recyclable plastics are common. For example, plastic code 6 is also called PS (polystyrene). This type of plastic may be familiar to students. It is commonly used in Styrofoam cups, food trays, and other packaging.

Content Background

The billions of microbes in a compost pile digest yard and kitchen wastes and create productive soil. Sometimes worms and insects help them. It is important to note that some organic wastes must never go into a compost pile. Chemically treated wood products can contain toxic levels of arsenic, chromium and copper. Diseased plants can infect a garden. Human and pet wastes can transmit diseases. Pernicious weeds can multiply in a new garden. Meat, bones, and fatty food wastes are slow to break down and will attract pests, including rodents.

Visual Learning

Ask students to examine the cans shown on this page. Have them try to identify the type of metal each is made of, and make a list of items in their homes made of this type of metal. Discuss whether any of the items at home might be further recycled.

Metals

A variety of metals are recyclable. Steel is the most common material recycled in the United States. Steel is recycled into any item new steel would be used for such as food cans, structural beams for buildings, and parts for automobiles. Aluminum is a commonly recycled material. It is recycled into new beverage cans, lawn chair frames, siding, and cookware. Even precious metals that are used in laboratories or in jewelry such as gold, silver, and platinum are recyclable. Recycling steel saves enough energy to supply one-fifth of the households in the United States (18 million homes) electricity for one year. A recycled aluminum beverage can uses 95 percent less energy to produce than a can made from new aluminum, which is enough energy to burn a 100W light bulb for three and a half ($3\frac{1}{2}$) hours.

Organic Waste

Organic waste such as yard trimmings, food waste, paper, and wood make up a large percentage of solid waste in the United States. Composting is one way to recycle organic wastes. Food and yard wastes can be placed in compost bins and converted into nutrient rich soil. Mulching is another way to recycle yard waste and wood. In some communities grass clippings, leaves, sticks, and other yard waste can be shredded at local recycling centers to make mulch. Mulch is used to reduce water loss from soil and to keep weeds from growing. As the mulch decays it enriches the soil.

Inclusion Strategies

Learning Disabled Have students visit several restaurants near their homes or their school. Have them meet with the restaurant manager or staff and determine what glass or metallic materials are used. Have students collect samples of the recyclable products used by the restaurants and determine how they should be separated for recycling.

Household Hazardous Wastes

Household Hazardous Wastes (HHWs) include household and car batteries, bleach, household cleaners, paint, paint thinner, motor oil, gasoline, herbicides, pesticides, solvents, and automotive fluids. They contain chemicals that can cause injury or are harmful if used, stored, or discarded improperly. HHWs are marked with a skull and crossbones, caution words or special handling directions. HHWs should not be sent with other garbage to landfills or to incinerators. Water seeps into landfill areas and the toxins could end up in the water supply. Burning may send toxins into the air you breathe. Garbage companies and recycling agencies have free HHW drop-off days or locations.

Follow These Steps to Reduce HHWs:

1. Whenever possible, buy nontoxic alternatives to hazardous products.
2. If you buy a hazardous product, buy only what you need to do the job.
3. Before you store leftover products on the shelf, try to find someone who can use them.

Quick Demo

Place a number of common household products that are HHWs on a table. Lift each one and ask those who have the product in their homes to raise their hands. Read the special handling instructions on the packaging and ask students what precautions they take in handling each product. Include items like flashlight batteries, a bottle of bleach, drain cleaner, a medical thermometer, and an aerosol can of insect killer.

Use Science Words

Word Meaning Have students use the word *toxin* in a sentence describing its characteristics. Possible answer: A poisonous substance harmful to living things is a toxin.

Discussion

Finding nontoxic alternatives to hazardous products is often easier than you might think. For example, baking soda and hydrogen peroxide can perform a similar function to chlorine-based scouring powder. **What other alternatives to hazardous household products can you think of?** Possible answers might include: using rechargeable batteries, using a plumber's "snake" to clear a clogged drain instead of using drain cleaner, buying citronella candles to ward off mosquitoes, buying a digital, non-mercury thermometer.

Curriculum Connection

Health Mercury is a hazardous waste that can make its way into water supplies and has caused serious health problems in humans who depend on local water. Research to find a significant episode of mercury pollution in terms of human health. Report on your findings to the class.

Organizing Information

As you study science, you will make many observations and conduct investigations and experiments. You will also research information that is available from many sources. These activities will involve organizing and recording data. The quality of the data you collect and the way you organize it will determine how well others can understand and use it. In **Figure 1,** the student is obtaining and recording information using a microscope.

Putting your observations in writing is an important way of communicating to others the information you have found and the results of your investigations and experiments.

Researching Information

Scientists work to build on and add to human knowledge of the world. Before moving in a new direction, it is important to gather the information that already is known about a subject. You will look for such information in various reference sources. Follow these steps to research information on a scientific subject:

Step 1 Determine exactly what you need to know about the subject. For instance, you might want to find out what happened to local plant life when Mount St. Helens erupted in 1980.

Step 2 Make a list of questions, such as: When did the eruption begin? How long did it last? How large was the area in which plant life was affected?

Step 3 Use multiple sources such as textbooks, encyclopedias, government documents, professional journals, science magazines, and the Internet.

Step 4 List where you found the sources. Make sure the sources you use are reliable and the most current available.

Figure 1
Making an observation is one way to gather information directly.

Evaluating Print and Nonprint Sources

Not all sources of information are reliable. Evaluate the sources you use for information, and use only those you know to be dependable. For example, suppose you want information about the digestion of fats and proteins. You might find two Websites on digestion. One Web site contains "Fat Zapping Tips" written by a company that sells expensive, high-protein supplements to help your body eliminate excess fat. The other is a Web page on "Digestion and Metabolism" written by a well-respected medical school. You would choose the second Web site as the more reliable source of information.

In science, information can change rapidly. Always consult the most current sources. A 1985 source about the human genome would not reflect the most recent research and findings.

Interpreting Scientific Illustrations

As you research a science topic, you will see drawings, diagrams, and photographs. Illustrations help you understand what you read. Some illustrations are included to help you understand an idea that you can't see easily by yourself. For instance, you can't see the bones of a blue whale, but you can look at a diagram of a whale skeleton as labeled in **Figure 2** that helps you understand them. Visualizing a drawing helps many people remember details more easily. Illustrations also provide examples that clarify difficult concepts or give additional information about the topic you are studying.

Most illustrations have a label or a caption. A label or caption identifies the illustration or provides additional information to better explain it. Can you find the caption or labels in **Figure 2?**

Figure 2
A labeled diagram of the skeletal structure of a blue whale.

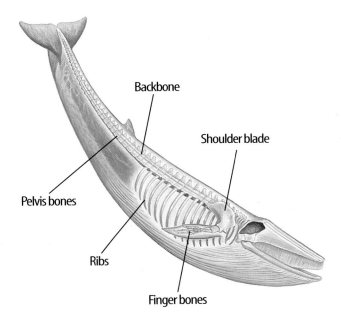

Backbone

Shoulder blade

Pelvis bones

Ribs

Finger bones

Concept Mapping

If you were taking a car trip, you might take some sort of road map. By using a map, you begin to learn where you are in relation to other places on the map.

A concept map is similar to a road map, but a concept map shows relationships among ideas (or concepts) rather than places. It is a diagram that visually shows how concepts are related. Because a concept map shows relationships among ideas, it can make the meanings of ideas and terms clear and help you understand what you are studying.

Overall, concept maps are useful for breaking large concepts down into smaller parts, making learning easier.

Venn Diagram

Although it is not a concept map, a Venn diagram illustrates how two subjects compare and contrast. In other words, you can see the characteristics that the subjects have in common and those that they do not.

The Venn diagram in **Figure 3** shows the relationship between two categories of organisms, plants and animals. Both share some basic characteristics as living organisms. However, there are differences in the ways they carry out various life processes, such as obtaining nourishment, that distinguish one from the other.

Figure 3
A Venn diagram shows how objects or concepts are alike and how they are different.

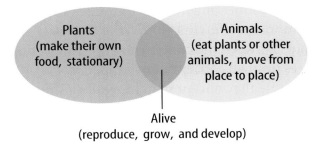

Plants
(make their own food, stationary)

Animals
(eat plants or other animals, move from place to place)

Alive
(reproduce, grow, and develop)

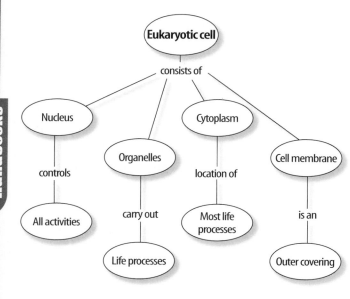

Figure 4
A network tree shows how concepts or objects are related.

Network Tree

Look at the concept map in **Figure 4,** that shows details about a eukaryotic cell. This is called a network tree concept map. Notice how some words are in ovals while others are written across connecting lines. The words inside the ovals are science terms or concepts. The words written on the connecting lines describe the relationships between the concepts.

When constructing a network tree, write the topic on a note card or piece of paper. Write the major concepts related to that topic on separate note cards or pieces of paper. Then arrange them in order from general to specific. Branch the related concepts from the major concept and describe the relationships on the connecting lines. Continue branching to more specific concepts. Write the relationships between the concepts on the connecting lines until all concepts are mapped. Then examine the concept map for relationships that cross branches, and add them to the concept map.

Events Chain

An events chain is another type of concept map. It models the order of items or their sequence. In science, an events chain can be used to describe a sequence of events, the steps in a procedure, or the stages of a process.

When making an events chain, first find the one event that starts the chain. This event is called the *initiating event.* Then, find the next event in the chain and continue until you reach an outcome. Suppose you are asked to describe the main stages in the growth of a plant from a seed. You might draw an events chain such as the one in **Figure 5.** Notice that connecting words are not necessary in an events chain.

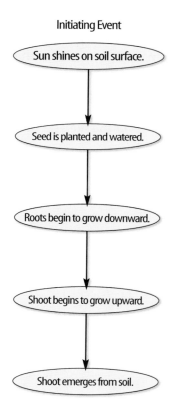

Figure 5
Events chains show the order of steps in a process or event.

Cycle Map A cycle concept map is a specific type of events chain map. In a cycle concept map, the series of events does not produce a final outcome. Instead, the last event in the chain relates back to the beginning event.

You first decide what event will be used as the beginning event. Once that is decided, you list events in order that occur after it. Words are written between events that describe what happens from one event to the next. The last event in a cycle concept map relates back to the beginning event. The number of events in a cycle concept varies, but is usually three or more. Look at the cycle map, as shown in **Figure 6.**

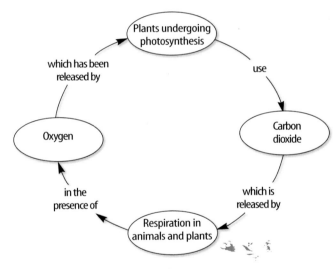

Figure 6
A cycle map shows events that occur in a cycle.

Spider Map A type of concept map that you can use for brainstorming is the spider map. When you have a central idea, you might find you have a jumble of ideas that relate to it but may not clearly relate to each other. The circulatory system spider map in **Figure 7** shows that if you write these ideas outside the main concept, then you can begin to separate and group unrelated terms so they become more useful.

Figure 7
A spider map allows you to list ideas that relate to a central topic but not necessarily to one another.

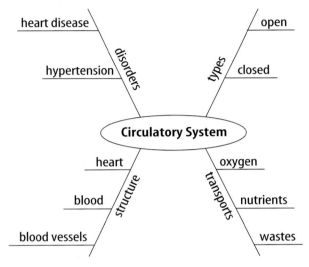

Writing a Paper

You will write papers often when researching science topics or reporting the results of investigations or experiments. Scientists frequently write papers to share their data and conclusions with other scientists and the public. When writing a paper, use these steps.

Step 1 Assemble your data by using graphs, tables, or a concept map. Create an outline.

Step 2 Start with an introduction that contains a clear statement of purpose and what you intend to discuss or prove.

Step 3 Organize the body into paragraphs. Each paragraph should start with a topic sentence, and the remaining sentences in that paragraph should support your point.

Step 4 Position data to help support your points.

Step 5 Summarize the main points and finish with a conclusion statement.

Step 6 Use tables, graphs, charts, and illustrations whenever possible.

You might say the work of a scientist is to solve problems. When you decide to find out why one corner of your yard is always soggy, you are problem solving, too. You might observe the corner is lower than the surrounding area and has less vegetation growing in it. You might decide to see if planting some grass will keep the corner drier.

Scientists use orderly approaches to solve problems. The methods scientists use include identifying a question, making observations, forming a hypothesis, testing a hypothesis, analyzing results, and drawing conclusions.

Scientific investigations involve careful observation under controlled conditions. Such observation of an object or a process can suggest new and interesting questions about it. These questions sometimes lead to the formation of a hypothesis. Scientific investigations are designed to test a hypothesis.

Identifying a Question

The first step in a scientific investigation or experiment is to identify a question to be answered or a problem to be solved. You might be interested in knowing why an animal like the one in **Figure 8** look the way they do.

Figure 8
When you see a bird, you might ask yourself, "How does the shape of this bird's beak help it feed?"

Forming Hypotheses

Hypotheses are based on observations that have been made. A hypothesis is a possible explanation based on previous knowledge and observations.

Perhaps a scientist has observed that bean plants grow larger if they are fertilized than if not. Based on these observations, the scientist can make a statement that he or she can test. The statement is a hypothesis. The hypothesis could be: *Fertilizer makes bean plants grow larger.* A hypothesis has to be something you can test by using an investigation. A testable hypothesis is a valid hypothesis.

Predicting

When you apply a hypothesis, or general explanation, to a specific situation, you predict something about that situation. First, you must identify which hypothesis fits the situation you are considering. People use predictions to make everyday decisions. Based on previous observations and experiences, you might form a prediction that if fertilizer makes bean plants grow larger, then fertilized plants will yield more beans than plants not fertilized. Someone could use this prediction to plan to grow fewer plants.

Testing a Hypothesis

To test a hypothesis, you need a procedure. A procedure is the plan you follow in your experiment. A procedure tells you what materials to use, as well as how and in what order to use them. When you follow a procedure, data are generated that support or do not support the original hypothesis statement.

For example, suppose you notice that your guppies don't seem as active as usual when your aquarium heater is not working. You wonder how water temperature affects guppy activity level. You decide to test the hypothesis, "If water temperature increases, then guppy activity should increase." Then you write the procedure shown in **Figure 9** for your experiment and generate the data presented in the table below.

> **Procedure**
> 1. Fill five identical glass containers with equal amounts of aquarium water.
> 2. Measure and record the temperature of the water in the first container.
> 3. Heat and cool the other containers so that two have higher and two have lower water temperatures.
> 4. Place a guppy in each container; count and record the number of movements each guppy makes in 5 minutes.

Figure 9
A procedure tells you what to do step by step.

Number of Guppy Movements		
Container	Temperature (°C)	Movements
1	38	56
2	40	61
3	42	70
4	36	46
5	34	42

Are all investigations alike? Keep in mind as you perform investigations in science that a hypothesis can be tested in many ways. Not every investigation makes use of all the ways that are described on these pages, and not all hypotheses are tested by investigations. Scientists encounter many variations in the methods that are used when they perform experiments. The skills in this handbook are here for you to use and practice.

Identifying and Manipulating Variables and Controls

In any experiment, it is important to keep everything the same except for the item you are testing. The one factor you change is called the independent variable. The factor that changes as a result of the independent variable is called the dependent variable. Always make sure you have only one independent variable. If you allow more than one, you will not know what causes the changes you observe in the dependent variable. Many experiments also have controls—individual instances or experimental subjects for which the independent variable is not changed. You can then compare the test results to the control results.

For example, in the guppy experiment, you made everything the same except the temperature of the water. The glass containers were identical. The volume of aquarium water in each container and beginning water temperature were the same. Each guppy was like the others, as much as possible. In this way, you could be sure that any difference in the number of guppy movements was caused by the temperature change—the independent variable. The activity level of the guppy was measured as the number of guppy movements—the dependent variable. The guppy in the container in which the water temperature was not changed was the control.

Collecting Data

Whether you are carrying out an investigation or a short observational experiment, you will collect data, or information. Scientists collect data accurately as numbers and descriptions and organize it in specific ways.

Observing Scientists observe items and events, then record what they see. When they use only words to describe an observation, it is called qualitative data. For example, a scientist might describe the color of a bird or the shape of a bird's beak as seen through binoculars. Scientists' observations also can describe how much there is of something. These observations use numbers, as well as words, in the description and are called quantitative data. For example, if a particular dog is described as being "furry, yellow, and short-haired," the data are clearly qualitative. Quantitative data for this dog might include "a mass of 14 kg, a height of 46 cm, and an age of 150 days." Quantitative data often are organized into tables. Then, from information in the table, a graph can be drawn. Graphs can reveal relationships that exist in experimental data.

When you make observations in science, you should examine the entire object or situation first, then look carefully for details. If you're looking at a plant, for instance, check general characteristics such as size and overall structure before using a hand lens to examine the leaves and other smaller structures such as flowers or fruits. Remember to record accurately everything you see.

Scientists try to make careful and accurate observations. When possible, they use instruments such as microscopes, metric rulers, graduated cylinders, thermometers, and balances. Measurements provide numerical data that can be repeated and checked.

Sampling When working with large numbers of objects or a large population, scientists usually cannot observe or study every one of them. Instead, they use a sample or a portion of the total number. To *sample* is to take a small, representative portion of the objects or organisms of a population for research. By making careful observations or manipulating variables within a portion of a group, information is discovered and conclusions are drawn that might apply to the whole population.

Estimating Scientific work also involves estimating. To *estimate* is to make a judgment about the size or the number of something without measuring or counting every object or member of a population. Scientists first count the number of objects in a small sample. Looking through a microscope lens, for example, a scientist can count the number of bacterial colonies in the 1-cm^2 frame shown in **Figure 10.** Then the scientist can multiply that number by the number of cm^2 in the petri dish to get an estimate of the total number of bacterial colonies present.

Figure 10

To estimate the total number of bacterial colonies that are present on a petri dish, count the number of bacterial colonies within a 1-cm^2 frame and multiply that number by the number of frames on the dish.

Measuring in SI

The metric system of measurement was developed in 1795. A modern form of the metric system, called the International System, or SI, was adopted in 1960. SI provides standard measurements that all scientists around the world can understand.

The metric system is convenient because unit sizes vary by multiples of 10. When changing from smaller units to larger units, divide by a multiple of 10. When changing from larger units to smaller, multiply by a multiple of 10. To convert millimeters to centimeters, divide the millimeters by 10. To convert 30 mm to centimeters, divide 30 by 10 (30 mm equal 3 cm).

Prefixes are used to name units. Look at the table below for some common metric prefixes and their meanings. Do you see how the prefix *kilo-* attached to the unit *gram* is *kilogram*, or 1,000 g?

Metric Prefixes			
Prefix	Symbol	Meaning	
kilo-	k	1,000	thousand
hecto-	h	100	hundred
deka-	da	10	ten
deci-	d	0.1	tenth
centi-	c	0.01	hundredth
milli-	m	0.001	thousandth

Now look at the metric ruler shown in **Figure 11.** The centimeter lines are the long, numbered lines, and the shorter lines are millimeter lines.

When using a metric ruler, line up the 0-cm mark with the end of the object being measured, and read the number of the unit where the object ends, in this instance it would be 4.5 cm.

Figure 11
This metric ruler shows centimeters and millimeter divisions.

Liquid Volume In some science activities, you will measure liquids. The unit that is used to measure liquids is the liter. A liter has the volume of 1,000 cm^3. The prefix *milli-* means "thousandth (0.001)." A milliliter is one thousandth of 1 L and 1 L has the volume of 1,000 mL. One milliliter of liquid completely fills a cube measuring 1 cm on each side. Therefore, 1 mL equals 1 cm^3.

You will use beakers and graduated cylinders to measure liquid volume. A graduated cylinder, as illustrated in **Figure 12,** is marked from bottom to top in milliliters. This graduated cylinder contains 79 mL of a liquid.

Figure 12
Graduated cylinders measure liquid volume.

Mass Scientists measure mass in grams. You might use a beam balance similar to the one shown in **Figure 13.** The balance has a pan on one side and a set of beams on the other side. Each beam has a rider that slides on the beam.

Before you find the mass of an object, slide all the riders back to the zero point. Check the pointer on the right to make sure it swings an equal distance above and below the zero point. If the swing is unequal, find and turn the adjusting screw until you have an equal swing.

Place an object on the pan. Slide the largest rider along its beam until the pointer drops below zero. Then move it back one notch. Repeat the process on each beam until the pointer swings an equal distance above and below the zero point. Sum the masses on each beam to find the mass of the object. Move all riders back to zero when finished.

Figure 13
A triple beam balance is used to determine the mass of an object.

You should never place a hot object on the pan or pour chemicals directly onto the pan. Instead, find the mass of a clean container. Remove the container from the pan, then place the chemicals in the container. Find the mass of the container with the chemicals in it. To find the mass of the chemicals, subtract the mass of the empty container from the mass of the filled container.

Making and Using Tables

Browse through your textbook and you will see tables in the text and in the activities. In a table, data, or information, are arranged so that they are easier to understand. Activity tables help organize the data you collect during an activity so results can be interpreted.

Making Tables To make a table, list the items to be compared in the first column and the characteristics to be compared in the first row. The title should clearly indicate the content of the table, and the column or row heads should tell the reader what information is found in there. The table below lists materials collected for recycling on three weekly pick-up days. The inclusion of kilograms in parentheses also identifies for the reader that the figures are mass units.

Recyclable Materials Collected During Week			
Day of Week	Paper (kg)	Aluminum (kg)	Glass (kg)
Monday	5.0	4.0	12.0
Wednesday	4.0	1.0	10.0
Friday	2.5	2.0	10.0

Using Tables How much paper, in kilograms, is being recycled on Wednesday? Locate the column labeled "Paper (kg)" and the row "Wednesday." The information in the box where the column and row intersect is the answer. Did you answer "4.0"? How much aluminum, in kilograms, is being recycled on Friday? If you answered "2.0," you understand how to read the table. How much glass is collected for recycling each week? Locate the column labeled "Glass (kg)" and add the figures for all three rows. If you answered "32.0," then you know how to locate and use the data provided in the table.

Recording Data

To be useful, the data you collect must be recorded carefully. Accuracy is key. A well-thought-out experiment includes a way to record procedures, observations, and results accurately. Data tables are one way to organize and record results. Set up the tables you will need ahead of time so you can record the data right away.

Record information properly and neatly. Never put unidentified data on scraps of paper. Instead, data should be written in a notebook like the one in **Figure 14.** Write in pencil so information isn't lost if your data gets wet. At each point in the experiment, record your data and label it. That way, your information will be accurate and you will not have to determine what the figures mean when you look at your notes later.

Figure 14
Record data neatly and clearly so it is easy to understand.

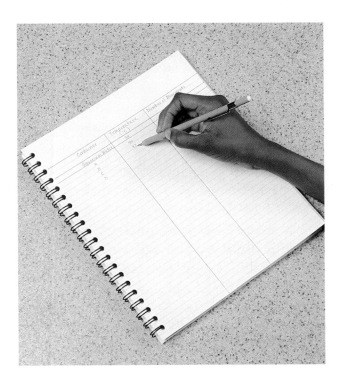

Recording Observations

It is important to record observations accurately and completely. That is why you always should record observations in your notes immediately as you make them. It is easy to miss details or make mistakes when recording results from memory. Do not include your personal thoughts when you record your data. Record only what you observe to eliminate bias. For example, when you record that a plant grew 12 cm in one day, you would note that this was the largest daily growth for the week. However, you would not refer to the data as "the best growth spurt of the week."

Making Models

You can organize the observations and other data you collect and record in many ways. Making models is one way to help you better understand the parts of a structure you have been observing or the way a process for which you have been taking various measurements works.

Models often show things that are very large or small or otherwise would be difficult to see and understand. You can study blood vessels and know that they are hollow tubes. The size and proportional differences among arteries, veins, and capillaries can be explained in words. However, you can better visualize the relative sizes and proportions of blood vessels by making models of them. Gluing different kinds of pasta to thick paper so the openings can be seen can help you see how the differences in size, wall thickness, and shape among types of blood vessels affect their functions.

Other models can be devised on a computer. Some models, such as disease control models used by doctors to predict the spread of the flu, are mathematical and are represented by equations.

Making and Using Graphs

After scientists organize data in tables, they might display the data in a graph that shows the relationship of one variable to another. A graph makes interpretation and analysis of data easier. Three types of graphs are the line graph, the bar graph, and the circle graph.

Line Graphs A line graph like in **Figure 15** is used to show the relationship between two variables. The variables being compared go on two axes of the graph. For data from an experiment, the independent variable always goes on the horizontal axis, called the *x*-axis. The dependent variable always goes on the vertical axis, called the *y*-axis. After drawing your axes, label each with a scale. Next, plot the data points.

A data point is the intersection of the recorded value of the dependent variable for each tested value of the independent variable. After all the points are plotted, connect them.

Bar Graphs Bar graphs compare data that do not change continuously. Vertical bars show the relationships among data.

To make a bar graph, set up the *y*-axis as you did for the line graph. Draw vertical bars of equal size from the *x*-axis up to the point on the *y*-axis that represents value of *x*.

Figure 16
The number of wing vibrations per second for different insects can be shown as a bar graph or circle graph.

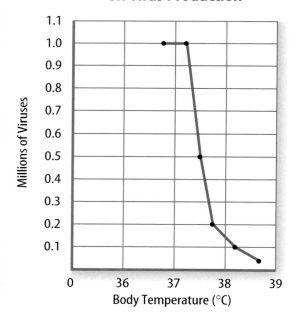

Wing Vibration Rates

Figure 15
This line graph shows the relationship between body temperature and the millions of infecting viruses present in a human body.

Circle Graphs A circle graph uses a circle divided into sections to display data as parts (fractions or percentages) of a whole. The size of each section corresponds to the fraction or percentage of the data that the section represents. So, the entire circle represents 100 percent, one-half represents 50 percent, one-fifth represents 20 percent, and so on.

Analyzing and Applying Results

Analyzing Results

To determine the meaning of your observations and investigation results, you will need to look for patterns in the data. You can organize your information in several of the ways that are discussed in this handbook. Then you must think critically to determine what the data mean. Scientists use several approaches when they analyze the data they have collected and recorded. Each approach is useful for identifying specific patterns in the data.

Forming Operational Definitions

An operational definition defines an object by showing how it functions, works, or behaves. Such definitions are written in terms of how an object works or how it can be used; that is, they describe its job or purpose.

For example, a ruler can be defined as a tool that measures the length of an object (how it can be used). A ruler also can be defined as something that contains a series of marks that can be used as a standard when measuring (how it works).

Classifying

Classifying is the process of sorting objects or events into groups based on common features. When classifying, first observe the objects or events to be classified. Then select one feature that is shared by some members in the group but not by all. Place those members that share that feature into a subgroup. You can classify members into smaller and smaller subgroups based on characteristics.

How might you classify a group of animals? You might first classify them by putting all of the dogs, cats, lizards, snakes, and birds into separate groups. Within each group,

you could then look for another common feature by which to further classify members of the group, such as size or color.

Remember that when you classify, you are grouping objects or events for a purpose. For example, classifying animals can be the first step in identifying them. You might know that a cardinal is a red bird. To find it in a large group of animals, you might start with the classification scheme mentioned above. You'll locate a cardinal within the red grouping of the birds that you separate from the rest of the animals. A male ruby-throated hummingbird could be located within the birds by its tiny size and the bright red color of its throat. Keep your purpose in mind as you select the features to form groups and subgroups.

Figure 17
Color is one of many characteristics that are used to classify animals.

Comparing and Contrasting

Observations can be analyzed by noting the similarities and differences between two or more objects or events that you observe. When you look at objects or events to see how they are similar, you are comparing them. Contrasting is looking for differences in objects or events. The table below compares and contrasts the nutritional value of two cereals.

Nutritional Values		
	Cereal A	**Cereal B**
Calories	220	160
Fat	10 g	10 g
Protein	2.5 g	2.6 g
Carbohydrate	30 g	15 g

Recognizing Cause and Effect

Have you ever gotten a cold and then suggested that you probably caught it from a classmate who had one recently? If so, you have observed an effect and inferred a cause. The event is the effect, and the reason for the event is the cause.

When scientists are unsure of the cause of a certain event, they design controlled experiments to determine what caused it.

Interpreting Data

The word *interpret* means "to explain the meaning of something." Look at the problem originally being explored in an experiment and figure out what the data show. Identify the control group and the test group so you can see whether or not changes in the independent variable have had an effect. Look for differences in the dependent variable between the control and test groups.

These differences you observe can be qualitative or quantitative. You would be able to describe a qualitative difference using only words, whereas you would measure a quantitative difference and describe it using numbers. If there are qualitative or quantitative differences, the independent variable that is being tested could have had an effect. If no qualitative or quantitative differences are found between the control and test groups, the variable that is being tested apparently had no effect.

For example, suppose that three pepper plants are placed in a garden and two of the plants are fertilized, but the third is left to grow without fertilizer. Suppose you are then asked to describe any differences in the plants after two weeks. A qualitative difference might be the appearance of brighter green leaves on fertilized plants but not on the unfertilized plant. A quantitative difference might be a difference in the height of the plants or the number of flowers on them.

Inferring Scientists often make inferences based on their observations. An inference is an attempt to explain, or interpret, observations or to indicate what caused what you observed. An inference is a type of conclusion.

When making an inference, be certain to use accurate data and accurately described observations. Analyze all of the data that you've collected. Then, based on everything you know, explain or interpret what you've observed.

Drawing Conclusions

When scientists have analyzed the data they collected, they proceed to draw conclusions about what the data mean. These conclusions are sometimes stated using words similar to those found in the hypothesis formed earlier in the process.

Conclusions To analyze your data, you must review all of the observations and measurements that you made and recorded. Recheck all data for accuracy. After your data are rechecked and organized, you are almost ready to draw a conclusion such as "Plants need sunlight in order to grow."

Before you can draw a conclusion, however, you must determine whether the data allow you to come to a conclusion that supports a hypothesis. Sometimes that will be the case, other times it will not.

If your data do not support a hypothesis, it does not mean that the hypothesis is wrong. It means only that the results of the investigation did not support the hypothesis. Maybe the experiment needs to be redesigned, but very likely, some of the initial observations on which the hypothesis was based were incomplete or biased. Perhaps more observation or research is needed to refine the hypothesis.

Avoiding Bias Sometimes drawing a conclusion involves making judgments. When you make a judgment, you form an opinion about what your data mean. It is important to be honest and to avoid reaching a conclusion if there were no supporting evidence for it or if it were based on a small sample. It also is important not to allow any expectations of results to bias your judgments. If possible, it is a good idea to collect additional data. Scientists do this all the time.

For example, animal behaviorist Katharine Payne made an important observation about elephant communication. While visiting a zoo, Payne felt the air vibrating around her. At the same time, she also noticed that the skin on an elephant's forehead was fluttering. She suspected that the elephants were generating the vibrations and that they might be using the low-frequency sounds to communicate.

Payne conducted an experiment to record these sounds and simultaneously observe the behavior of the elephants in the zoo. She later conducted a similar experiment in Namibia in southwest Africa, where elephant herds roam. The additional data she collected supported the judgment Payne had made, which was that these low-frequency sounds were a form of communication between elephants.

Evaluating Others' Data and Conclusions

Sometimes scientists have to use data that they did not collect themselves, or they have to rely on observations and conclusions drawn by other researchers. In cases such as these, the data must be evaluated carefully.

How were the data obtained? How was the investigation done? Has it been duplicated by other researchers? Did they come up with the same results? Look at the conclusion, as well. Would you reach the same conclusion from these results? Only when you have confidence in the data of others can you believe it is true and feel comfortable using it.

Communicating

The communication of ideas is an important part of the work of scientists. A discovery that is not reported will not advance the scientific community's understanding or knowledge. Communication among scientists also is important as a way of improving their investigations.

Scientists communicate in many ways, from writing articles in journals and magazines that explain their investigations and experiments, to announcing important discoveries on television and radio, to sharing ideas with colleagues on the Internet or presenting them as lectures.

Computer Skills

People who study science rely on computers to record and store data and to analyze results from investigations. Whether you work in a laboratory or just need to write a lab report with tables, good computer skills are a necessity.

Using a Word Processor

Suppose your teacher has assigned a written report. After you've completed your research and decided how you want to write the information, you need to put all that information on paper. The easiest way to do this is with a word processing application on a computer.

A computer application that allows you to type your information, change it as many times as you need to, and then print it out so that it looks neat and clean is called a word processing application. You also can use this type of application to create tables and columns, add bullets or cartoon art to your page, include page numbers, and even check your spelling.

Helpful Hints

- If you aren't sure how to do something using your word processing program, look in the help menu. You will find a list of topics there to click on for help. After you locate the help topic you need, just follow the step-by-step instructions you see on your screen.
- Just because you've spell checked your report doesn't mean that the spelling is perfect. The spell check feature can't catch misspelled words that look like other words. If you've accidentally typed *wind* instead of *wing*, the spell checker won't know the difference. Always reread your report to make sure you didn't miss any mistakes.

Figure 18
You can use computer programs to make graphs and tables.

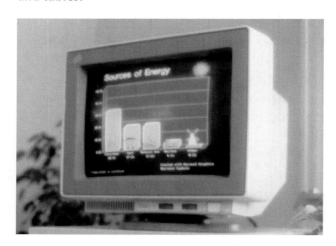

Using a Database

Imagine you're in the middle of a research project busily gathering facts and information. You soon realize that it's becoming more difficult to organize and keep track of all the information. The tool to use to solve information overload is a database. Just as a file cabinet organizes paper records, a database organizes computer records. However, a database is more powerful than a simple file cabinet because at the click of a mouse, the contents can be reshuffled and reorganized. At computer-quick speeds, databases can sort information by any characteristics and filter data into multiple categories.

Helpful Hints

- Before setting up a database, take some time to learn the features of your database software by practicing with established database software.
- Periodically save your database as you enter data. That way, if something happens such as your computer malfunctions or the power goes off, you won't lose all of your work.

Skill Handbooks

Doing a Database Search

When searching for information in a database, use the following search strategies to get the best results. These are the same search methods used for searching Internet databases.

■ Place the word *and* between two words in your search if you want the database to look for any entries that have both the words. For example, "fox *and* mink" would give you information that mentions both fox and mink.

■ Place the word *or* between two words if you want the database to show entries that have at least one of the words. For example "fox *or* mink" would show you information that mentions either fox or mink.

■ Place the word *not* between two words if you want the database to look for entries that have the first word but do not have the second word. For example, "canine *not* fox" would show you information that mentions the term canine but does not mention the fox.

In summary, databases can be used to store large amounts of information about a particular subject. Databases allow biologists, Earth scientists, and physical scientists to search for information quickly and accurately.

Using an Electronic Spreadsheet

Your science fair experiment has produced lots of numbers. How do you keep track of all the data, and how can you easily work out all the calculations needed? You can use a computer program called a spreadsheet to record data that involve numbers. A spreadsheet is an electronic mathematical worksheet.

Type in your data in rows and columns, just as in a data table on a sheet of paper. A spreadsheet uses simple math to do data calculations. For example, you could add, subtract, divide, or multiply any of the values in the spreadsheet by another number. You also could set up a series of math steps you want to apply to the data. If you want to add 12 to all the numbers and then multiply all the numbers by 10, the computer does all the calculations for you in the spreadsheet. Below is an example of a spreadsheet that records data from an experiment with mice in a maze.

Helpful Hints

■ Before you set up the spreadsheet, identify how you want to organize the data. Include any formulas you will need to use.

■ Make sure you have entered the correct data into the correct rows and columns.

■ You also can display your results in a graph. Pick the style of graph that best represents the data with which you are working.

Figure 19
A spreadsheet allows you to display large amounts of data and do calculations automatically.

Test Runs	Time	Distance	Number of turns
Mouse 1	15 seconds	1 meter	3
Mouse 2	12 seconds	1 meter	2
Mouse 3	20 seconds	1 meter	5

Using a Computerized Card Catalog

When you have a report or paper to research, you probably go to the library. To find the information you need in the library, you might have to use a computerized card catalog. This type of card catalog allows you to search for information by subject, by title, or by author. The computer then will display all the holdings the library has on the subject, title, or author requested.

A library's holdings can include books, magazines, databases, videos, and audio materials. When you have chosen something from this list, the computer will show whether an item is available and where in the library to find it.

Helpful Hints

- Remember that you can use the computer to search by subject, author, or title. If you know a book's author but not the title, you can search for all the books the library has by that author.
- When searching by subject, it's often most helpful to narrow your search by using specific search terms, such as *and, or,* and *not.* If you don't find enough sources, you can broaden your search.
- Pay attention to the type of materials found in your search. If you need a book, you can eliminate any videos or other resources that come up in your search.
- Knowing how your library is arranged can save you a lot of time. The librarian will show you where certain types of materials are kept and how to find specific holdings.

Using Graphics Software

Are you having trouble finding that exact piece of art you're looking for? Do you have a picture in your mind of what you want but can't seem to find the right graphic to represent your ideas? To solve these problems, you can use graphics software. Graphics software allows you to create and change images and diagrams in almost unlimited ways. Typical uses for graphics software include arranging clip art, changing scanned images, and constructing pictures from scratch. Most graphics software applications work in similar ways. They use the same basic tools and functions. Once you master one graphics application, you can use any other graphics application relatively easily.

Figure 20
Graphics software can use your data to draw bar graphs.

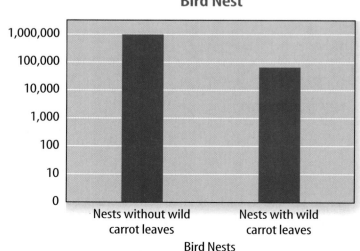

Number of Mites per Bird Nest

Figure 21
Graphics software can use your data to draw circle graphs.

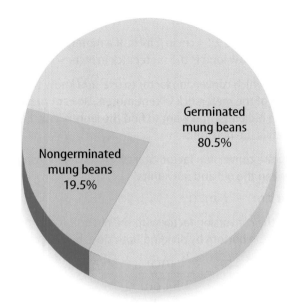

Helpful Hints

■ As with any method of drawing, the more you practice using the graphics software, the better your results will be.

■ Start by using the software to manipulate existing drawings. Once you master this, making your own illustrations will be easier.

■ Clip art is available on CD-ROMs and the Internet. With these resources, finding a piece of clip art to suit your purposes is simple.

■ As you work on a drawing, save it often.

Developing Multimedia Presentations

It's your turn—you have to present your science report to the entire class. How do you do it? You can use many different sources of information to get the class excited about your presentation. Posters, videos, photographs, sound, computers, and the Internet can help show your ideas.

First, determine what important points you want to make in your presentation. Then, write an outline of what materials and types of media would best illustrate those points. Maybe you could start with an outline on an overhead projector, then show a video, followed by something from the Internet or a slide show accompanied by music or recorded voices. You might choose to use a presentation builder computer application that can combine all these elements into one presentation. Make sure the presentation is well constructed to make the most impact on the audience.

Figure 22
Multimedia presentations use many types of print and electronic materials.

Helpful Hints

■ Carefully consider what media will best communicate the point you are trying to make.

■ Make sure you know how to use any equipment you will be using in your presentation.

■ Practice the presentation several times.

■ If possible, set up all of the equipment ahead of time. Make sure everything is working correctly.

Use this Math Skill Handbook to help solve problems you are given in this text. You might find it useful to review topics in this Math Skill Handbook first.

Converting Units

In science, quantities such as length, mass, and time sometimes are measured using different units. Suppose you want to know how many miles are in 12.7 km?

Conversion factors are used to change from one unit of measure to another. A conversion factor is a ratio that is equal to one. For example, there are 1,000 mL in 1 L, so 1,000 mL equals 1 L, or:

$$1{,}000 \text{ mL} = 1 \text{ L}$$

If both sides are divided by 1 L, this equation becomes:

$$\frac{1{,}000 \text{ mL}}{1 \text{ L}} = 1$$

The **ratio** on the left side of this equation is equal to one and is a conversion factor. You can make another conversion factor by dividing both sides of the top equation by 1,000 mL:

$$1 = \frac{1 \text{ L}}{1{,}000 \text{ mL}}$$

To **convert units,** you multiply by the appropriate conversion factor. For example, how many milliliters are in 1.255 L? To convert 1.255 L to milliliters, multiply 1.255 L by a conversion factor.

Use the **conversion factor** with new units (mL) in the numerator and the old units (L) in the denominator.

$$1.255 \text{ L} \times \frac{1{,}000 \text{ mL}}{1 \text{ L}} = 1{,}255 \text{ mL}$$

The unit L divides in this equation, just as if it were a number.

Example 1 There are 2.54 cm in 1 inch. If a meterstick has a length of 100 cm, how long is the meterstick in inches?

Step 1 Decide which conversion factor to use. You know the length of the meterstick in centimeters, so centimeters are the old units. You want to find the length in inches, so inch is the new unit.

Step 2 Form the conversion factor. Start with the relationship between the old and new units.

$$2.54 \text{ cm} = 1 \text{ inch}$$

Step 3 Form the conversion factor with the old unit (centimeter) on the bottom by dividing both sides by 2.54 cm.

$$1 = \frac{2.54 \text{ cm}}{2.54 \text{ cm}} = \frac{1 \text{ inch}}{2.54 \text{ cm}}$$

Step 4 Multiply the old measurement by the conversion factor.

$$100 \text{ cm} \times \frac{1 \text{ inch}}{2.54 \text{ cm}} = 39.37 \text{ inches}$$

The meter stick is 39.37 inches long.

Example 2 There are 365 days in one year. If a person is 14 years old, what is his or her age in days? (Ignore leap years)

Step 1 Decide which conversion factor to use. You want to convert years to days.

Step 2 Form the conversion factor. Start with the relation between the old and new units.

$$1 \text{ year} = 365 \text{ days}$$

Step 3 Form the conversion factor with the old unit (year) on the bottom by dividing both sides by 1 year.

$$1 = \frac{1 \text{ year}}{1 \text{ year}} = \frac{365 \text{ days}}{1 \text{ year}}$$

Step 4 Multiply the old measurement by the conversion factor:

$$14 \text{ years} \times \frac{365 \text{ days}}{1 \text{ year}} = 5{,}110 \text{ days}$$

The person's age is 5,110 days.

Practice Problem A cat has a mass of 2.31 kg. If there are 1,000 g in 1 kg, what is the mass of the cat in grams? 2,310 g

Using Fractions

A **fraction** is a number that compares a part to the whole. For example, in the fraction $\frac{2}{3}$, the 2 represents the part and the 3 represents the whole. In the fraction $\frac{2}{3}$, the top number, 2, is called the numerator. The bottom number, 3, is called the denominator.

Sometimes fractions are not written in their simplest form. To determine a fraction's **simplest form,** you must find the greatest common factor (GCF) of the numerator and denominator. The greatest common factor is the largest common factor of all the factors the two numbers have in common.

For example, because the number 3 divides into 12 and 30 evenly, it is a common factor of 12 and 30. However, because the number 6 is the largest number that evenly divides into 12 and 30, it is the **greatest common factor.**

After you find the greatest common factor, you can write a fraction in its simplest form. Divide both the numerator and the denominator by the greatest common factor. The number that results is the fraction in its **simplest form.**

Example Twelve of the 20 corn plants in a field are over 1.5 m tall. What fraction of the corn plants in the field are over 1.5 m tall?

Step 1 Write the fraction.

$$\frac{\text{part}}{\text{whole}} = \frac{12}{20}$$

Step 2 To find the GCF of the numerator and denominator, list all of the factors of each number.

Factors of 12: 1, 2, 3, 4, 6, 12 (the numbers that divide evenly into 12)

Factors of 20: 1, 2, 4, 5, 10, 20 (the numbers that divide evenly into 20)

Step 3 List the common factors.

1, 2, 4.

Step 4 Choose the greatest factor in the list of common factors.

The GCF of 12 and 20 is 4.

Step 5 Divide the numerator and denominator by the GCF.

$$\frac{12 \div 4}{20 \div 4} = \frac{3}{5}$$

In the field, $\frac{3}{5}$ of the corn plants are over 1.5 m tall.

Practice Problem There are 90 duck eggs in a population. Of those eggs, 66 hatch over a one-week period. What fraction of the eggs hatch over a one-week period? Write the fraction in simplest form. $\frac{11}{15}$

Math Skill Handbook

Calculating Ratios

A **ratio** is a comparison of two numbers by division.

Ratios can be written 3 to 5 or 3:5. Ratios also can be written as fractions, such as $\frac{3}{5}$. Ratios, like fractions, can be written in simplest form. Recall that a fraction is in **simplest form** when the greatest common factor (GCF) of the numerator and denominator is 1.

Example From a package of sunflower seeds, 40 seeds germinated and 64 did not. What is the ratio of germinated to not germinated seeds as a fraction in simplest form?

Step 1 Write the ratio as a fraction.
$$\frac{\text{germinated}}{\text{not germinated}} = \frac{40}{64}$$

Step 2 Express the fraction in simplest form. The GCF of 40 and 64 is 8.
$$\frac{40}{64} = \frac{40 \div 8}{64 \div 8} = \frac{5}{8}$$

The ratio of germinated to not germinated seeds is $\frac{5}{8}$.

Practice Problem Two children measure 100 cm and 144 cm in height. What is the ratio of their heights in simplest fraction form? $\frac{25}{36}$

Using Decimals

A **decimal** is a fraction with a denominator of 10, 100, 1,000, or another power of 10. For example, 0.854 is the same as the fraction $\frac{854}{1,000}$.

In a decimal, the decimal point separates the ones place and the tenths place. For example, 0.27 means twenty-seven hundredths, or $\frac{27}{100}$, where 27 is the **number of units** out of 100 units. Any fraction can be written as a decimal using division.

Example Write $\frac{5}{8}$ as a decimal.

Step 1 Write a division problem with the numerator, 5, as the dividend and the denominator, 8, as the divisor. Write 5 as 5.000.

Step 2 Solve the problem.

$$
\begin{array}{r}
0.625 \\
8\overline{)5.000} \\
\underline{48} \\
20 \\
\underline{16} \\
40 \\
\underline{40} \\
0
\end{array}
$$

Therefore, $\frac{5}{8} = 0.625$.

Practice Problem Write $\frac{19}{25}$ as a decimal. 0.76

Using Percentages

The word *percent* means "out of one hundred." A **percent** is a ratio that compares a number to 100. Suppose you read that 77 percent of all fish on Earth live in the Pacific Ocean. That is the same as reading that the Earth's fish that live in the Pacific Ocean is $\frac{77}{100}$. To express a fraction as a percent, first find an equivalent decimal for the fraction. Then, multiply the decimal by 100 and add the percent symbol. For example, $\frac{1}{2} = 1 \div 2 = 0.5$. Then $0.5 = 0.50 = 50\%$.

Example Express $\frac{13}{20}$ as a percent.

Step 1 Find the equivalent decimal for the fraction.

$$
\begin{array}{r}
0.65 \\
20\overline{)13.00} \\
\underline{120} \\
100 \\
\underline{100} \\
0
\end{array}
$$

Step 2 Rewrite the fraction $\frac{13}{20}$ as 0.65.

Step 3 Multiply 0.65 by 100 and add the % sign.

$0.65 \cdot 100 = 65 = 65\%$

So, $\frac{13}{20} = 65\%$.

Practice Problem In an experimental population of 365 sheep, 73 were brown. What percent of the sheep were brown? 20%

Using Precision and Significant Digits

When you make a **measurement,** the value you record depends on the precision of the measuring instrument. When adding or subtracting numbers with different precision, the answer is rounded to the smallest number of decimal places of any number in the sum or difference. When multiplying or dividing, the answer is rounded to the smallest number of significant figures of any number being multiplied or divided. When counting the number of **significant figures,** all digits are counted except zeros at the end of a number with no decimal such as 2,500, and zeros at the beginning of a decimal such as 0.03020.

Example The lengths 5.28 and 5.2 are measured in meters. Find the sum of these lengths and report the sum using the least precise measurement.

Step 1 Find the sum.

$$
\begin{array}{ll}
5.28 \text{ m} & 2 \text{ digits after the decimal} \\
\underline{+\ 5.2\ \ \text{m}} & 1 \text{ digit after the decimal} \\
10.48 \text{ m} &
\end{array}
$$

Step 2 Round to one digit after the decimal because the least number of digits after the decimal of the numbers being added is 1.

The sum is 10.5 m.

Practice Problem Multiply the numbers in the example using the rule for multiplying and dividing. Report the answer with the correct number of significant figures. 27.5 m^2

Math Skill Handbook

Solving One-Step Equations

An **equation** is a statement that two things are equal. For example, $A = B$ is an equation that states that A is equal to B.

Sometimes one side of the equation will contain a **variable** whose value is not known. In the equation $3x = 12$, the variable is x.

The equation is solved when the variable is replaced with a value that makes both sides of the equation equal to each other. For example, the solution of the equation $3x = 12$ is $x = 4$. If the x is replaced with 4, then the equation becomes $3 \cdot 4 = 12$, or $12 = 12$.

To solve an equation such as $8x = 40$, divide both sides of the equation by the number that multiplies the variable.

$$8x = 40$$
$$\frac{8x}{8} = \frac{40}{8}$$
$$x = 5$$

You can check your answer by replacing the variable with your solution and seeing if both sides of the equation are the same.

$$8x = 8 \cdot 5 = 40$$

The left and right sides of the equation are the same, so $x = 5$ is the solution.

Sometimes an equation is written in this way: $a = bc$. This also is called a **formula.** The letters can be replaced by numbers, but the numbers must still make both sides of the equation the same.

Example 1 Solve the equation $10x = 35$.

Step 1 Find the solution by dividing each side of the equation by 10.

$$10x = 35 \qquad \frac{10x}{10} = \frac{35}{10} \qquad x = 3.5$$

Step 2 Check the solution.

$$10x = 35 \qquad 10 \times 3.5 = 35 \qquad 35 = 35$$

Both sides of the equation are equal, so $x = 3.5$ is the solution to the equation.

Example 2 In the formula $a = bc$, find the value of c if $a = 20$ and $b = 2$.

Step 1 Rearrange the formula so the unknown value is by itself on one side of the equation by dividing both sides by b.

$$a = bc$$
$$\frac{a}{b} = \frac{bc}{b}$$
$$\frac{a}{b} = c$$

Step 2 Replace the variables a and b with the values that are given.

$$\frac{a}{b} = c$$
$$\frac{20}{2} = c$$
$$10 = c$$

Step 3 Check the solution.

$$a = bc$$
$$20 = 2 \times 10$$
$$20 = 20$$

Both sides of the equation are equal, so $c = 10$ is the solution when $a = 20$ and $b = 2$.

Practice Problem In the formula $h = gd$, find the value of d if $g = 12.3$ and $h = 17.4$. $d = 1.4$

A **proportion** is an equation that shows that two ratios are equivalent. The ratios $\frac{2}{4}$ and $\frac{5}{10}$ are equivalent, so they can be written as $\frac{2}{4} = \frac{5}{10}$. This equation is an example of a proportion.

When two ratios form a proportion, the **cross products** are equal. To find the cross products in the proportion $\frac{2}{4} = \frac{5}{10}$, multiply the 2 and the 10, and the 4 and the 5. Therefore $2 \cdot 10 = 4 \cdot 5$, **or** $20 = 20$.

Because you know that both proportions are equal, you can use cross products to find a missing term in a proportion. This is known as **solving the proportion.** Solving a proportion is similar to solving an equation.

Example The heights of a tree and a pole are proportional to the lengths of their shadows. The tree casts a shadow of 24 m at the same time that a 6-m pole casts a shadow of 4 m. What is the height of the tree?

Step 1 Write a proportion.

$$\frac{\text{height of tree}}{\text{height of pole}} = \frac{\text{length of tree's shadow}}{\text{length of pole's shadow}}$$

Step 2 Substitute the known values into the proportion. Let h represent the unknown value, the height of the tree.

$$\frac{h}{6} = \frac{24}{4}$$

Step 3 Find the cross products.

$$h \cdot 4 = 6 \cdot 24$$

Step 4 Simplify the equation.

$$4h = 144$$

Step 5 Divide each side by 4.

$$\frac{4h}{4} = \frac{144}{4}$$

$$h = 36$$

The height of the tree is 36 m.

Practice Problem The proportions of bluefish are stable by the time they reach a length of 30 cm. The distance from the tip of the mouth to the back edge of the gill cover in a 35-cm bluefish is 15 cm. What is the distance from the tip of the mouth to the back edge of the gill cover in a 59-cm bluefish? 25.3 cm

Math Skill Handbook

Statistics is the branch of mathematics that deals with collecting, analyzing, and presenting data. In statistics, there are three common ways to summarize the data with a single number—the mean, the median, and the mode.

The **mean** of a set of data is the arithmetic average. It is found by adding the numbers in the data set and dividing by the number of items in the set.

The **median** is the middle number in a set of data when the data are arranged in numerical order. If there were an even number of data points, the median would be the mean of the two middle numbers.

The **mode** of a set of data is the number or item that appears most often.

Another number that often is used to describe a set of data is the range. The **range** is the difference between the largest number and the smallest number in a set of data.

A **frequency table** shows how many times each piece of data occurs, usually in a survey. The frequency table below shows the results of a student survey on favorite color.

Color	Tally	Frequency
red	||||	4
blue	⊬||	5
black	||	2
green	|||	3
purple	⊬|| ||	7
yellow	⊬|| |	6

Based on the frequency table data, which color is the favorite?

Example The high temperatures (in °C) on five consecutive days in a desert habitat under study are 39°, 37°, 44°, 36°, and 44°. Find the mean, median, mode, and range of this set.

To find the mean:
Step 1 Find the sum of the numbers.

$$39 + 37 + 44 + 36 + 44 = 200$$

Step 2 Divide the sum by the number of items, which is 5.

$$200 \div 5 = 40$$

The mean high temperature is 40°C.

To find the median:
Step 1 Arrange the temperatures from least to greatest.

$$36, \ 37, \ \underline{39}, \ 44, \ 44$$

Step 2 Determine the middle temperature.

The median high temperature is 39°C.

To find the mode:
Step 1 Group the numbers that are the same together.

$$44, 44, 36, 37, 39$$

Step 2 Determine the number that occurs most in the set.

$$\underline{44, 44}, 36, 37, 39$$

The mode measure is 44°C.

To find the range:
Step 1 Arrange the temperatures from largest to smallest.

$$44, 44, 39, 37, 36$$

Step 2 Determine the largest and smallest temperature in the set.

$$\underline{44}, 44, 39, 37, \underline{36}$$

Step 3 Find the difference between the largest and smallest temperatures.

$$44 - 36 = 8$$

The range is 8°C.

Practice Problem Find the mean, median, mode, and range for the data set 8, 4, 12, 8, 11, 14, 16.

mean, 10; median, 11; mode, 8; range 12

Safety in the Science Classroom

1. Always obtain your teacher's permission to begin an investigation.

2. Study the procedure. If you have questions, ask your teacher. Be sure you understand any safety symbols shown on the page.

3. Use the safety equipment provided for you. Goggles and a safety apron should be worn during most investigations.

4. Always slant test tubes away from yourself and others when heating them or adding substances to them.

5. Never eat or drink in the lab, and never use lab glassware as food or drink containers. Never inhale chemicals. Do not taste any substances or draw any material into a tube with your mouth.

6. Report any spill, accident, or injury, no matter how small, immediately to your teacher, then follow his or her instructions.

7. Know the location and proper use of the fire extinguisher, safety shower, fire blanket, first aid kit, and fire alarm.

8. Keep all materials away from open flames. Tie back long hair and tie down loose clothing.

9. If your clothing should catch fire, smother it with the fire blanket, or get under a safety shower. NEVER RUN.

10. If a fire should occur, turn off the gas then leave the room according to established procedures.

Follow these procedures as you clean up your work area

1. Turn off the water and gas. Disconnect electrical devices.

2. Clean all pieces of equipment and return all materials to their proper places.

3. Dispose of chemicals and other materials as directed by your teacher. Place broken glass and solid substances in the proper containers. Make sure never to discard materials in the sink.

4. Clean your work area. Wash your hands thoroughly after working in the laboratory.

First Aid	
Injury	**Safe Response ALWAYS NOTIFY YOUR TEACHER IMMEDIATELY**
Burns	Apply cold water.
Cuts and Bruises	Stop any bleeding by applying direct pressure. Cover cuts with a clean dressing. Apply ice packs or cold compresses to bruises.
Fainting	Leave the person lying down. Loosen any tight clothing and keep crowds away.
Foreign Matter in Eye	Flush with plenty of water. Use eyewash bottle or fountain.
Poisoning	Note the suspected poisoning agent.
Any Spills on Skin	Flush with large amounts of water or use safety shower.

Care and Use of a Microscope

Eyepiece Contains magnifying lenses you look through.

Arm Supports the body tube.

Low-power objective Contains the lens with the lowest power magnification.

Stage clips Hold the microscope slide in place.

Fine adjustment Sharpens the image under high magnification.

Coarse adjustment Focuses the image under low power.

Body tube Connects the eyepiece to the revolving nosepiece.

Revolving nosepiece Holds and turns the objectives into viewing position.

High-power objective Contains the lens with the highest magnification.

Stage Supports the microscope slide.

Light source Provides light that passes upward through the diaphragm, the specimen, and the lenses.

Base Provides support for the microscope.

Reference Handbook

Caring for a Microscope

1. Always carry the microscope holding the arm with one hand and supporting the base with the other hand.

2. Don't touch the lenses with your fingers.

3. The coarse adjustment knob is used only when looking through the lowest-power objective lens. The fine adjustment knob is used when the high-power objective is in place.

4. Cover the microscope when you store it.

Using a Microscope

1. Place the microscope on a flat surface that is clear of objects. The arm should be toward you.

2. Look through the eyepiece. Adjust the diaphragm so light comes through the opening in the stage.

3. Place a slide on the stage so the specimen is in the field of view. Hold it firmly in place by using the stage clips.

4. Always focus with the coarse adjustment and the low-power objective lens first. After the object is in focus on low power, turn the nosepiece until the high-power objective is in place. Use ONLY the fine adjustment to focus with the high-power objective lens.

Making a Wet-Mount Slide

1. Carefully place the item you want to look at in the center of a clean, glass slide. Make sure the sample is thin enough for light to pass through.

2. Use a dropper to place one or two drops of water on the sample.

3. Hold a clean coverslip by the edges and place it at one edge of the water. Slowly lower the coverslip onto the water until it lies flat.

4. If you have too much water or a lot of air bubbles, touch the edge of a paper towel to the edge of the coverslip to draw off extra water and draw out unwanted air.

Diversity of Life: Classification of Living Organisms

A six-kingdom system of classification of organisms is used today. Two kingdoms—Kingdom Archaebacteria and Kingdom Eubacteria—contain organisms that do not have a nucleus and that lack membrane-bound structures in the cytoplasm of their cells. The members of the other four kingdoms have a cell or cells that contain a nucleus and structures in the cytoplasm, some of which are surrounded by membranes. These kingdoms are Kingdom Protista, Kingdom Fungi, Kingdom Plantae, and Kingdom Animalia.

Kingdom Archaebacteria

one-celled; some absorb food from their surroundings; some are photosynthetic; some are chemosynthetic; many found in extremely harsh environments including salt ponds, hot springs, swamps, and deep-sea hydrothermal vents

Kingdom Eubacteria

one-celled; most absorb food from their surroundings; some are photosynthetic; some are chemosynthetic; many are parasites; many are round, spiral, or rod-shaped; some form colonies

Kingdom Protista

Phylum Euglenophyta one-celled; photosynthetic or take in food; most have one flagellum; euglenoids

Phylum Bacillariophyta one-celled; photosynthetic; have unique double shells made of silica; diatoms

Phylum Dinoflagellata one-celled; photosynthetic; contain red pigments; have two flagella; dinoflagellates

Phylum Chlorophyta one-celled, many-celled, or colonies; photosynthetic; contain chlorophyll; live on land, in freshwater, or salt water; green algae

Phylum Rhodophyta most are many-celled; photosynthetic; contain red pigments; most live in deep, saltwater environments; red algae

Phylum Phaeophyta most are many-celled; photosynthetic; contain brown pigments; most live in saltwater environments; brown algae

Phylum Rhizopoda one-celled; take in food; are free-living or parasitic; move by means of pseudopods; amoebas

Kingdom Eubacteria
Bacillus anthracis

Phylum Chlorophyta
Desmids

Amoeba

Phylum Zoomastigina one-celled; take in food; free-living or parasitic; have one or more flagella; zoomastigotes

Phylum Ciliophora one-celled; take in food; have large numbers of cilia; ciliates

Phylum Sporozoa one-celled; take in food; have no means of movement; are parasites in animals; sporozoans

Phylum Myxomycota
Slime mold

Phylum Oomycota
Phytophthora infestans

Phyla Myxomycota and Acrasiomycota one- or many-celled; absorb food; change form during life cycle; cellular and plasmodial slime molds

Phylum Oomycota many-celled; are either parasites or decomposers; live in freshwater or salt water; water molds, rusts and downy mildews

Kingdom Fungi

Phylum Zygomycota many-celled; absorb food; spores are produced in sporangia; zygote fungi; bread mold

Phylum Ascomycota one- and many-celled; absorb food; spores produced in asci; sac fungi; yeast

Phylum Basidiomycota many-celled; absorb food; spores produced in basidia; club fungi; mushrooms

Phylum Deuteromycota members with unknown reproductive structures; imperfect fungi; *Penicillium*

Mycophycota organisms formed by symbiotic relationship between an ascomycote or a basidiomycote and green alga or cyanobacterium; lichens

Lichens

Kingdom Plantae

Divisions Bryophyta (mosses), **Anthocerophyta** (hornworts), **Hepatophytal** (liverworts), **Psilophytal** (whisk ferns) many-celled nonvascular plants; reproduce by spores produced in capsules; green; grow in moist, land environments

Division Lycophyta many-celled vascular plants; spores are produced in conelike structures; live on land; are photosynthetic; club mosses

Division Sphenophyta vascular plants; ribbed and jointed stems; scalelike leaves; spores produced in conelike structures; horsetails

Division Pterophyta vascular plants; leaves called fronds; spores produced in clusters of sporangia called sori; live on land or in water; ferns

Division Ginkgophyta deciduous trees; only one living species; have fan-shaped leaves with branching veins and fleshy cones with seeds; ginkgoes

Division Cycadophyta palmlike plants; have large, featherlike leaves; produces seeds in cones; cycads

Division Coniferophyta deciduous or evergreen; trees or shrubs; have needlelike or scalelike leaves; seeds produced in cones; conifers

Division Anthophyta
Tomato plant

Division Gnetophyta shrubs or woody vines; seeds are produced in cones; division contains only three genera; gnetum

Division Anthophyta dominant group of plants; flowering plants; have fruits with seeds

Kingdom Animalia

Phylum Porifera aquatic organisms that lack true tissues and organs; are asymmetrical and sessile; sponges

Phylum Cnidaria radially symmetrical organisms; have a digestive cavity with one opening; most have tentacles armed with stinging cells; live in aquatic environments singly or in colonies; includes jellyfish, corals, hydra, and sea anemones

Phylum Platyhelminthes bilaterally symmetrical worms; have flattened bodies; digestive system has one opening; parasitic and free-living species; flatworms

Division Bryophyta
Liverwort

Phylum Platyhelminthes
Flatworm

Phylum Chordata

Phylum Nematoda round, bilaterally symmetrical body; have digestive system with two openings; free-living forms and parasitic forms; roundworms

Phylum Mollusca soft-bodied animals, many with a hard shell and soft foot or footlike appendage; a mantle covers the soft body; aquatic and terrestrial species; includes clams, snails, squid, and octopuses

Phylum Annelida bilaterally symmetrical worms; have round, segmented bodies; terrestrial and aquatic species; includes earthworms, leeches, and marine polychaetes

Phylum Arthropoda largest animal group; have hard exoskeletons, segmented bodies, and pairs of jointed appendages; land and aquatic species; includes insects, crustaceans, and spiders

Phylum Echinodermata marine organisms; have spiny or leathery skin and a water-vascular system with tube feet; are radially symmetrical; includes sea stars, sand dollars, and sea urchins

Phylum Chordata organisms with internal skeletons and specialized body systems; most have paired appendages; all at some time have a notochord, nerve cord, gill slits, and a postanal tail; include fish, amphibians, reptiles, birds, and mammals

This glossary defines each key term that appears in bold type in the text. It also shows the chapter, section, and page number where you can find the words used.

A

abiotic: nonliving, physical features of the environment, including air, water, sunlight, soil, temperature, and climate. (Chap. 2, Sec. 1, p. 36)

acid precipitation: precipitation with a pH below 5.6—which occurs when air pollutants from the burning of fossil fuels react with water in the atmosphere to form strong acids—that can pollute water, kill fish and plants, and damage soils. (Chap. 4, Sec. 2, p. 103)

acid rain: forms when sulfur dioxide and nitrogen oxide from industries and car exhausts combine with water vapor in the air; can wash nutrients from soil and damage trees and aquatic life. (Chap. 5, Sec. 1, p. 135)

atmosphere: air surrounding Earth; is made up of gases, including 78 percent nitrogen, 21 percent oxygen, and 0.03 percent carbon dioxide. (Chap. 2, Sec. 1, p. 37)

B

biodiversity: variety of life in an ecosystem, most commonly measured by the number of species that live in a given area. (Chap. 5, Sec. 1, p. 126)

biomes (BI ohmz): large geographic areas with similar climates and ecosystems; includes tundra, taiga, desert, temperate deciduous forest, temperate rain forest, tropical rain forest, and grassland. (Chap. 3, Sec. 2, p. 68)

biosphere: part of Earth that supports life, including the top portion of Earth's crust, the atmosphere, and all the water on Earth's surface. (Chap. 1, Sec. 1, p. 8)

biotic (bi AHT ik): features of the environment that are alive or were once alive. (Chap. 2, Sec. 1, p. 36)

C

captive population: population of organisms that is cared for by humans. (Chap. 5, Sec. 2, p. 142)

carbon cycle: model describing how carbon molecules move between the living and nonliving world. (Chap. 2, Sec. 2, p. 49)

carrying capacity: largest number of individuals of a particular species that an ecosystem can support over time. (Chap. 1, Sec. 2, p. 15)

chemosynthesis (kee moh SIN thuh sus): process in which producers make energy-rich nutrient molecules from chemicals. (Chap. 2, Sec. 3, p. 51)

climate: average weather conditions of an area over time, including wind, temperature, and rainfall or other types of precipitation such as snow or sleet. (Chap. 2, Sec. 1, p. 41)

climax community: stable, end stage of ecological succession in which the plants and animals of a community use resources efficiently and balance is maintained by disturbances such as fire. (Chap. 3, Sec. 1, p. 67)

commensalism: a type of symbiotic relationship in which one organism benefits and the other organism is not affected. (Chap. 1, Sec. 3, p. 22)

community: all the populations of different species that live in an ecosystem. (Chap. 1, Sec. 1, p. 10)

condensation: process that takes place when a gas changes to a liquid. (Chap. 2, Sec. 2, p. 45)

conservation biology: study of methods for protecting Earth's biodiversity; uses strategies such as reintroduction programs and habitat restoration and works to preserve threatened and endangered species. (Chap. 5, Sec. 2, p. 138)

English Glossary

consumer: organism that cannot create energy-rich molecules but obtains its food by eating other organisms. (Chap. 1, Sec. 3, p. 21)

coral reef: diverse ecosystem formed from the calcium carbonate shells secreted by corals. (Chap. 3, Sec. 3, p. 81)

D

desert: driest biome on Earth with less than 25 cm of rain each year; has dunes or thin soil with little organic matter and plants and animals specially adapted to survive extreme conditions. (Chap. 3, Sec. 2, p. 74)

E

ecology: study of the interactions that take place among organisms and their environment. (Chap. 1, Sec. 1, p. 9)

ecosystem: all the living organisms that live in an area and the nonliving features of their environment. (Chap. 1, Sec. 1, p. 9)

endangered species: species that is in danger of becoming extinct because of factors such as habitat loss, overhunting, and pollution. (Chap. 5, Sec. 1, p. 131)

energy pyramid: model that shows the amount of energy available at each feeding level in an ecosystem. (Chap. 2, Sec. 3, p. 53)

erosion: movement of soil from one place to another. (Chap. 4, Sec. 2, p. 109)

estuary: extremely fertile area where a river meets an ocean; contains a mixture of freshwater and saltwater and serves as a nursery for many species of fish. (Chap. 3, Sec. 3, p. 82)

evaporation: process that takes place when a liquid changes to a gas. (Chap. 2, Sec. 2, p. 44)

extinct species: species that was once present on Earth but has died out. (Chap. 5, Sec. 1, p. 130)

F

food web: model that shows the complex feeding relationships among organisms in a community. (Chap. 2, Sec. 3, p. 52)

fossil fuels: nonrenewable energy resources—coal, oil, and natural gas—that formed in Earth's crust over hundreds of millions of years. (Chap. 4, Sec. 1, p. 96)

G

geothermal energy: heat energy within Earth's crust, available only where natural geysers or volcanoes are located. (Chap. 4, Sec. 1, p. 99)

grasslands: temperate and tropical regions with 25 cm to 75 cm of precipitation each year that are dominated by climax communities of grasses; ideal for growing crops and raising cattle and sheep. (Chap. 3, Sec. 2, p. 75)

greenhouse effect: heat-trapping feature of the atmosphere that keeps Earth warm enough to support life. (Chap. 4, Sec. 2, p. 104)

H

habitat: place where an organism lives and that provides the types of food, shelter, moisture, and temperature needed for survival. (Chap. 1, Sec. 1, p. 11)

habitat restoration: process of bringing a damaged habitat back to a healthy condition. (Chap. 5, Sec. 2, p. 141)

hazardous wastes: waste materials, such as pesticides and leftover paints, that are harmful to human health or poisonous to living organisms. (Chap. 4, Sec. 2, p. 110)

hydroelectric power: electricity produced when the energy of falling water turns the blades of a generator turbine. (Chap. 4, Sec. 1, p. 97)

I

intertidal zone: part of the shoreline that is under water at high tide and exposed to the air at low tide. (Chap. 3, Sec. 3, p. 82)

introduced species: species that moves into an ecosystem as a result of human actions and can reduce or eliminate populations of native species. (Chap. 5, Sec. 1, p. 134)

L

limiting factor: anything that can restrict the size of a population, including living and nonliving features of an ecosystem, such as predators or drought. (Chap. 1, Sec. 2, p. 14)

M

mutualism: a type of symbiotic relationship in which both organisms benefit. (Chap. 1, Sec. 3, p. 22)

N

native species: original organisms in an ecosystem. (Chap. 5, Sec. 1, p. 134)

natural resources: parts of Earth's environment that supply materials useful or necessary for the survival of living organisms. (Chap. 4, Sec. 1, p. 94)

niche: in an ecosystem, refers to the unique ways an organism survives, obtains food and shelter, and avoids danger. (Chap. 1, Sec. 3, p. 23)

nitrogen cycle: model describing how nitrogen moves from the atmosphere to the soil, to living organisms, and then back to the atmosphere. (Chap. 2, Sec. 2, p. 46)

nitrogen fixation: process in which some types of bacteria in the soil change nitrogen gas into a form of nitrogen that plants can use. (Chap. 2, Sec. 2, p. 46)

nonrenewable resources: natural resources, such as petroleum, minerals, and metals, that are used more quickly than they can be replaced by natural processes. (Chap. 4, Sec. 1, p. 95)

nuclear energy: energy produced from the splitting apart of billions of uranium nuclei by a nuclear fission reaction. (Chap. 4, Sec. 1, p. 98)

O

ozone depletion: thinning of Earth's ozone layer caused by chlorofluorocarbons (CFCs) leaking into the air and reacting chemically with ozone, breaking the ozone molecules apart. (Chap. 4, Sec. 2, p. 105)

ozone layer: protective layer of gas in Earth's atmosphere, about 15 km to 30 km above Earth's surface, that absorbs ultraviolet radiation from the Sun. (Chap. 5, Sec. 1, p. 136)

P

parasitism: a type of symbiotic relationship in which one organism benefits and the other organism is harmed. (Chap. 1, Sec. 3, p. 22)

petroleum: nonrenewable resource formed over hundreds of millions of years mostly from the remains of microscopic marine organisms buried in Earth's crust. (Chap. 4, Sec. 1, p. 95)

pioneer species: a group of hardy organisms, such as lichens, found in the primary stage of succession and that begin an area's soil-building process. (Chap. 3, Sec. 1, p. 64)

pollutant: substance that contaminates any part of the environment. (Chap. 4, Sec. 2, p. 102)

population: all the organisms that belong to the same species living in a community. (Chap. 1, Sec. 1, p. 10)

producer: organism, such as a green plant or alga, that uses an outside source of energy like the Sun to create energy-rich food molecules. (Chap. 1, Sec. 3, p. 20)

R

recycling: conservation method that is a form of reuse and requires changing or reprocessing an item or natural resource. (Chap. 4, Sec. 3, p. 113)

reintroduction program: conservation strategy that returns organisms to an area where the species once lived and may involve seed banks, captive populations, and relocation. (Chap. 5, Sec. 2, p. 142)

renewable resources: natural resources, such as water, sunlight, and crops, that are constantly being recycled or replaced by nature. (Chap. 4, Sec. 1, p. 94)

S

soil: mixture of mineral and rock particles, the remains of dead organisms, air, and water that forms the topmost layer of Earth's crust and supports plant growth. (Chap. 2, Sec. 1, p. 38)

succession: natural, gradual changes in the types of species that live in an area; can be primary or secondary. (Chap. 3, Sec. 1, p. 64)

symbiosis: any close relationship between species, including mutualism, commensalism, and parasitism. (Chap. 1, Sec. 3, p. 22)

T

taiga (TI guh): world's largest biome, located south of the tundra between 50°N and 60°N latitude; has long, cold winters, precipitation between 35 cm and 100 cm each year, cone-bearing evergreen trees, and dense forests. (Chap. 3, Sec. 2, p. 70)

temperate deciduous forest: biome usually having four distinct seasons, annual precipitation between 75 cm and 150 cm, and climax communities of deciduous trees. (Chap. 3, Sec. 2, p. 71)

temperate rain forest: biome with 200 cm to 400 cm of precipitation each year, average temperatures between 9°C and 12°C, and forests dominated by trees with needlelike leaves. (Chap. 3, Sec. 2, p. 71)

threatened species: species that is likely to become endangered in the near future because of factors such as overhunting, introduced species, and pollution. (Chap. 5, Sec. 1, p. 131)

tropical rain forest: most biologically diverse biome; has an average temperature of 25°C and receives between 200 cm and 600 cm of precipitation each year. (Chap. 3, Sec. 2, p. 72)

tundra: cold, dry, treeless biome with less than 25 cm of precipitation each year, a short growing season, permafrost, and winters that can be six to nine months long. (Chap. 3, Sec. 2, p. 69)

W

water cycle: model describing how water moves from Earth's surface to the atmosphere and back to the surface again through evaporation, condensation, and precipitation. (Chap. 2, Sec. 2, p. 45)

wetland: a region that is wet most or all of the year. (Chap. 3, Sec. 3, p. 79)

Este glosario define cada término clave que aparece en negrillas en el texto. También muestra el capítulo, la sección y el número de página en donde se usa dicho término.

A

abiotic / abióticos: factores físicos inanimados del medio ambiente, que incluyen el aire, el agua, la luz solar, el suelo, la temperatura y el clima. (Cap. 2, Sec. 1, pág. 36)

acid precipitation / precipitación ácida: precipitación con un pH menor de 5.6 (la cual ocurre cuando los contaminantes del aire, provenientes de la quema de combustibles fósiles, reaccionan con el agua de la atmósfera para formar ácidos fuertes) capaz de contaminar el agua, matar peces y plantas y perjudicar los suelos. (Cap. 4, Sec. 2, pág. 103)

acid rain / lluvia ácida: se produce cuando el dióxido de azufre y el óxido de nitrógeno provenientes de las industrias y de los tubos de escape de los vehículos se combinan con el vapor de agua en el aire; puede arrastrar nutrientes del suelo y perjudicar los árboles y la vida acuática. (Cap. 5, Sec. 1, pág. 135)

atmosphere / atmósfera: el aire que rodea la Tierra; está compuesta por gases, entre los cuales se incluye un 78 por ciento de nitrógeno, un 21 por ciento de oxígeno y 0.03 por ciento de dióxido de carbono. (Cap. 2, Sec. 1, pág. 37)

B

biodiversity / biodiversidad: variedad de vida en un ecosistema, que se mide principalmente por el número de especies que viven en un área dada. (Cap. 5, Sec. 1, pág. 126)

biomes / biomas: áreas geográficas extensas con climas y ecosistemas similares; incluye la tundra, la taiga, el desierto, los bosques caducifolios de zonas templadas, los bosques pluviales de zonas templadas, los bosques pluviales tropicales y las praderas. (Cap. 3, Sec. 2, pág. 68)

biosphere / biosfera: parte de la Tierra que sostiene la vida; incluye la parte superior de la corteza terrestre, la atmósfera y toda el agua sobre la superficie de la Tierra. (Cap. 1, Sec. 1, pág. 8)

biotic / bióticos: factores del medio ambiente que son seres vivos o seres que alguna vez estuvieron vivos. (Cap. 2, Sec. 1, pág. 36)

C

captive population / población en cautiverio: población de organismos que los seres humanos cuidan. (Cap. 5, Sec. 2, pág. 142)

carbon cycle / ciclo del carbono: modelo que describe cómo las células del carbono se movilizan entre el mundo vivo y el inanimado. (Cap. 2, Sec. 2, pág. 49)

carrying capacity / capacidad de carga: el número mayor de individuos de una especie en particular que puede mantener un ecosistema de manera prolongada. (Cap. 1, Sec. 2, pág. 15)

chemosynthesis / quimiosíntesis: proceso en el cual los productores elaboran moléculas nutritivas ricas en energía a partir de sustancias químicas. (Cap. 2, Sec. 3, pág. 51)

climate / clima: condiciones meteorológicas promedio de una región durante un período de tiempo, entre las cuales se incluyen el viento, la temperatura y la precipitación pluvial u otro tipo de precipitación como la nieve o la cellisca. (Cap. 2, Sec. 1, pág. 41)

climax community / comunidad clímax: etapa final estable de la sucesión ecológica, en que las plantas y los animales de una comunidad usan eficientemente los recursos y en la cual se mantiene el equilibrio mediante perturbaciones como los incendios. (Cap. 3, Sec. 1, pág. 67)

commensalism / comensalismo: tipo de relación simbiótica en el cual un organismo se beneficia y el otro organismo no se ve afectado. (Cap. 1, Sec. 3, pág. 22)

community / comunidad: todas las poblaciones de diferentes especies que viven en un ecosistema. (Cap. 1, Sec. 1, pág. 10)

condensation / condensación: proceso que se efectúa cuando un gas se convierte en un líquido. (Cap. 2, Sec. 2, pág. 45)

conservation biology / biología de la conservación: estudio de métodos para proteger la biodiversidad terrestre; utiliza estrategias como programas de reintroducción y restauración de hábitats y se esfuerza por preservar las especies amenazadas y aquellas en peligro de extinción. (Cap. 5, Sec. 2, pág. 138)

consumer / consumidor: organismo que no puede fabricar moléculas ricas en energía, sino que obtiene su alimento al alimentarse de otros organismos. (Cap. 1, Sec. 3, pág. 21)

coral reef / arrecife de coral: ecosistema diverso formado de las conchas de carbonato de calcio secretadas por los corales. (Cap. 3, Sec. 3, pág. 81)

D

desert / desierto: el bioma más seco de la Tierra, con menos de 25 cm de lluvia anual; tiene dunas o suelo delgado con poca materia orgánica, y plantas y animales especialmente adaptados para sobrevivir condiciones extremas. (Cap. 3, Sec. 2, pág. 74)

E

ecology / ecología: estudio de las interacciones que se llevan a cabo entre los organismos y su ambiente. (Cap. 1, Sec. 1, pág. 9)

ecosystem / ecosistema: todos los organismos vivos que habitan en un área y las cosas inanimadas en su ambiente. (Cap. 1, Sec. 1, pág. 9)

endangered species / especie en peligro de extinción: especie que está en peligro de extinguirse debido a factores como la pérdida de hábitat, la caza excesiva y la contaminación. (Cap. 5, Sec. 1, pág. 131)

energy pyramid / pirámide de energía: modelo que muestra la cantidad de energía disponible en cada nivel alimenticio de un ecosistema. (Cap. 2, Sec. 3, pág. 53)

erosion / erosión: movimiento del suelo de un lugar a otro. (Cap. 4, Sec. 2, pág. 109)

estuary / estuario: área estremadamente fértil donde un río desemboca en un océano; contiene una mezcla de agua dulce y agua salada y sirve de vivero para muchas especies de peces. (Cap. 3, Sec. 3, pág. 82)

evaporation / evaporación: proceso que se lleva a cabo cuando un líquido se convierte en un gas. (Cap. 2, Sec. 2, pág. 44)

extinct species / especie extinta: especie que alguna vez vivió en la Tierra, pero que ha desaparecido. (Cap. 5, Sec. 1, pág. 130)

F

food web / red alimenticia: modelo que muestra las complejas relaciones alimenticias entre los organismos de una comunidad. (Cap. 2, Sec. 3, pág. 52)

fossil fuels / combustibles fósiles: recursos energéticos no renovables (carbón, petróleo y gas natural) que se formaron en la corteza terrestre durante un período de cientos de millones de años. (Cap. 4, Sec. 1, pág. 96)

G

geothermal energy / energía geotérmica: energía calorífica en el interior de la corteza terrestre, disponible solamente cuando se localizan géisers naturales o volcanes. (Cap. 4, Sec. 1, pág. 99)

grasslands / praderas: regiones tropicales y de zonas templadas cuya precipitación anual varía de 25 a 75 cm; dominadas por comunidades clímax de pastos; ideales para el crecimiento de cosechas y el pastoreo del ganado vacuno y bovino. (Cap. 3, Sec. 2, pág. 75)

greenhouse effect / efecto invernadero: fenómeno de la atmósfera que atrapa el calor y que mantiene la Tierra con suficiente calor como para sostener la vida. (Cap. 4, Sec. 2, pág. 104)

H

habitat / hábitat: lugar en donde vive un organismo y que le provee los tipos de alimento, refugio, humedad y temperaturas necesarias para la sobrevivencia. (Cap. 1, Sec. 1, pág. 11)

habitat restoration / restauración de hábitats: proceso de restablecer condiciones saludables en un hábitat que ha sufrido daño. (Cap. 5, Sec. 2, pág. 141)

hazardous wastes / residuos peligrosos: materiales de desecho, como los pesticidas y los restos de pintura, que son dañinos para la salud humana o venenosos para los organismos vivos. (Cap. 4, Sec. 2, pág. 110)

hydroelectric power / energía hidroeléctrica: electricidad producida cuando la fuerza hidráulica hace girar las aspas de una turbina generadora de electricidad. (Cap. 4, Sec. 1, pág. 97)

I

intertidal zone / zona intermareal: parte de la costa cubierta de agua durante la marea alta y que está expuesta al aire durante la marea baja. (Cap. 3, Sec. 3, pág. 82)

introduced species / especie introducida: especie que llega a un ecosistema como resultado de acciones humanas y que puede reducir o eliminar poblaciones de especies nativas. (Cap. 5, Sec. 1, pág. 134)

L

limiting factor / factor limitativo: cualquier cosa que puede limitar el tamaño de una población, incluye los rasgos vivos y los inanimados de un ecosistema, como los depredadores o la sequía. (Cap. 1, Sec. 2, pág. 14)

M

mutualism / mutualismo: tipo de relación simbiótica en que ambos organismos se benefician. (Cap. 1, Sec. 3, pág. 22)

N

native species / especie autóctona: organismos originales de un ecosistema. (Cap. 5, Sec. 1, pág. 134)

natural resources / recursos naturales: partes del medio ambiente terrestre que suministran materiales útiles o necesarios para la sobreviviencia de los organismos vivos. (Cap. 4, Sec. 1, pág. 94)

niche / nicho: en un ecosistema, se refiere a las maneras particulares en que un organismo sobrevive, obtiene alimentos y refugio y evita peligros. (Cap. 1, Sec. 3, pág. 23)

nitrogen cycle / ciclo del nitrógeno: modelo que describe cómo se mueve el nitrógeno de la atmósfera al suelo, pasando luego a los organismos vivos y, finalmente, de regreso a la atmósfera. (Cap. 2, Sec. 2, pág. 46)

nitrogen fixation / fijación del nitrógeno: proceso en el cual algunos tipos de bacterias que se hallan en el suelo convierten el gas de nitrógeno en una forma de nitrógeno que pueden usar las plantas. (Cap. 2, Sec. 2, pág. 46)

nonrenewable resources / recursos no renovables: recursos naturales, como el petróleo crudo, los minerales y los metales, que se usan con mayor rapidez de lo que se pueden reemplazar por procesos naturales. (Cap. 4, Sec. 1, pág. 95)

nuclear energy / energía nuclear: energía producida a partir de la separación de billones de núcleos de uranio mediante una reacción de fisión nuclear. (Cap. 4, Sec. 1, pág. 98)

O

ozone depletion / agotamiento del ozono: enrarecimiento de la capa de ozono de la Tierra debido a los clorofluorocarbonos que se escapan al aire y reaccionan químicamente con el ozono, separando sus moléculas. (Cap. 4, Sec. 2, pág. 105)

ozone layer / capa de ozono: capa de gas protectora en la atmósfera terrestre, unos 15 km a 30 km encima de la superficie de la Tierra, que absorbe la radiación ultravioleta proveniente del Sol. (Cap. 5, Sec. 1, pág. 136)

P

parasitism / parasitismo: tipo de relación simbiótica en que un organismo se beneficia y el otro organismo es perjudicado. (Cap. 1, Sec. 3, pág. 22)

petroleum / petróleo crudo: recurso no renovable que se ha formado durante el transcurso de cientos de millones de años, principalmente de los restos de organismos marinos microscópicos enterrados en la corteza terrestre. (Cap. 4, Sec. 1, pág. 95)

pioneer species / especie pionera: grupo de organismos, como los líquenes, que se encuentran en la etapa primaria de sucesión y que comienza el proceso de formación del suelo. (Cap. 3, Sec. 1, pág. 64)

pollutant / contaminante: sustancia que contamina cualquier parte del medio ambiente. (Cap. 4, Sec. 2, pág. 102)

population / población: todos los organismos que pertenecen a la misma especie y que viven en una comunidad. (Cap. 1, Sec. 1, pág. 10)

producer / productor: organismo que utiliza fuentes externas de energía como el Sol, para fabricar moléculas ricas en energía; por ejemplo, las plantas o algas verdes. (Cap. 1, Sec. 3, pág. 20)

R

recycling / reciclaje: método de conservación que constituye una forma de reutilización y que requiere la transformación o reprocesamiento de un artículo o de un recurso natural. (Cap. 4, Sec. 3, pág. 113)

reintroduction program / *programa de reintroducción*: estrategia de conservación que devuelve organismos a un área donde una vez vivieron tales especies y que puede implicar bancos de semilla, poblaciones en cautiverio y reubicación. (Cap. 5, Sec. 2, pág. 142)

renewable resources / *recursos renovables*: recursos naturales, como el agua, la luz solar y los cultivos, que la naturaleza recicla o reemplaza constantemente. (Cap. 4, Sec. 1, pág. 94)

S

soil / *suelo*: mezcla de partículas minerales y rocosas, restos de organismos muertos, aire y agua que forma la capa superior de la corteza terrestre y que sostiene el crecimiento vegetal. (Cap. 2, Sec. 1, pág. 38)

succession / *sucesión*: cambios graduales naturales en los tipos de especies que moran en un área; puede ser primaria o secundaria. (Cap. 3, Sec. 1, pág. 64)

symbiosis / *simbiosis*: cualquier relación estrecha entre especies, incluye el mutualismo, el comensalismo y el parasitismo. (Cap. 1, Sec. 3, pág. 22)

T

taiga / *taiga*: el bioma más grande del mundo, ubicado al sur de la tundra entre las latitudes de 50° N y 60° N; tiene inviernos fríos y largos, precipitación anual entre 35 cm y 100 cm, árboles coníferos siempreverdes y bosques densos. (Cap. 3, Sec. 2, pág. 70)

temperate deciduous forest / *bosque caducifolio de zona templada*: bioma que por lo general presenta cuatro estaciones bien marcadas, una precipitación anual entre 75 cm y 150 cm y comunidades clímax de árboles caducifolio. (Cap. 3, Sec. 2, pág. 71)

temperate rain forest / *bosque pluvial de zona templada*: bioma cuya precipitación anual varía de 200 cm a 400 cm, con temperaturas promedio entre 9°C y 12°C y bosques dominados por árboles con hojas en forma de agujas. (Cap. 3, Sec. 2, pág. 71)

threatened species / *especie amenazada*: especie propensa a hallarse en peligro de extinción en un futuro cercano, debido a factores como la caza excesiva, la introducción de especies y la contaminación. (Cap. 5, Sec. 1, pág. 131)

tropical rain forest / *bosque pluvial tropical*: el bioma más diverso biológicamente; tiene una temperatura promedio de 25°C y recibe entre 200 cm y 600 cm de precipitación anual. (Cap. 3, Sec. 2, pág. 72)

tundra / *tundra*: bioma sin árboles, frío y seco con menos de 25 cm de precipitación cada año, una temporada de crecimiento corta, permagel e inviernos que duran entre seis y nueve meses. (Cap. 3, Sec. 2, pág. 69)

W

water cycle / *ciclo del agua*: modelo que describe cómo se mueve el agua de la superficie de la Tierra a la atmósfera para regresar nuevamente a la superficie a través de la evaporación, condensación y precipitación. (Cap. 2, Sec. 2, pág. 45)

wetland / *zonas pantanosas*: áreas que se mantienen mojadas la mayor parte del año. (Cap. 3, Sec. 3, pág. 79)

Index

The index for *Ecology* will help you locate major topics in the book quickly and easily. Each entry in the index is followed by the number of the pages on which the entry is discussed. A page number given in boldfaced type indicates the page on which that entry is defined. A page number given in italic type indicates a page on which the entry is used in an illustration or photograph. The abbreviation *act.* indicates a page on which the entry is used in an activity.

Index

Index

Index

Art Credits

Glencoe would like to acknowledge the artists and agencies who participated in illustrating this program: Absolute Science Illustration; Andrew Evansen; Argosy; Articulate Graphics; Craig Attebery represented by Frank & Jeff Lavaty; CHK America; Gagliano Graphics; Pedro Julio Gonzalez represented by Melissa Turk & The Artist Network; Robert Hynes represented by Mendola Ltd.; Morgan Cain & Associates; JTH Illustration; Laurie O'Keefe; Matthew Pippin represented by Beranbaum Artist's Representative; Precision Graphics; Publisher's Art; Rolin Graphics, Inc.; Wendy Smith represented by Melissa Turk & The Artist Network; Kevin Torline represented by Berendsen and Associates, Inc.; WILDlife ART; Phil Wilson represented by Cliff Knecht Artist Representative; Zoo Botanica.

Photo Credits

Abbreviation key: AA=Animals Animals; AH=Aaron Haupt; AMP=Amanita Pictures; BC=Bruce Coleman, Inc.; CB=CORBIS; DM=Doug Martin; DRK=DRK Photo; ES=Earth Scenes; FP=Fundamental Photographs; GH=Grant Heilman Photography; IC=Icon Images; KS=KS Studios; LA=Liaison Agency; MB=Mark Burnett; MM=Matt Meadows; PE=PhotoEdit; PD=PhotoDisc; PQ=PictureQuest; PR=Photo Researchers; SB=Stock Boston; TSA=Tom Stack & Associates; TSM=The Stock Market; VU=Visuals Unlimited.

Cover Darrell Gulin/Stone; **v** Kenneth Murray/PR; **vi** MM; **vii** Jacques Jangoux/Peter Arnold, Inc.; **2** (t)Darren Bennett/AA, (b)Collection of Glenbow Museum,Calgary, Canada; **3** (t)Mathew Cavanaugh/AP Photo, (b)Helen Hardin 1971; **4** (t)GH, (b)Rick Poley/VU; **5** (t)Jeff Cooper/The Salina Journal/Associated Press, (b)Fletcher & Baylus/PR; **6** David Cavagnaro/DRK; **6-7** Johnny Johnson/DRK; **7** John D. Cunningham/VU; **8** (tl)Richard Kolar/AA, (tr)G. Carleton Ray/PR, (bl)Adam Jones/PR, (br)Tom Van Sant/Geosphere Project, Santa Monica/Science Photo Library/PR; **9** (t)John W. Bova/PR, (b)David Young/TSA; **11** (l)Zig Leszczynski/AA, (r)Gary W. Carter/VU; **14** Mitsuaki Iwago/Minden Pictures; **15** Joel Sartore from GH; **17** (t)Norm Thomas/PR, (b)Maresa Pryor/ES; **18** (t)Wyman P. Meinzer, (c)Bud Neilson/Words & Pictures/PQ, (b)Wyman P. Meinzer; **20** (tl)Michael Abbey/PR, (tr)OSF/AA, (b)Michael P. Gadomski/PR; **21** (t, l to r)William J. Weber, Larry Kimball/VU, William J. Weber, George D. Lepp/PR, (b, l to r)Lynn M. Stone, Stephen J. Krasemann/Peter Arnold, Inc., William J. Weber, Mark Steinmetz; **22** (t)Milton Rand/TSA, (c)Marian Bacon/AA, (b)Sinclair Stammers/Science Photo Library/PR; **23** (tl)Raymond A. Mendez/AA, (bl)Donald Specker/AA, (br)Joe McDonald/AA; **24** Ted Levin/AA; **25** Richard L. Carlton/PR; **26** (t)Jean Claude Revy/PhotoTake NYC, (b)OSF/AA; **27** Runk/Schoenberger from GH; **29** (l)courtesy US Census, (r)Eric Larravadieu/Stone; **30** (t)Tui De Roy/Minden Pictures, (c)Maslowski/PR, (b)Stephen J. Krasemann/DRK; **31** (l)C.K. Lorenz/PR, (r)Hans Pfletschinger/Peter Arnold, Inc.; **32** Scott Camazine/PR; **34** Dr. Jeremy Burgess/Science Photo Library/PR; **34-35** Steve Bly/International Stock; **35** Jeff Greenberg/VU; **36** Kenneth Murray/PR; **37** (t)Jerry L. Ferrara/PR, (b)Art Wolfe/PR; **38** (t)Telegraph Colour Library/FPG, (b)Hal Beral/VU; **39** (l)Fritz Polking/VU, (r)R. Arndt/VU; **40** Tom Uhlman/VU; **44** (l)Jim Grattan, (r)Bruce S. Cushing/VU; **47** (t)Rob & Ann Simpson/VU, (c b)Runk/Schoenberger from GH; **48** Stephen R. Wagner; **50** (l)WHOI/VU, (r)Wolfgang Baumeister/Science Photo Library/PR; **54** (t)MM, (b)Gerald and Buff Corsi/VU; **55** Jeff J. Daly/VU; **56** Gordon Wiltsie/Peter Arnold, Inc.; **58** (tl)Dwight Kuhn, (tr)Stephen J. Krasemann/DRK, (bl)Gregory K. Scott/PR, (br)Simon Battensby/Stone; **59** (l)Soames Summerhay/PR, (r)Tom Uhlman/VU; **62** Les Christman/VU; **62-63** William Campbell/CB Sygma; **63** AH; **64** Jeff Greenberg/VU; **65** Larry Ulrich/DRK; **66** (bkgd)Craig Fujii/Seattle Times, (t)Jeff Henry, (c)Kevin R. Morris/CB, (b)Jeff Henry; **67** Rod Planck/PR; **69** (t)Steve McCutcheon/

VU, (bl)Pat O'Hara/DRK, (br)Erwin & Peggy Bauer/TSA; **70** (tl)Peter Ziminski/VU, (tr)Leonard Rue III/VU, (bl)C.C. Lockwood/DRK, (br)Larry Ulrich/DRK; **71** (t)Fritz Polking/VU, (b)William Grenfell/VU; **72** Lynn M. Stone/DRK; **74** (l)Joe McDonald/DRK, (r)Steve Solum/AMP; **75** Kevin Schafer; **77** W. Banaszewski/VU; **78** (l)Dwight Kuhn, (r)Mark E. Gibson/VU; **79** James R. Fisher/DRK; **80** D. Foster/WHOI/VU; **81** (l)C.C. Lockwood/AMP, (r)Steve Wolper/DRK; **82** (t)Dwight Kuhn, (c)Glenn Oliver/VU, (b)Stephen J. Krasemann/DRK; **83** (l)John Kaprielian/PR, (r)Jerry Sarapochiello/AMP; **84** (t)Dwight Kuhn, (b)John Gerlach/DRK; **85** Fritz Polking/AMP; **86 87** Courtesy Albuquerque Public Schools; **88** (tl)Bob Gurr/DRK, (tr)M.C. Chamberlain/DRK, (b)David Pearson/VU; **89** (l)James P. Rowan/DRK, (r)John Shaw/TSA; **92** Rannels from GH; **92-93** GH; **93** AMP; **94** (l)Keith Lanpher/LA, (r)Richard Thatcher/David R. Frazier Photolibrary; **95** (t)Solar Cookers International, (bl)Brian F. Peterson/TSM, (br)Ron Kimball Photography; **96** Larry Mayer/LA; **99** (t)Torleif Svenson/TSM, (c)Les Gibbon/Cordaiy Photo Library Ltd./CB, (b)Rob Williamson; **100** Sean Justice; **101** (t)Lowell Georgia/Science Source/PR, (cl)NASA, (c)CB, (cr)Sean Sprague/Impact Visuals/PQ, (bl)Lee Foster/AMP, (br)Robert Perron; **102** Philippe Renault/LA; **103** (l)NYC Parks Photo Archive/FP, (r)Kristen Brochmann/FP; **106** AH; **107** (l)Jeremy Walker/Science Photo Library/PR, (c)John Colwell from GH, (r)Telegraph Colour Library/FPG; **109** (tl)Larry Mayer/LA, (tr)ChromoSohm/TSM, (c)David R. Frazier Photolibrary, (b)Inga Spence/VU; **110** (tl)AMP, (tr)Andrew Holbrooke/TSM, (bl)IC, (br)AH; **112** Paul A. Souders/CB; **113** IC; **116** Larry Lefever from GH; **116** (t)Howard Buffett from GH, (b)Solar Cookers International; **117** John D. Cunningham/VU; **118** Frank Cezus/FPG; **118** Wilford Haven/LA; **119** Nic Paget-Clarke; **120** (t)MB, (c)David R. Frazier Photolibrary, (b)George Diebold/TSM; **121** (l)Lebrum/LA, (r)Spencer Grant/PE;

122 (l)James N. Westwater, (r)Steve McCutcheon/VU; **124** Gordon Wiltsie/Peter Arnold, Inc.; **124-125** Bob Firth; **125** Geoff Butler; **126** (l)Andy Sacks/Stone, (r)Erwin & Peggy Bauer/AMP; **127** (t)Leonard Lee Rue III/PR, (c)Chuck Pefley/Stone, (b)Charles W. Mann/PR; **128** (l)Gilbert S. Grant/PR, (lc)Rexford Lord/PR, (rc)Ray Pfortner/Peter Arnold, Inc., (r)William D. Adams; **129** William D. Adams; **131** (t)Joe McDonald/TSA, (b)Len Rue, Jr./AA; **132** (bkgd) Kennan Word/CB, (tl)Joel Sartore, (tr)William H. Amos, (c)Joseph Van Wormer/AMP/PQ, (b)Erwin & Peggy Bauer/AMP/PQ; **133** (l)Jim Baron/The Image Finders, (r)Melissa Hathaway/ODNR Div. of Wildlife; **134** (l)University of MN Sea Grant Program, (r)Marcia Griffen/ES; **135** SuperStock; **137** A. Greth/BIOS/Peter Arnold, Inc.; **138** Michael Pogany/Columbus Zoo; **139** (l)Bill Pogue/Stone, (r)Daniel J. Cox/Stone; **141** Save The Bay® People for Narragansett Bay; **142** Leonard L.T. Rhodes/AA; **143** Hal Beral/VU; **144** Zig Leszczynski/ES; **146** (t)Jacques Jangoux/PR, (b)Michael Fogden/DRK; **147** F. Gilson/Bios/Peter Arnold, Inc.; **148** (t)David Woodfall/Stone, (c)David Campbell/VU, (b)Kenneth W. Fink/AMP; **149** (l)Inga Spence/VU, (c)Bogart Photography, (r)Juan Manuel Renjifo/ES; **154-155** PD; **156** Greg Probst/Stone; **157** (t)GH, (b)George Ranalli/PR; **158** (t)AH, (b)Tom Bean/Stone; **159** (t)Tom Bean/DRK, (b)Gary Braasch/Stone; **160** Tony Freeman/PE/PQ; **161** (t)Dominic Oldershaw, (b)Mary Kate Denny/PE; **162** (t)file photo, (b)John Evans; **163** (t)KS, (b)Ken Lax; **164** Timothy Fuller; **168** First Image; **171** Dominic Oldershaw; **172** StudiOhio; **173** First Image; **175** Richard Day/AA; **178** Paul Barton/TSM; **181** Charles Gupton/TSM; **190** MM; **191** (t)NIBSC/Science Photo Library/PR, (bl)Dr. Richard Kessel, (br)David John/VU; **192** (t)Runk/Schoenberger from GH, (bl)Andrew Syred/Science Photo Library/PR, (br)Rich Brommer; **193** (t)G.R. Roberts, (bl)Ralph Reinhold/ES, (br)Scott Johnson/AA; **194** Martin Harvey/DRK.

PERIODIC TABLE OF THE ELEMENTS

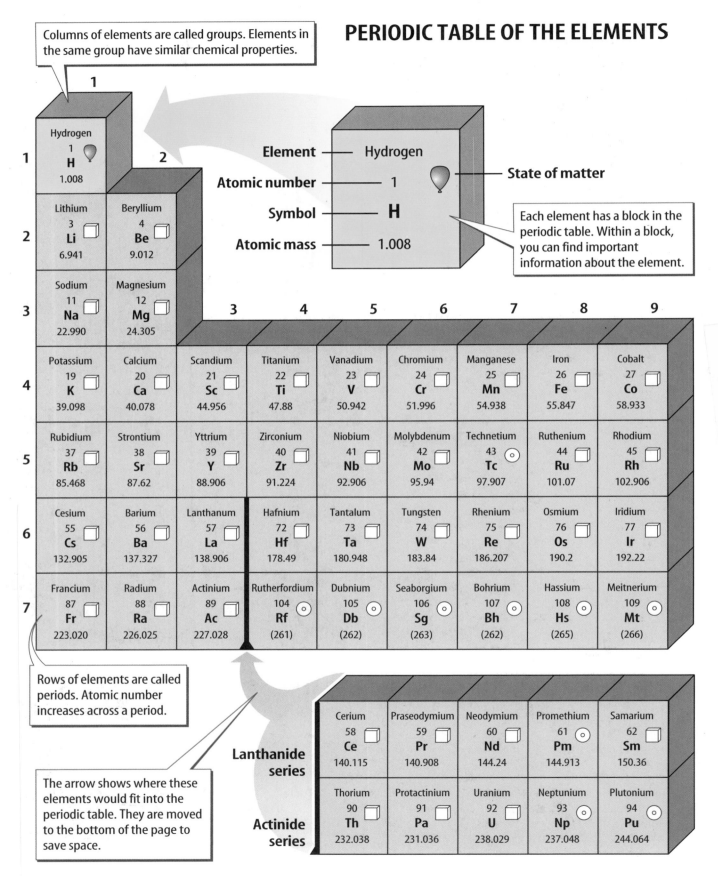

Columns of elements are called groups. Elements in the same group have similar chemical properties.

Element — Hydrogen
Atomic number — 1
Symbol — H
Atomic mass — 1.008
State of matter

Each element has a block in the periodic table. Within a block, you can find important information about the element.

Rows of elements are called periods. Atomic number increases across a period.

The arrow shows where these elements would fit into the periodic table. They are moved to the bottom of the page to save space.

Group	1	2	3	4	5	6	7	8	9
1	Hydrogen 1 H 1.008								
2	Lithium 3 Li 6.941	Beryllium 4 Be 9.012							
3	Sodium 11 Na 22.990	Magnesium 12 Mg 24.305							
4	Potassium 19 K 39.098	Calcium 20 Ca 40.078	Scandium 21 Sc 44.956	Titanium 22 Ti 47.88	Vanadium 23 V 50.942	Chromium 24 Cr 51.996	Manganese 25 Mn 54.938	Iron 26 Fe 55.847	Cobalt 27 Co 58.933
5	Rubidium 37 Rb 85.468	Strontium 38 Sr 87.62	Yttrium 39 Y 88.906	Zirconium 40 Zr 91.224	Niobium 41 Nb 92.906	Molybdenum 42 Mo 95.94	Technetium 43 Tc 97.907	Ruthenium 44 Ru 101.07	Rhodium 45 Rh 102.906
6	Cesium 55 Cs 132.905	Barium 56 Ba 137.327	Lanthanum 57 La 138.906	Hafnium 72 Hf 178.49	Tantalum 73 Ta 180.948	Tungsten 74 W 183.84	Rhenium 75 Re 186.207	Osmium 76 Os 190.2	Iridium 77 Ir 192.22
7	Francium 87 Fr 223.020	Radium 88 Ra 226.025	Actinium 89 Ac 227.028	Rutherfordium 104 Rf (261)	Dubnium 105 Db (262)	Seaborgium 106 Sg (263)	Bohrium 107 Bh (262)	Hassium 108 Hs (265)	Meitnerium 109 Mt (266)

Lanthanide series	Cerium 58 Ce 140.115	Praseodymium 59 Pr 140.908	Neodymium 60 Nd 144.24	Promethium 61 Pm 144.913	Samarium 62 Sm 150.36
Actinide series	Thorium 90 Th 232.038	Protactinium 91 Pa 231.036	Uranium 92 U 238.029	Neptunium 93 Np 237.048	Plutonium 94 Pu 244.064